FINANCIAL MANAGEMENT FOR HEALTH-SYSTEM PHARMACISTS

FINANCIAL MANAGEMENT FOR HEALTH-SYSTEM PHARMACISTS

2nd Edition

Robert P. Granko, BS Pharm, PharmD, MBA, FASHP, FNCAP

System Director of Enterprise Pharmacy, Geisinger
Associate Professor of Pharmacy
Department of Medical Education at the
Geisinger Commonwealth School of Medicine
Danville, Pennsylvania
Associate Professor of Clinical Education
UNC Eshelman School of Pharmacy
Chapel Hill, North Carolina

Any correspondence regarding this publication should be sent to the publisher, American Society of Health-System Pharmacists, 4500 East-West Highway, suite 900, Bethesda, MD 20814, attention: Special Publishing.

The information presented herein reflects the opinions of the contributors and advisors. It should not be interpreted as an official policy of ASHP or as an endorsement of any product.

Because of ongoing research and improvements in technology, the information and its applications contained in this text are constantly evolving and are subject to the professional judgment and interpretation of the practitioner due to the uniqueness of a clinical situation. The editors and ASHP have made reasonable efforts to ensure the accuracy and appropriateness of the information presented in this document. However, any user of this information is advised that the editors and ASHP are not responsible for the continued currency of the information, for any errors or omissions, and/or for any consequences arising from the use of the information in the document in any and all practice settings. Any reader of this document is cautioned that ASHP makes no representation, guarantee, or warranty, express or implied, as to the accuracy and appropriateness of the information contained in this document and specifically disclaims any liability to any party for the accuracy and/or completeness of the material or for any damages arising out of the use or non-use of any of the information contained in this document.

Vice President, Publishing Office: Daniel J. Cobaugh, PharmD, DABAT, FAACT

Editorial Director, Special Publishing: Ryan E. Owens, PharmD, BCPS

Editorial Coordinator, Special Publishing: Elaine Jimenez

Director, Production and Platform Services, Publishing Operations: Johnna M. Hershey, BA

Cover Design: DeVall Advertising

Cover Art: iamchamp - stock.adobe.com

Page Design: David Wade

Library of Congress Cataloging-in-Publication Data

Names: Granko, Robert P., editor. | American Society of Health-System Pharmacists, issuing body.

Title: Financial management for health-system pharmacists / [edited by] Robert P. Granko.

Description: Second edition. | Bethesda, MD : American Society of Health-System Pharmacists, [2023] | Includes bibliographical references and index. | Summary: "The second edition of Financial Management for Health-System Pharmacists will be a contemporary and forward looking reference written by today's and tomorrow's future pharmacy leaders encompassing progressive and contemporary issues as well as emerging opportunities impacting our practices and patients. This resource supports the management of Enterprise Pharmacy Finance across business and care continuums providing a confluence of business and financial acumen for Health-System Pharmacy Leaders, Executives, and Learners"—Provided by publisher.

Identifiers: LCCN 2022043638 (print) | LCCN 2022043639 (ebook) | ISBN 9781585287123 (paperback) | ISBN 9781585287130 (adobe pdf) | ISBN 9781585287147 (epub)

Subjects: MESH: Pharmacy Service, Hospital—economics | Pharmacy Service, Hospital—organization & administration | Financial Management—methods | Costs and Cost Analysis

Classification: LCC RA975.5.P5 (print) | LCC RA975.5.P5 (ebook) | NLM WX 179 | DDC 362.17/820681—dc23/eng/20221019

LC record available at https://lccn.loc.gov/2022043638

LC ebook record available at https://lccn.loc.gov/2022043639

Print ISBN: 978-1-58528-712-3

PDF ISBN: 978-1-58528-713-0

ePub ISBN: 978-1-58528-714-7

DOI: 10.37573/9781585287130

10 9 8 7 6 5 4 3 2 1

DEDICATION

This book is dedicated to my wife, Hazar, and my two sons, Kaiden and Rowan, for their unending love and support.

I would like to thank my past and present colleagues, mentors, and ASHP for their leadership of health-system pharmacy.

TABLE OF CONTENTS

DOI 10.37573/9781585287130.FM

FOREWORD

Today, more than ever, healthcare organizations depend on pharmacy leaders to be experts in financial management to actively support the clinical and economic success of their organizations. In the past, a pharmacy leader's focus was primarily on expense management and charge capture in the acute care arena, but today successful directors and managers must also have a deep understanding of revenue, managing the revenue cycle, and projecting financial performance accurately across multiple and diverse patient-care settings. While the COVID-19 pandemic created new opportunities for health-system pharmacists, it also created significant operational and financial challenges for pharmacy leaders.

You will find this book an up-to-date and forward-looking reference written by and for future pharmacy leaders. It aims to incorporate contemporary and advanced topics as well as evolving opportunities which will affect the practice of pharmacy as we care for patients. As a pharmacy leader, you already possess the knowledge and skills to proficiently manage the complex world of modern pharmacy budgets and the juxtaposition of ensuring optimal patient care, driving innovation, and healthcare sustainability. Senior leaders in healthcare organizations are also expecting you to have a deep understanding of how the use of data analytics can be leveraged to effectively project financial performance while also managing supply chain challenges, purchasing contracts, regulatory compliance, and strategic growth opportunities for pharmacy.

This book is comprised of two distinct parts: ten traditional chapters covering a wide range of financial management topics, followed by thirteen business cases that will assist the reader in applying the concepts learned in each chapter and employing critical thinking to solve problems. By developing a thorough understanding of pharmacy finances across continuums of care, pharmacy leaders will build trust with senior finance leaders and health-system executives, which will enable them to achieve greater success when recommending new resources for the expansion of pharmacy services and exploring new sources of revenue or other entrepreneurial opportunities in pharmacy. Ultimately, health-system executives are dependent on pharmacy leaders to manage multiple complex operations that influence the overall financial performance of their health systems. Pharmacy leaders of today are uniquely positioned to demonstrate the value of pharmacy services to senior leaders by not just focusing on expense and productivity management, but on business development and growth, all while maintaining a keen eye on the quality, efficiency, and safety of the medication-use process, no matter the practice setting.

Thank you for your endless dedication to the patients and families you serve.

Tad Gomez

DOI 10.37573/9781585287130.FM

PREFACE

I am pleased to present to you the 2nd edition of *Financial Management for Health-System Pharmacists*. The 1st edition, authored over a decade ago under the leadership of Andrew L. Wilson, PharmD, FASHP, laid the foundation for health-system pharmacy financial stewardship, helping the reader develop a thorough understanding of the framework, and detailing corresponding recommendations for the financial management of health-system pharmacy.

Building on the cornerstone principles set forth in the 1st edition, the vision behind the undertaking of the 2nd edition was to provide the reader a contemporary and forward-looking reference written by current and future pharmacy leaders that would encompass progressive and contemporary topics. Interspersed throughout this new edition are insightful perspectives from over 50 outstanding authors from across the country. The 2nd edition engages the reader with a mix of chapters, some new to this edition, along with a trove of new health-system pharmacy financial business cases. As leaders look to transform their organizations, the principles and practices provided herein will give the reader the knowledge and guidance to craft a new path forward as they look to improve the provision of pharmacy and patient-care services.

Undoubtedly, we face continued challenges in leading health-system pharmacy. As we work against those headwinds, this resource will serve as a guidebook to support the management of enterprise pharmacy finance across business and care continuums. Further, it will provide a confluence of business and financial acumen for health-system pharmacy leaders, executives, and learners to further support the strategies behind comprehensive enterprise pharmacy-level services.

I would like to recognize Andy's contribution to the field in spearheading the authoring of the 1st edition of *Financial Management for Health-System Pharmacists*. Andy was critical in leading the way, and I am grateful for his friendship and support in developing this revised body of work.

Robert P. Granko, BS Pharm, PharmD, MBA, FASHP, FNCAP

DOI 10.37573/9781585287130.FM

CONTRIBUTORS

EDITOR

Robert P. Granko, BS Pharm, PharmD, MBA, FASHP, FNCAP
System Director of Enterprise Pharmacy, Geisinger
Associate Professor of Pharmacy
Department of Medical Education at the Geisinger Commonwealth School of Medicine
Danville, Pennsylvania
Associate Professor of Clinical Education
UNC Eshelman School of Pharmacy
Chapel Hill, North Carolina

CONTRIBUTORS

Jeanette A. Alava, PharmD
Resident, PGY-2 Health System Pharmacy Administration and Leadership
Lee Health
Fort Myers, Florida

John A. Armitstead, MS, RPh, FASHP
System Director of Pharmacy
Lee Health
Fort Myers, Florida

Jared A. Austin, PharmD, BCPS, BCOP
Pharmacy Supervisor
Beaumont Home Infusion
Royal Oaks, Michigan

Elaine Bedell, RPh, PharmD, BCPS
National Pharmacy Practice Manager
Ascension
Austin, Texas

Lori Berg, BS
Vice President, Pharmacy Finance Operations
Fairview Health Services
Minneapolis, Minnesota

Gretchen Brummel, PharmD, BCPS
Pharmacy Executive Director, Center for Pharmacy Practice Excellence
Vizient, Inc.

DOI 10.37573/9781585287130.FM

Philip Brummond, PharmD, MS, FASHP

Senior Vice President
Visante
St. Paul, Minnesota

Scott L. Canfield, PharmD, CSP

Assistant Director for Clinical Program Development
Johns Hopkins Home Care Group
Johns Hopkins Medicine
Baltimore, Maryland

Christine Collins, MBA, RPh, FASHP

Vice President/Chief Pharmacy Officer
Lifespan
Kingston, Rhode Island

Michelle C. Corrado, PharmD, DPLA, MHA, FACHE

System Director, Pharmacy Business Operations
Lifespan
Providence, Rhode Island

Ginny Crisp, PharmD

Owner
Prescription Benefit Solutions
Charleston, South Carolina

Brian Davis, MS, RPh

Pharmacy Strategy and Partnerships
University of California Health
University of California Office of the President
Oakland, California

Michael DeCoske, PharmD, BCPS, FASHP

Assistant Vice President, Ambulatory Pharmacy
Baptist Health South Florida
Miami, Florida

Stephen F. Eckel, PharmD, MHA, FASHP

Associate Dean, Global Engagement
Associate Professor
UNC Eshelman School of Pharmacy
Chapel Hill, North Carolina

Polly Fox, BBA

Kaiser Permanente Northwest Region
Pharmacy Administration
Portland, Oregon

Michael J. Freudiger, PharmD, APh, BCPS, BCSCP
Compounding and Regulatory Compliance
Valley Children's Healthcare
Madera, California

Adrianne "Maxie" Friemel, PharmD, MS, BCPS, CRCR
Senior Director, Pharmacy Revenue Cycle Services
Visante
St. Paul, Minnesota

Eric Friestrom, PharmD, MS
Senior Consultant
Visante
St. Paul, Minnesota

David Hager, PharmD, BCPS
Senior Director
Visante
St. Paul, Minnesota

Kevin N. Hansen, PharmD, MS, BCPS, BCSCP
Director of Pharmacy
Compounding Services and Data Analytics
Cone Health
Greensboro, North Carolina

Seth Hartman, PharmD, MBA
Executive Director, Pharmacy Informatics
The University of Chicago
UChicago Medicine
Chicago, Illinois

Christopher A. Hatwig, MS, RPh, FASHP
President
Apexus LLC
Irving, Texas

Joel Hennenfent, PharmD, MBA, BCPS, FASHP
Senior Vice President
Pharmacy Member Services
Vizient, Inc.
Irving, Texas

Miriam Jarvinen, BS
Director, Integrated Hospital Pharmacy Finance Operations
Fairview Health Services
Minneapolis, Minnesota

Chad Johnson, PharmD, MBA, 340B ACE

Manager, 340B Education & Compliance Support
Apexus
Irving, Texas

Patricia J. Killingsworth, AB Pharm

National Director Pharmacy Integration
Ascension Health
St. Louis, Missouri

Randall Knoebel, PharmD, MPH, BCOP

Pharmacy Director Health Analytics & Drug Policy
Research Associate Professor, Department of Medicine
Residency Program Director, PGY1 Pharmacy Residency
Pharmacy Director, Pain Stewardship
UChicago Medicine
Chicago, Illinois

Calvin H. Knowlton, PhD, BS Pharm

Chief Executive and Chairman
Tabula Rasa HealthCare Inc.
Moorestown, New Jersey

Orsula V. Knowlton

Co-President and Chief Marketing Officer
Tabula Rasa HealthCare Inc.
Moorestown, New Jersey

Sarah LeMay, PharmD

Resident, PGY-1 Health-Systems Pharmacy Administration and Leadership
William S. Middleton Memorial Veterans Hospital
Madison, Wisconsin

Steven Lucio, PharmD, BCPS

Senior Principal, Center for Pharmacy Practice Excellence
Vizient, Inc.
Irving, Texas

Alfred E. Lyman, Jr., PharmD, BCPS

Executive Director, Regional Pharmacy Services
Kaiser Permanente Northwest Region
Pharmacy Administration
Portland, Oregon

Halena Leah Marcelin, PharmD, MS

Director, Pharmacy Business Affairs
Baptist Health South Florida
Miami, Florida

Lisa Mascardo, PharmD, MBA, FASHP

Director, Ambulatory Pharmacy
Department of Pharmaceutical Care
University of Iowa Health Care
Iowa City, Iowa

Matthew Maughan, PharmD, MHCDS

Director of Pharmacy Operations
Dartmouth-Hitchcock Medical Center
Lebanon, New Hampshire

Caron Misita, PharmD, BCPS

Director, Pharmacy Benefits
Prescription Benefit Solutions
Pittsboro, North Carolina

Agatha Nolen, PhD, CRCR, FASHP

Certified Revenue Cycle Representative Visante
St. Paul, Minnesota

John Pastor III, PharmD, FASHP, FMSHP

System Vice President, Pharmacy and Respiratory Care
Fairview Health Services
Minneapolis, Minnesota

Ravi Patel, PharmD, MBA, MS

Lead Innovation Advisor
School of Pharmacy
University of Pittsburgh
Pittsburgh, Pennsylvania

Fern Paul-Aviles, PharmD, MS, BCPS

Assistant Vice President, Pharmacy
340B, Pharmacy Population Health Strategy, and Non-acute Pharmacy Service Lines
Atrium Health

Zachary Pollock, PharmD, MS

Associate Director, Clinical Cancer Services
Holden Comprehensive Cancer Center
University of Iowa Health Care
Iowa City, Iowa

Eric Reimer, PharmD

Regional Manager
Credena Health – Alaska, Montana & Washington
Spokane, Washington

Matthew H. Rim, PharmD, MS, FASHP

Clinical Assistant Professor, Department of Pharmacy Practice
Residency Program Director, PGY2 SPAL
College of Pharmacy, University of Illinois Chicago
Senior Associate Director, Specialty and Infusion Pharmacies
Ambulatory Pharmacy Services
UI Health
Chicago, Illinois

Steve Rough, MS, RPh, FASHP

Senior Vice President
Visante
St. Paul, Minnesota

Wayne Russell, PharmD, FASHP

Vice President, Pharmacy
Premier, Inc.
Charlotte, North Carolina

Lucas Schulz, PharmD

Clinical Pharmacist
University of Wisconsin Hospital and Clinics
Madison, Wisconsin

Mark Siska, RPh, MBA/TM, FASHP

Chief Pharmacy Informatics Officer, Pharmacy Services
Mayo Clinic
Rochester, Minnesota

Kelly M. Smith, PharmD, FASHP, FCCP

Dean and Professor
University of Georgia College of Pharmacy
Athens, Georgia

Scott Sterrett, PharmD, MBA

Director of Pharmacy
Beaumont Home Infusion & Specialty Pharmacy
Royal Oak, Michigan

Kristin Tiry, PharmD, MHA

Pharmacy Manager
Froedtert and Medical College of Wisconsin
Milwaukee, Wisconsin

Candy Tsourounis, PharmD, FCSHP

Professor of Clinical Pharmacy, Department of Clinical Pharmacy
Pharmacoeconomics and Drug Use Management Supervisor
UCSF Health
San Francisco, California

Susan M. Wescott, RPh, MBA

Senior Director of Pharmacy, Managed Care, Mayo Clinic
Executive Lead, Clinical Services, Alluma
Mayo Clinic
Rochester, Minnesota

Jennifer Wood, PharmD, BCPS

Clinical Pharmacist Practitioner, Ambulatory Care
William S. Middleton Memorial Veterans Hospital
Madison, Wisconsin

ASPECTS OF FINANCIAL MANAGEMENT: COST AND PREDICTIVE ACCOUNTING

John Pastor III, Lori Berg, and Miriam Jarvinen

This chapter will provide an overview of the healthcare industry and health system financial accounting and reporting. The reader will gain insight into the industry and into the accounting and reporting issues facing health system leaders today. This chapter will provide important background for more in-depth information in the chapters that follow.

THE "BUSINESS" OF HEALTHCARE

Healthcare is business—big business. Healthcare spending continues to rise sharply, and in the United States in 2020 it reached $4.1 trillion which equates to $12,530 per person. The portion of the Gross Domestic Product (GDP) attributed to healthcare spending rose to a record 19.7% in 2020. The unprecedented spending in 2020 was primarily due to the significant increase in federal expenditures for healthcare that occurred in response to the COVID-19 pandemic. Additionally, health spending is projected to grow at an average annual rate of 5.4% and reach $6.2 trillion by the year 2028.[1]

This level of spending creates enormous pressure on health system leaders at all levels to manage their organizations more effectively than many other businesses, whether organized as community-based/not-for-profit, for-profit, or as an academic medical center. Operating efficiently and generating a margin is crucial for all health systems, regardless of ownership, to maintain infrastructure, replace equipment, and implement modern technologies to keep up with consumer demand. For many health systems another important aspect of efficient operations is making interest payments on bonds and other indebtedness or making dividend payments to shareholders.

MISSION AND COMMUNITY FOCUS

Hospitals and health systems are community-focused, mission-driven organizations, which sets them apart from most other businesses. Organizations must make sound business decisions while demonstrating their core values in addressing the needs of the communities being served. For many hospitals, especially critical access, or sole community hospitals, running an efficient operation simply equates to survival.

Another area that distinguishes hospitals and health systems from most other businesses is the number of stakeholders involved. How many other businesses provide services to customers (patients) as ordered by independent practitioners (physicians not always employed by the hospital) and paid for by a third party? Many of the supplies used by hospitals are dictated by the preferences of physicians who have no fiscal responsibility for the cost of those supplies. Other stakeholders include the employed caregivers, lenders, owners, vendors, and the community at large. These various relationships create a complex operational environment not found in many other businesses.

Efficient operations, defined by an excess of revenues over expenses, are often equated to margin. Some argue that generating margin is somehow fundamentally wrong in healthcare. However, generating a margin (or return on investment) is critical in order to replace aging equipment and facilities and to provide new technology for tomorrow's healthcare needs. These uses of margin support the mission of the hospital/health system and it has been said that "without margin, there is no mission."

GOVERNANCE

In 2021, the United States had 6,090 hospitals. Of those, 48% were nonprofit/community hospitals and 20% were for-profit or investor owned. The remaining 32% were government, psychiatric, or other specialty institutions.[2]

Nonprofit community hospitals and health systems are generally organized as tax-exempt and qualify as charities under the Internal Revenue Service regulations (501 (c)(3)). As result of that tax-exempt status, they generally do not pay property tax, state or federal income tax, or sales tax. In exchange for this, they are required to reinvest monies and services back into their communities. Access to capital for these organizations is mainly through donations (usually tax deductible to the donor), bonds and other debt instruments, and by managing operations efficiently. These organizations face regular scrutiny by policymakers charged with ensuring they contribute to their communities in a meaningful way that justifies the significant tax exemptions they receive.

Beyond contributing to the community, academic medical centers have as part of their mission the responsibility to teach new healthcare professionals and funding medical research. These additional responsibilities carry a higher cost structure, which is often offset in some measure by other funding sources, such as grants, state legislative funding, and so forth.

Conversely, for-profit hospitals are investor-owned and organized as taxable entities. They are different from nonprofit organizations in that they are expected to make profits for shareholders or owners. Access to capital is mainly through the sale of stock, debt instruments, and efficient operations.

All hospitals and health systems are governed by a board of trustees, regardless of how they are organized and structured. The board is responsible for hiring or firing the Chief Executive Officer (CEO), advising the CEO and executive leadership team, and approving policies and major decisions for the organization. The board, in effect, supervises the CEO and monitors organizational performance with a focus on both current performance and long-term sustainability.

The CEO, or president, is responsible for developing and executing the strategies needed to operate the organization. This includes all aspects of clinical care and operations, financial performance, along with quality and safety. The CEO and their team are accountable to the board of directors/trustees.

In addition to the CEO, senior leadership may include a Chief Financial Officer, a Chief Operating Officer, a Chief Medical Officer, a Chief Nursing Executive, a Chief Pharmacy Officer as well as other administrative officers (legal, human resources, public affairs, digital, and information technology). Titles will vary depending upon the facility's size, style, and organization. These senior leaders are accountable to the CEO and board for the strategic and tactical decisions made for the operation of the facility. Department leaders, such as the pharmacy director, are responsible for the day-to-day operational decisions made in the facility.

ENVIRONMENTAL FACTORS

Hospital and health system operations are subject to regulatory oversight by numerous agencies and accreditation bodies. The Centers for Medicare & Medicaid Services (CMS), their approved accrediting organizations such as The Joint Commission (TJC) and DNV Healthcare (DNV), the state board of pharmacy, and the state department of health are examples of a few of the many regulatory organizations that seek to reshape the way healthcare will be delivered in the future. Consumer, payer, and employer groups have also been formed in recent years to address the issue of rising healthcare costs and how to improve healthcare outcomes. All these organizations will impact the pharmacy leader's role in managing across the entire pharmacy enterprise.

The rising cost of caring for the indigent, uninsured, and underinsured is threatening the financial well-being of many of America's hospitals and health systems. The number of Americans living below 200% of the Federal Poverty Level (as published by the federal government each spring) continues to increase. Although some citizens seek healthcare in free clinics, many use hospital emergency rooms for primary and urgent care. This comes at an excessive cost and, for most, is an inappropriate setting for routine healthcare.

Because of the increasing cost of health insurance premiums, many employees have found coverage to be either unaffordable or unavailable. Many Americans have decided to risk being uninsured to divert financial resources into other areas of their lives. Others may have become temporarily uninsured while in between jobs. To reduce health insurance premiums, some employers have offered health plans with high deductibles, which is the amount that beneficiaries must pay before their health insurance will begin to pay, or high co-payments, which is the total amount that the beneficiary must pay. Although these plans reduce monthly premium costs, they may become financially stressful when services are needed.

Providing care for indigent, uninsured, and underinsured Americans is challenging the resources of the healthcare system. All organizations are wrestling with this issue. The Affordable Care Act (ACA) was enacted in 2010 to improve health insurance markets for individuals and small businesses, lower healthcare costs and increase the number of people with healthcare insurance. Charity care write-offs and debt expense are among the top financial problems for hospitals. It will take a collaboration of hospitals, health systems, safety net providers, communities, payers, and the government to solve the issue. Pharmacy leaders can also play a significant role in creating pharmacy solutions for low income or indigent patients. Many pharmaceutical manufacturers offer programs that provide drugs for patients who cannot afford their medications. Dedicating resources to assist in obtaining access to these programs is a valuable contribution from today's pharmacy leader.

DEFINITIONS OF COST AND PREDICTIVE ACCOUNTING

Accounting had always been a profession focused on reviewing historical performance. However, that focus has changed and there is a growing focus on leveraging tools to accurately predict future performance.

Cost accounting refers to a set of procedures for recording and reporting revenues and the cost of goods and services in the aggregate and in detail. It includes methods for identifying, classifying, allocating, aggregating, and reporting. Cost accounting provides leaders the detailed cost information to facilitate decision making when managing current operations as well as helping them plan.

Recently there has been a significant shift in accounting strategy within health systems. Enterprise-wide integration of information and billing systems, along with advanced analytics and artificial intelligence, are providing finance operations leaders with the necessary information to be more forward-looking with predictive accounting. Predictive accounting processes enable decision makers to get a credible look into future performance to make better present-day decisions.

The new buzz word in today's healthcare is Predictive Analytics. Predictive Analytics captures variables from past occurrences combined with statistical modeling via Artificial Intelligence (AI) to discover correlations and provide actionable recommendations. As data sets become larger, manual analysis is becoming less feasible. Predictive Analytics allows one to make decisions early in the process to improve patient outcomes and achieve financial goals. Wikipedia defines artificial intelligence (AI) in healthcare as technology that "uses algorithms and software to approximate human cognition in the analysis of complex medical data. The primary aim of health-related AI applications is to analyze relationships between prevention or treatment techniques and patient outcomes."

By embedding predictive analytic models across the continuum of care, healthcare systems can leverage analytics for meaningful improvement:

- **Population Health Management**—Patients at high-risk of developing a chronic condition can be identified early to avoid costly treatments later.

- **Risk Management**—Identify high-risk patients who can be treated with medications which results in improved quality of care and reduced costs.

- **Readmissions**—Identify patients with a high probability of being readmitted within 30 days of discharge. Clinicians can implement predischarge interventions and adjust care plans, thus avoiding readmissions.

- **Medication Adherence**—Identify patients who are at high-risk for nonadherence. Early intervention will improve patient outcomes.

- **Resources**—Patients who are most likely to miss appointments can be identified. The health system can send reminders or provide transportation to minimize workflow disruptions.

- **Finance**—Data can be applied to streamline budgeting, clinical processes, quality metrics, and key performance indicators (KPIs).

Improving prediction is one of the key challenges healthcare faces in advancing patient care. Enhancing diagnosis, treatment plans, and understanding disease progression are key components. The advantages of improved outcomes, lowered costs, and reduced patient risk make the adoption of Predictive Analytics a priority in bringing healthcare to a new level.

OVERVIEW OF THE FISCAL SERVICES DEPARTMENT

Fiscal Services is the collective name for numerous financial functions often led by the chief financial officer (CFO). **Table 1-1 Typical Departments within Fiscal Services** lists the departments often associated with the CFO, the responsibilities, and the typical position that manages the department. Titles and specific positions vary among hospitals and health systems, and the reporting roll up of departments may vary.

The CFO often reports to the Chief Executive Officer (CEO) or president and is responsible for the financial operation of the hospital or health system. CFOs play a key role in the strategic direction and are part of an integrated team of leaders across the organization functions. CFOs must have an appreciation for the full complexities of operations to fully align the financial objectives with the strategic objectives of the organization. The CFO must also ensure the integrity of the financial reporting, financial systems, and financial health of the organization. In addition, the CFO ensures

TABLE 1-1. Typical Departments within Fiscal Services

Department	Responsibilities	Typical Person in Charge
Accounting	Manages all general ledger accounting, monthly reporting, and subsidiary ledger accounting for the organization; responsible for compilation of financial statements, maintaining fixed asset records, reconciling general ledger accounts, and communicating health system performance and performance drivers to health system leaders.	Controller
Business Office/Revenue Cycle Management	Manages all aspects of billing and collections for third party and patient accounts including financial securing, charge capture, claims billing, claims payment follow-up to ensure accurate payment receipt, denial management, and payer/claims audit management.	Revenue cycle management or business office vice president or director
Managed Care Contracting	Manages all aspects of managed care contracts including contract negotiation, contract management, and total cost of care performance reporting.	Managed care vice president or director
Financial Operations/Analytics	Partners with organization leaders to analyze financial and clinical data across the organization to understand financial performance, drivers, identify opportunities and improvements, and support strategic decision making. Also manages the forecasting and budgeting processes with organization leaders.	Financial operations vice president or director
Payroll	Manages all payroll functions for the health system.	Payroll manager
Accounts Payable	Manages all payments to vendors for the health system.	Accounts payable manager
Supply Chain or Purchasing and Materials Management	Handles all procurement and materials warehousing and distribution for the health system.	Supply chain or materials vice president or director
Treasury	Manages the organization's cash and investment portfolio, balance sheet and cash forecasting, capital management and acquisition, risk management and insurance, and tax.	Treasurer or director of treasury
Cost Reporting	Prepares annual cost reports for Medicare and other governmental payers as required and keeps the organization current on changing regulations.	Reimbursement or cost reporting director
Development	Organizes and conducts fund raising for community-based/ not-for-profit health systems.	Director of development

compliance with financial regulations, including billing, cost reporting, accounting standards and financial covenants.

THE ACCOUNTING CYCLE

The accounting cycle includes revenue cycle, the expense cycle, "capital" items, the budget, and the monthly close and reporting process. The accounting cycle is detailed below.

THE REVENUE CYCLE

Revenues are generated when services or goods are provided to patients. See the **Income Statement** section for a more detailed description of revenues, discounts, and net revenue. All healthcare organizations have a system in place to capture the charges for the services provided. Charge capture is when charges are entered into the patient accounting system (billing system) for services provided and bills are generated (often referred to as "dropped"). Health systems bill the patient's insurance carrier on behalf of the patient and keep the patient informed as to the status of the claim. The insurance carrier will also inform the patient of bills received from the health system in the form of an Explanation of Benefits (EOB) statement. The EOB will provide the patient detailed information from the insurance carrier of bills received, contractual discounts taken, amounts covered by the insurance plan, and amounts that are a secondary insurance or patient responsibility based on the patient's insurance plan coverage (such as co-payment, deductibles, or coinsurance). Once the insurance carrier (or governmental payer) pays the health system for the claim, the health system will write off the contractual discounts as appropriate and bill the patient for any patient portion due as identified by the carrier. For retail pharmacy prescription charges, the claims are typically adjudicated at the time of dispense at the contractual rate by the Pharmacy Benefits Manager (PBM) and the patient portion is identified at that time. A PBM is a third-party administrator acting on behalf of the insurer/health plan.

The revenue cycle is affected by the clinical department's successful capture of charges for the services provided, the complexities of the negotiated contracts with the carrier, and the timeliness of submitting the bill payments receipt from the carrier and the patient. Charge capture is a crucial part of the revenue cycle process and requires accurate documentation of the care provided to ensure all services provided are billed. Ongoing training of staff on billing rules and regulations, continuous communication between interdisciplinary teams, documented processes, and consistent charge standards are crucial in successful charge capture. In addition, organizations should leverage technology platforms to automate and streamline the process. The goal is to accurately capture all services provided and shorten the time between when the service is provided and when the bill is produced to ensure the services are billed in accordance with regulations or payer requirements and to accelerate cash receipt. Quick turnaround of accounts receivable (amounts billed to carriers and patients that have not been collected) is crucial to provide ongoing cash flow to the organization.

Another key component to the revenue cycle is collection, and retention, of billed amounts. Billed claims should be reconciled to ensure correct and timely payment is received from the payer. This not only includes ensuring that payment for the claim is received, but also that the payment is accurate per the contractual rates. For retail pharmacy claims, this also includes reviewing the amounts adjudicated by the PBMs (pharmacy benefit managers) against contractual rates. Processes should also be in place to review, validate, and follow-up on subsequent take back of payments to ensure the organization is not only receiving, but retaining amounts contractually due. And processes should also be in place to track and manage payer claim audits. This includes providing the documentation within the time required by the audit and retaining audited amounts contractually due. As with claims capture, organizations should leverage technology platforms to automate and streamline these processes to better ensure accurate payment and payment retention.

The billing and payment accounting system is generally automated and linked with the general ledger accounting system. In some cases, the interface between the two may be manual.

THE EXPENSE CYCLE

Expenses are the result of commitments for costs incurred in the provision of patient services or the operation of the health system. Successful health systems have a defined process to bind the organization to financial commitments. A typical process starts with a purchase request or requisition to be completed by the department leader. This document includes information on the proposed purchase, including vendor, amount, a description of item to be purchased, the general ledger account code, the budgeted amount, and the business justification for the purchase. Purchase requisitions have established approval levels required before the final purchase order is communicated to the vendor. This can include supervisor or manager level up to senior administration, depending on the amount of the requisition. In some organizations, the purchasing department communicates the final approved purchase order to the vendor, and in others the department leader manages this. Once the items are appropriately received by the health system and an invoice is received, the accounts payable department will match the invoice with the original purchase order. If the amounts match, the invoice will be paid. If not, the documents are often returned to the originating department to resolve the discrepancy. Accounts payable will typically not pay a vendor's invoice until all discrepancies are resolved.

Like the patient accounting system, the purchasing and accounts payable systems are most often automated and linked with the general ledger accounting system. In some cases, the interface between the systems may be manual.

CAPITAL ITEMS

Certain high dollar items with a useful life of greater than one year are generally referred to as "capital" items. They derive this name because they are reported on the balance sheet as an asset when acquired rather than on the income statement as an expense. Because capital items have a benefit of greater than one year and are high dollar items, these items are expensed, or depreciated, over the expected life of the asset. This allows the expense of the purchase to be recognized over the period the asset is used rather than all at the time of purchase. Each organization will establish the financial threshold of when an expenditure is considered capital, determine the capital budget, and establish the capital approval process.

Frequently the capital budget is divided into subcategories such as replacement infrastructure, strategic, technology, or break/fix. For many healthcare organizations capital needs can be high when compared against the capital budget available. To determine which capital items to prioritize, capital expenditures require additional review and consideration. Further analysis of the expenditure can include a pro forma, a return-on-investment calculation, and a value proposition describing the need for capital, the benefits, risks, and alternatives. Frequently subject matter experts are engaged in this process to ensure full needs of a capital purchase or project are considered before approving, such as facilities, information technology, finance, and supply chain. Many health systems have established groups or committees to review requests for prioritization and final approval. Departmental leadership should consult with the CFO to understand the specific requirements for capital purchases.

THE BUDGET

The budget is the roadmap for the organization to obtain its strategic objectives. Historically, the development of the budget was a lengthy, complicated process; however, because of enhancements in budgeting and analytical tools, and the dynamically changing healthcare industry, organizations are moving toward a more lean and timely budget process. Budgets are frequently paired with timelier monthly or quarterly forecasts that can shift with changing business and industry trends and allow leaders to adjust business plans to address these changes. Budgets are typically compiled with cross-functional teams that include department leaders, administration, and finance teams, including the CFO, the controller, and decision support analysts that closely analyze historical trends and future projections. The pharmacy director should consult with the CFO to understand the specific responsibilities for budget development.

The budget process should factor in numerous variables such as historical financial performance paired with anticipated changes in future performance including payer mix, payer contracts, patient mix, patient volumes, industry changes, and individual health system initiatives such as focused growth initiatives. These should be carried through for all service areas within the health system impacted by these factors. The completed budget is subjected to an extensive review and approval process. Approvals are obtained from senior leadership, the board of trustees, and any other governing entity. Once approved, the budget becomes the measuring stick against which monthly performance is compared.

In most health systems, department leaders are responsible for analyzing and explaining performance variances with the budget. Action plans are often required for ongoing performance that is projected to vary significantly from the budget. This requires a thorough understanding of the departmental operations or responsibility reports and the general accounting processes influencing those reports.

THE MONTHLY CLOSE

The controller and staff close the general ledger at the end of every month. The general ledger close accumulates all activity from the current month and resets the general ledger for the next month. For accrual basis accounting, the close includes all revenue and expenses that were incurred during the period and will include accruals for accounts receivable, accounts payable, payroll, and other liabilities. For cash basis accounting, the close will include all cash transactions for the month (see **Accounting Methods** below). The general ledger is typically held open for a designated number of days in the following month, many within five to 10 business days, to allow for compilation of the monthly activity, ensure accruals are made, and accounts are reviewed, complete, and accurate.

The monthly close process involves compiling many sources of data into the general ledger including the electronic health record charges, payment reconciliation system(s), accounts payable system, payroll system, and capital management system. In many organizations some of these are integrated into the same platform (such as the electronic health record and payment reconciliation, or general ledger, payroll, and capital management on one enterprise management system).

Once the general ledger is closed, the financial statements and departmental reports can be prepared and distributed for management to review. These reports include the Income Statement, Balance Sheet, and Statement of Cash Flows (see **Financial Reporting** below). For successful financial management it is imperative to include analysis of the financial results to understand performance drivers. These drivers should be used to determine any changes in operational processes to maximize financial performance and address any performance shortfalls. This analysis is typically performed by the financial operations analysts, department leaders, and the controller.

To further assist with this process, department leaders should ensure that invoices are processed promptly, ensure critical information about trends and operational changes is communicated to the controller and the financial operations team in a timely manner, and work with the finance operations/analytics team.

ACCOUNTING METHODS

There are three basic accounting methods used by healthcare organizations: cash basis, accrual basis, and fund accounting.

Cash-basis accounting recognizes income and expense only when cash is received or disbursed. It is a simple method of accounting that does not factor in liabilities for purchases made but not yet received, and assets earned but not yet collected. Financial reports generated by cash-basis accounting can be grossly misleading and inaccurate to actual performance because it does not represent revenue when earned and the related expenses incurred. This can produce misleading income results, does not show the balance sheet asset, liability, and equity position of the organization, and does not accurately reflect the financial position of the organization. Cash-basis accounting is typically limited to individuals or small community organizations.

Accrual basis accounting accrues revenues and expenses in the proper period they were earned or incurred. This method of accounting is used for most organizations. This is a large part of the monthly closing process for the controller and staff. For accurate monthly financial statements, the controller and staff must ensure that all transactions for the month are properly recorded, regardless of whether cash has been received or paid. This method will better reflect the financial position of an organization, its revenue, expenses, income, assets, liabilities, and equity. Most of the examples and discussion in the remainder of this chapter focus on the accrual basis of accounting.

Fund accounting is typically used by governmental entities and academic medical centers. Fund accounting establishes specific funds for a variety of uses. Two examples include an equipment replacement fund and the general fund. The equipment replacement fund would be used to replace specific equipment in the future. The general fund serves as the operating fund for the entity. Many of the funds extend beyond the normal one-year cycle. This makes budgeting and maintenance of the funds a bit more complex.

GENERAL LEDGER CHART OF ACCOUNTS

The general ledger uses a set of accounts organized according to their type. The chart of accounts (COA) refers to an index of all these accounts that is organized into main categories for asset, liability, equity, revenue, and expense, typically assigned numerically in that order. These are further broken down into more detailed subcategories. Each account is given a multidigit identification code and a brief description. The number of digits in the accounts varies by health system; the examples below use six. The following table demonstrates a typical configuration for organizing the chart of accounts:

Account Range	General Account Category
1xx.xxx	Assets
2xx.xxx	Liabilities
3xx.xxx	Equity or Fund Balance
4xx.xxx	Revenues
5xx.xxx	Deductions from Revenues
6xx.xxx	Expenses

General ledger accounts are further broken down and organized within the category listed above, as noted in the examples below. Some health systems maintain more detailed general ledgers using a separate account for tracking specific details. Other health systems organize the general ledger in a broader manner and use subsidiary ledgers for further detail.

Assets typically have numerical categories assigned based on the asset type, where the first three digits are often the general asset type, with the first digit identified by the general account category (1 above). As an example, 110.xxx may be used for the cash accounts and 120.xxx may be used for receivable accounts. The last three digits are typically used for detailed breakout of these asset types. For example, accounts receivable may be broken out by patient receivables in 120.110 and third-party payer receivables in 120.120.

Liabilities (2 above) are assigned numerical categories like assets. Examples are 210.xxx may be used for accounts payable and 220.xxx may be used for accrued wages; and within accrued wages, accrued payroll may be 220.110 and accrued health insurance 220.120.

Revenue also has numerical categories assigned, where the first three digits are often the type of revenue (such as inpatient and outpatient) with the first digit as identified in the revenue chart of accounts (4 above). For example, inpatient revenue may be assigned 410 and outpatient revenue 420. For the last three digits, each revenue-producing department type is typically assigned a revenue center code. For example, the lab department may be assigned 310, the full general ledger account code for inpatient and outpatient lab revenue would be 410.310 and 420.310, respectively.

Deductions from Revenues (5 above) represent amounts that will not be collected from the gross billed charges in revenues. Deductions from revenues can include contractual discounts, provision for bad, and charity care. Contractual discounts are the difference between the health system established billed rates for the care provided and the contractual rates with the insurance carrier, government agency, or other third party. Provision for bad debt includes an estimate of the amount due to the health system that will not be realized because of non-collection. Charity care, also referred to as uncompensated care, represents care provided with no charge or at a reduced charge to people with limited income that are unable to pay for their care. Health systems have an established policy on its charity care program including qualification criteria and the amount of assistance provided.

Expenses (6 above) have numerical categories assigned based on the expense type. As an example, 610 may be used for salary and wage expense and 630 may be used for purchased services expense. The last three digits further break out each expense type, for example purchased laundry services may be 630.110 and purchased food services may be 630.120.

Department leaders should understand the organization of the chart of accounts and the appropriate use of the accounts because they are often responsible for coding purchase requisitions and invoices as well as managing performance results within their departments.

FINANCIAL REPORTING

Financial reporting for healthcare organizations is regulated by several different entities. The Financial Accounting Standards Board (FASB) and Governmental Accounting Standards Board (GASB) establish Generally Accepted Accounting Principles (GAAP) that organizations must follow. The American Institute of Certified Public Accountants (AICPA) publishes an Audit and Accounting Guide for Healthcare Organizations that summarizes the reporting requirements. This section introduces the basic financial statements and their application to operational management.

THE BALANCE SHEET

The balance sheet is a valuable statement that represents the overall financial condition of an organization. The balance sheet lists assets owned by the organization on the left side of the report, and the liabilities owed and the equity of the organization on the right side of the report. Equity, or fund balance, represents the difference between the assets and the liabilities. It is called "net assets" because it reflects the amount of ownership in the organization after payment of liabilities. The balance sheet represents a given date in time and is often referred to as a "snapshot" of the entity's assets and liabilities as of that specific date. The financial statement derives its name from the fact that the total assets must equal, or "balance" to, total liabilities and equity.

TABLE 1-2. Typical Balance Sheets as of December 31, 2021 and 2020

	December 31	
ASSETS	**2021**	**2020**
Current Assets		
Cash and Cash Equivalents	$42,130	$40,020
Accounts Receivable for Medical Services	$360,860	$342,820
Less: Allowance for Contractual Deductions	$(187,650)	$(178,270)
Less: Allowance for Bad Debts	$(10,830)	$(10,290)
Net Accounts Receivable for Medical Services	$162,380	$154,260
Receivable under Third Party Payer Contracts	$4,230	$4,020
Inventories	$64,140	$60,930
Prepaid Expenses	$2,120	$2,010
Other Receivables	$10,460	$9,940
Other Current Assets	$60,160	$57,150
Total Current Assets	$345,620	$328,330
Land, Buildings, and Equipment		
Land and Land Improvement	$50,820	$48,280
Buildings and Building Improvement	$842,650	$800,520
Equipment	$402,500	$382,380
Finanaced Leased Facilities and Equipment	$30,160	$28,650
Construction In Process	$58,920	$55,970
Accumulated Depreciation	$(760,120)	$(722,110)
Net Land, Buildings, and Equipment	$624,930	$593,690
Investments	$996,540	$946,710
Other Assets		
Intangible Assets, Net	$26,790	$25,450
Right of Use Operating Leases Assets	$58,280	$55,370
Investment in Related Parties	$40,150	$38,140
Other Long Term Assets	$13,100	$12,450
Total Other Long Term Assets	$138,320	$131,410
TOTAL ASSETS	**$2,105,410**	**$2,000,140**

TABLE 1-2. continued

		December 31	
ASSETS		**2021**	**2020**
LIABILITIES AND NET ASSETS			
Current Liabilities			
Accounts Payable		$140,830	$133,790
Accrued Wages		$160,460	$152,440
Right of Use Operating Lease Obligations		$8,940	$8,490
Current Maturities of Long Term Debt		$36,250	$34,440
Other Current Liabilities		$41,440	$39,370
Total Current Liabilities		$387,920	$368,530
Long Term Debt		$590,390	$560,870
Other Liabilities			
Right of Use Operating Lease Obligations		$53,370	$50,700
Other Long Term Obligations		$68,450	$65,030
Total Other Liabilities		$121,820	$115,730
Total Liabilities		$1,100,130	$1,045,130
Net Assets			
Retained Earnings - Start of Year		$934,305	$894,164
Net Income - Current Year		$70,975	$60,846
Total Net Assets		$1,005,280	$955,010
TOTAL LIABILITIES AND NET ASSETS		**$2,105,410**	**$2,000,140**

TABLE 1-3. Balance Sheet Definitions

Assets		
Cash and Cash Equivalents		This represents the cash on hand and short term cash investments as of the balance sheet date.
Accounts Receivable for Medical Services		
	Accounts Receivable for Medical Services	This represents the accounts receivable from patients or payers on behalf of patients (Medicare, Medicaid, Blue Cross, Cigna, etc.). For some payers, the receivable is reduced to the net amount expected to be collected and is shown on this line at the net amount. For other payers, the gross receivable is shown on this line and an allowance for deductions from revenue is accrued.
	Allowance for Deductions	This represents the difference between negotiated or regulated rates expected to be received and the gross charges in accounts receivable. An allowance is calculated and accrued for all payers whose accounts are not discounted and reported net in the line above. Often referred to as Allowance for Discounts and Contractual Adjustments.
	Allowance for Bad Debt	This represents the estimated amount of bad debt included in patient receivables.
	Net Patient Receivables	This represents the net amount expected to be collected from patients or payers on behalf of patients.

TABLE 1-3. continued

Assets		
Receivable under Third Party Payer Contracts		This represents receivables (or payables) anticipated from filed Medicare and Medicaid cost reports, total cost of care contracts, or other ongoing or future contract provisions. These amounts are not finalized until these items are filed and finalized.
Inventories		This represents supplies on hand as of the balance sheet date. Supplies includes pharmaceutical drugs, medical and surgical supplies, lab, and diagnostic imaging.
Prepaid Expenses		This represents invoices paid which benefit future periods and are therefore expensed over those future periods.
Other Receivables		This represents miscellaneous receivables not from patients and patient services.
Other Current Assets		This represents assets which are highly liquid. Generally, current assets are assets that are expected to be converted to cash in less than one year.
Land, Buildings, and Equipment		
	Land and Land Improvements	This represents the historical cost of land and any improvements (such as sidewalks and landscaping). Depreciation is not calculated on land.
	Buildings and Building Improvements	This represents the historical cost of the buildings and building improvements.
	Equipment	This represents the historical cost of major moveable equipment (typically large, stationary equipment that is capable of being moved, such as lab analyzers, imaging equipment, and autos), fixed equipment (typically large equipment attached to the buildings, such as boilers, HVAC, and backup electrical generators), and certain minor equipment (typically office furnishings and equipment greater than an established dollar threshhold...amounts below that threshhold are typically expensed to supplies).
	Financed Leased Facilities and Equipment	This represents leased facilities and equipment that have characteristics of owned assets in accordance with ASC 842, where the economic benefits and risks of the underlying asset transfer to the lessee. This includes transfer of ownership to the lessee or an option to purchase underlying assets, or the lease term is for the majority of the economic life of the underlying asset, or the lease payments are more than substantially all of the fair value of the underlying asset.
	Construction in Progress	This represents the costs of construction projects currently in progress that have not yet been placed in service.
	Accumulated Depreciation	This represents the depreciation expense recorded over time associated with the property, plant and equipment assets noted above. Depreciation is not calculated on land and on construction in progress.
	Net Land, Buildings, and Equipment	Often referred to as "net book value," this represents the depreciated cost of the land, building, and equipment assets.
Investments		This represents the cost of long-term investments. Often, specific investment categories will be reported on the Balance Sheet.

TABLE 1-3. continued

Assets		
Other Assets		
	Intangible Assets, Net	This represents specific intangible assets associated with the organization. Goodwill from a purchase of the facility is one example.
	Right of Use Operating Leases Assets	This represents the lessee's right to use an underlying asset over the lease term in accordance with ASC 842.
Liabilities		
Accounts Payable		This represents invoices and check request that are awaiting payment. This includes invoices and payment requests received by accounts payable as well as received but not invoiced items.
Accrued Salary & Benefits		This represents an accrual for the end of period payroll expense (payroll earned by employees but not yet paid), and accruals for other compensation related liabilities such as FICA, retirement benefits, paid time off, and health benefits.
Right of Use Operating Lease Obligations		A lessee's obligation to make the lease payments arising from a lease, measured on a discounted basis, broken out between current (due in less than one year) and long term (due in greater than one year).
Current Maturities of Long Term Debt		This represents the portion of a debt liabilities that are coming due in the next year.
Other Current Liabilities		This represents other organization liabilities that are expected to be paid within one year.
Long Term Debt		This represents the portion of a debt liabilities that are due in greater than one year.
Other Long-Term Obligations		This represents other long-term debt or commitments by the facility.
Net Assets		
Retained Earnings		This represents the accumulated earnings (losses) of the organization since its inception.
Net Income - Current Year		This represents the current year's net income.

Assets are separated into short-term and long-term. Short-term assets are those that can be converted to cash in a short period of time, typically within a year, and include cash, accounts receivable, and inventory. Long-term assets include fixed assets such as property, plant, and equipment. Liabilities are also separated into short-term and long-term. Short-term liabilities include accounts payable, accrued salaries and wages, accrued liabilities due within a year, and short-term debts. Long-term liabilities include loans or other amounts repaid over many years. Equity, or fund balance, represents the difference between the assets and the liabilities. It is called "net assets" because it reflects the amount of ownership in the organization after payment of liabilities.

The balance sheet is necessary for managing an effective organization and understanding how much cash the organization has, and how quickly assets can be converted to cash for funding operations and working capital. Department leaders can use the balance sheet to assess operational performance such as inventory turn, with a goal to maximize inventory turns. Net days in patient

TABLE 1-4. Typical Income Statement for the Years Ended December 31, 2021 and 2020

	12/31/2021				12/31/2020		
	Actual	Budget	Variance	Var %	Prior Year	Variance	Var %
Operating Revenue							
Inpatient Revenue	$3,012,720	$2,979,580	$33,140	1.1%	$2,895,224	$117,496	3.9%
Outpatient Revenue	$2,215,400	$2,233,123	$(17,723)	−0.8%	$ 2,166,661	$ 48,739	2.2%
Other Patient Revenue	$980,400	$976,478	$3,922	0.4%	$950,988	$29,412	3.0%
Gross Patinet Revenue	$6,208,520	$6,189,182	$19,338	0.3%	$6,012,873	$195,647	3.3%
Discounts	$(3,319,860)	$(3,303,261)	$(16,599)	−0.5%	$(3,213,624)	$(106,236)	−3.2%
Uncompensated Care	$(31,370)	$(31,150)	$(220)	−0.7%	$(30,743)	$(627)	−2.0%
Bad Debt	$(52,280)	$(51,757)	$(523)	−1.0%	$(50,712)	$(1,568)	−3.0%
Shared Savings	$18,425	$17,872	$553	3.0%	$17,688	$737	4.0%
Net Patient Revenue	$2,823,435	$2,820,886	$2,549	0.1%	$2,735,482	$87,953	3.2%
Other Operating Revenue	$101,480	$100,465	$1,015	1.0%	$100,465	$1,015	1.0%
Total Operating revenue	$2,924,915	$2,921,351	$3,564	0.1%	$2,835,948	$88,967	3.1%
Operating Expenses							
Salaries and Benefits	$1,697,015	$1,698,712	$1,697	0.1%	$1,646,105	$(50,910)	−3.0%
Contract Labor	$52,485	$52,275	$(210)	−0.4%	$51,173	$(1,312)	−2.5%
Professional Fees	$128,176	$127,663	$(513)	−0.4%	$124,203	$(3,973)	−3.1%
Purchased Services	$32,044	$32,685	$641	2.0%	$31,019	$(1,025)	−3.2%
Supplies	$740,680	$737,717	$(2,963)	−0.4%	$719,200	$(21,480)	−2.9%
Utilities, Repair, and Maintenance	$96,840	$96,549	$(291)	−0.3%	$94,903	$(1,937)	−2.0%
Insurance and Rent	$39,140	$39,179	$39	0.1%	$38,357	$(783)	−2.0%
Other Expenses	$26,750	$26,670	$(80)	−0.3%	$26,162	$(589)	−2.2%
Operating Expenses	$2,813,130	$2,811,451	$(1,679)	−0.1%	$2,731,121	$(82,009)	−3.0%
EBIDTA	$111,785	$109,900	$1,885	1.7%	$104,827	$6,958	6.6%
Depreciation and Amortization	$52,260	$52,365	$105	0.2%	$52,103	$(157)	−0.3%
Operating Margin	$59,525	$57,535	$1,990	3.5%	$52,724	$6,801	12.9%
Interest Expense	$16,020	$16,020	$ –	0.0%	$16,020	$ –	0.0%
Net Operating Income	$43,505	$41,515	$1,990	4.8%	$36,704	$6,801	18.5%
Realized Investment Income	$45,490	$44,125	$1,365	3.0%	$43,216	$2,275	5.0%
Unrealized Investment Income	$(20,560)	$(22,616)	$2,056	10.0%	$(21,588)	$1,028	5.0%
Other Non-Operating Income	$2,540	$2,591	$(51)	−2.0%	$2,515	$25	1.0%
Net Income	$70,975	$65,615	$5,360	8.2%	$60,846	$10,129	16.6%

TABLE 1-5. Income Statement Definitions

Gross Patient Revenue	
Inpatient Revenue	Gross charges generated from all services provided for inpatient care such as facility, physician services, lab, imaging, operating room, and inpatient pharmacy.
Outpatient Revenue	Gross charges generated from all services provided for inpatient care such as facility, physician services, lab, imaging, operating room, and inpatient pharmacy.
Other Patient Revenue	Revenues generated from other sources such as nonhosptial based clinics, retail pharmacy, home infusion, and durable medical equipment rental.
Deductions from Revenue	
Discounts	Represents the discounts negotiated with insurance and managed care payers, and the mandated contractual adjustments from governmental payers.
Uncompensated Care	Discounts provided to indigent patients in accordance with established facility policies. Many health systems provide a partial or full discount for patients that meet income guidelines as established in the system policy, many times a sliding scale based on a percentage of the Federal Poverty Level (FPL).
Bad Debts	Represents the write-off of uncollectible accounts for patients who are unwilling to pay their balance. Hospitals are required to have a collection process and to ensure that every patient account follows that process to completion.
Shared Savings	Represents the organizations portion of shared savings from programs with managed care plans.
Net Patient Revenue	Represents the amount of gross revenue expected to be collected from the appropriate payers.
Other Operating Revenue	Revenues from federal or other awards and grants, gift shop, cafeteria, or other nonpatient related activity the health system has.
Operating Expenses	
Salaries and Benefits	Represents the cost of payroll and related benefits.
Contract Labor	Represents the cost of outsourced labor, such as temporary nursing labor.
Supplies	Represents the cost of drugs, medical, surgical, and office supplies used by the organization. Often includes the cost of minor equipment (such as office equipment and furnishings). For organizations with a retail pharmacy presence, many times drugs will be separated from general supplies.
Professional Fees	Represents the cost of fees to professional medical staff for services rendered under contract. Examples may include physician services, emergency room services, medical directorships, clinical reading contracts, etc.
Contract Services	Represents the cost of services outsourced under contract to external organizations and professional and other purchased services. Examples may include an outsourced lab, housekeeping, or a grounds keeping contract, marketing, and legal and professional fees.
Repairs and Maintenance	Represents the cost of repairs and maintenance on equipment and buildings, including maintenance agreements.
Rent and Utilities	Represents the cost of leases for equipment and buildings, and the cost of building utilities (such as gas, water, and electric).
Other Operating Expenses	Represents a variety of miscellaneous operating expenses such banking fees, postage, subscriptions, licenses, and community events and donations.
EBIDTA	Represents Earnings Before Interest, Depreciation, Taxes, and Amortization.
Depreciation	Represents the expense allocation of the cost of an asset over its determined useful life.
Interest Expense	Represents the expense incurred on borrowed funds/debt.
Income Taxes	Represents an estimate of the income taxes due on the pretax income shown. Includes both federal and state taxes.

accounts receivable can be managed by the revenue cycle leader. Many of the other balance sheet measures are organization wide and are used by senior leadership and the board rather than by department leaders.

THE INCOME OR OPERATING STATEMENT

The income statement, also referred to as the operating statement, the statement of revenues and expenses, and the profit and loss statement (P&L) reports the financial performance of the organization for a designated period. The designated period may be the end of the month and the year-to-date period ended that month. The income statement details the revenues earned and the related expenses incurred in the operation of the organization, the difference is the net operating income.

The income statement is a key financial report used by leadership to manage the financial performance of the organization. It is reported at many different roll up levels including overall organization performance, by type of operations, by individual department, and any other grouping or breakout used by the organization to manage performance. The income statement is generally presented with the prior year's information and the current year's budget. This assists management in analyzing performance to plan and trends.

STATEMENT OF CASH FLOWS

The statement identifies the sources and uses of cash in the organization. The statement of cash flows must tie to the cash balance reported on the balance sheet and complement both the balance sheet and income statement. It is meant to show where cash is generated and spent and how much cash is available (referred to as liquidity) to fund operating expenses and pay down liabilities.

The three components of the statement of cash flows are cash generated from or used in operating activities, investing activities, and financing activities. Operating activities include cash generation and use from the organization's business activities including cash from the sale of goods and services, payment for goods and supplies used in business activities, employee wage payments, rent, and any other type of operating expense. Investing activities include the purchase or sale of assets such as plants and equipment, other noncurrent assets, and investments not included in cash equivalents. Financing activities include the issuance or payment of debt and other investing activities such as bonds, common stock, and dividends.

STATISTIC ACCOUNTS

Statistic accounts quantify nonmonetary activity that can be used to maintain statistical information for a variety of metrics. Many statistical accounts are included in the income statement and performance reports distributed to department leaders and administration.

Common statistical accounts include volume and labor measurements. A common volume statistic is Units of Service (UOS). The UOS will vary by department and function and include admissions, discharges, adjusted patient days, administrations, prescription dispenses, and procedures. A common labor statistic is full-time equivalents (FTEs). An FTE is a full-time equivalent employee which is calculated by dividing the number of person hours for the period by the number of person hours a full-time employee would be paid for that period. Another common labor statistic is hours worked.

Statistic accounts can be used at their reported value and add even more value to performance assessment when combined with other financial and nonfinancial data for performance metrics at ratios.

PERFORMANCE METRICS

In addition to financial statements and statistics, performance metrics are also measured, reported, and analyzed. Organizations establish Key Performance Indicators (KPIs) which are quantifiable measures that are important to the organization and are indicators of the health of the organization. Although a KPI is a metric, a metric is not always a KPI. The key difference is that KPIs represent value drivers of the organization, whereas metrics may represent the measurement of any business activity. Good KPIs should be well defined, quantifiable, indicative of the financial performance and success of the organization, and thoroughly communicated. **Table 1-6 Sample Pharmacy KPIs and Metrics** provides a summary of KPIs and metrics that can be used to measure department performance. An organization's specific KPIs and metrics should be determined based on the operational focus and strategic goals.

TABLE 1-6. Sample Pharmacy KPIs and Metrics

KPI Measure		
Volume adjusted expense	Measures expenses adjusted to account for the change in volumes	
	Volume adjusted wage expense	(Wage Expense/UOS variance) × (Actual Volume)
	Volume adjusted supply expense	(Wage Expense/UOS variance) × (Actual Volume)
	Total Operating Expense (TOE)	(TOE/UOS variance) × (Actual Volume)
Pharmacy Workload Hours	Measures the time it takes to dispense and manage medications	Relative Value Unit (RVU) × # doses
Hours Per Unit of Service (HPU)	Measures how much labor is utilized to manage department volumes	(All productive (worked) hours in the department)/UOS
Productivity Index (PI)	Measures the staffing efficiency of a department.	Productive Target FTE / Productive Actual FTE
		(An index ≥100% is favorable; an index <100% is unfavorable)
Other Performance Metrics		
Revenue per UOS	Measures the revenue generated per UOS	Gross revenue/UOS
Wage expense per UOS	Measures the wage expense incurred per UOS	Wage expense/UOS
Supplies expense per UOS	Measures the supplies expense incurred per UOS	Supplies expense/UOS
Pharmaceutical expense per UOS	Measures the pharmaceutical expense incurred per UOS; separate out pharmaceutical expense from total supplies expense	Pharmaceutical expense/UOS
Total operating expense per UOS	Measures the total operating expenses incurred per UOS	Total operating expense/UOS
Net operating margin per UOS	Measures the net operating margin generated per UOS	Net operating margin/UOS
COGS %	Measures the drug expense of the revenue generated, as a percent of revenue	Drug expense/gross revenue
Discount %	Measures discounts as a percent of revenue	Discounts/gross revenue

TABLE 1-6. continued

Other Performance Metrics		
Bad debt expense %	Meaures bad debt expense as a percent of revenue	Bad debt/gross revenue
UOS per FTE	Measures the number of units processed per FTE	UOS/Total FTEs
Wage expense per FTE	Measures the wage expense incurred per FTE	Wage expense/Total FTEs
Net operating margin %	Measures the net profitability of the activity in a department	(Net Revenue – Total Operating Expenses)/Net Revenue

RATIOS

Ratios are a concise and systemic way to organize the data contained in financial statements into a framework that creates meaningful information. A ratio is the quantitative relation between two amounts showing the number of times one value contains or is contained within the other. Ratios provide a way to bring relational comparisons to the revenue, expense, balance sheet, and metric measured activity. This is key in understanding fluctuations and trends in performance, analyzing performance trends over an extended period of time, benchmarking performance to industry and competitors, identifying strength and weak areas, and assisting the management in decision making. **Table 1-7 Typical Performance Ratios** lists typical performance ratios used by organizations to measure performance.

TABLE 1-7. Typical Performance Ratios

Profitability Ratios (measures some aspects of profitability)		
Current ratio	Measures the number of times short-term obligations can be met by short-term creditors	Current Assets
		Current Liabilities
Quick ratio	Includes only liquid assets (cash, marketable securities, and accounts receivable)	Cash + Marketability Securities + Net Accts Receivable
		Current Liabilities
Net days in patient accounts receivable	Measures the efficiency of the collections function	Net Patient Accounts Receivable
		(Net Patient Service Revenue)/365
Average payment period	Measures how quickly an organization pays its bills	Current Liabilities
		(Operating Expense – Depreciation)/365
Days cash on hand	Measures survival period of an organization receiving no further cash inflows	Cash + Marketable Securities + Unrestricted LT Investments
		(Operating Expense – Depreciation)/365
Utilization Indicators (commonly used operating indicators)		
Length of stay (LOS)	Measures efficiency in containing inpatient service costs	Total Inpatient Days
		Total Discharges
Occupancy rate	Measures volume and utilization of inpatient services	Total Inpatient Days
		Staffed Beds × Days in Period

TABLE 1-7. continued

Utilization Indicators (commonly used operating indicators)		
Case mix index	Measures how sick patients are; used to make patient care costs comparable	Sum of (cases in each DRG × weight for that DRG)
		Total Cases
Adjusted admissions	"Adjusted" means that outpatient revenue is converted into admissions	Total Gross Charges × Inpatient Discharges
		Inpatient Charges
Adjusted patient days	When divided by 365 also called Adjusted Occupied Beds	Total Gross Charges × Inpatient Days
		Inpatient Charges
Average daily census	Measures what percentage of beds are occupied	Inpatient Days
		365
Case mix adjusted cost per patient day	Severity adjusts cost per patient day	Cost Per Patient Day
		Case Mix Index
Activity Ratios (measures how efficiently assets are used in operations)		
Total asset turnover	Measures how many times a year total assets are turned into revenue	Total Operating Revenue
		Total Assets
Fixed asset turnover	Measures how many times a year fixed assets are turned into revenue	Total Operating Revenue
		Net Fixed Assets
Current asset turnover	Measures how many times a year current assets are turned into revenue	Total Operating Revenue
		Current Assets
Inventory turnover	Measures how many times a year inventory is completely replaced	Total Operating Revenue
		Inventory
Capital Structure Ratios (measure the degree to which assets are leveraged and used for acquiring debt)		
Equity financing ratio	Measures how much of the balance sheet is owned vs financed via credit and debt	Net Assets
		Total Assets
Cash flow to total debt	Measures how much cash there is to pay off all debt (ST and LT)	Net Income + Depreciation
		Current Liabilities + LT Debt
Long-term debt to equity	Measures how much leverage the company is taking	LT Liabilities
		Net Assets
Fixed assets financing	Measures extent to which LT debt is financed through fixed assets	LT Liabilities
		Net Fixed Assets
Times interest earned	Measures how much income is generated to cover interest payments	Net Income + Interest Expense
		Interest Expense
Debt service coverage	Measures how much income is generated to cover principal + interest payments	Net Income + Interest Expense + Depreciation
		Principal Payment + Interest Expense
Debt capitalization	Measures total outstanding debt as a percentage of total capitalization	Total Debt
		Net Assets + Total Debt

COST ACCOUNTING SYSTEMS

Many hospitals use a cost accounting system, also called a decision support system (DSS) to further support performance and financial management. These systems use information from the hospital's general ledger system applied to individual patient account activity from the hospital's billing system to perform detailed data analysis on issues affecting more than a single department of the hospital. The cost accounting systems used in hospitals today would be more accurately described as cost allocation systems, as they allocate the hospital's total cost to the patient database and make no comparisons to budget, or a standard cost. Nonetheless, they are a valuable tool in managing the hospital's finances.

Classification of expenses in cost accounting are different than classification of expenses on the general ledger. On the general ledger, expenses are classified as either direct or indirect. In the cost accounting process expenses are classified as fixed and variable.

Fixed expenses are defined as those expenses that do not fluctuate as volumes in the hospital change. An example of a fixed expense would be the monthly lease payment for office space or equipment. In the cost accounting process, many other expenses are considered fixed, including core staffing levels in some revenue-producing departments, and central support departments such as administration, human resources, and fiscal services.

Variable expenses are defined as those expenses that do fluctuate as volumes in the hospital change. Pharmacy drug cost is an example of a variable expense—generally the more patients that the hospital has, the higher the total drug cost is, and vice versa. Other factors, such as type of patients (cardiac, chemotherapy) also contribute to fluctuations in drug cost.

There are two drivers for the success of any cost accounting system. The first is proper determination of the fixed and variable costs associated with each item for which the hospital generates a patient charge. The second is the methodology for which variable costs are allocated within a department. The more correlated the methodology with the actual charge line item expense, the more accurate the cost accounting results. To accomplish this, an accountant, or system specialist, will conduct detailed "costing" meetings with each department manager. For example, the amount of time to prepare an IV admixture must be assigned to the drugs administered in this manner, making them more expensive in pharmacist time than a drug administered orally or by injection.

Once the costing process is complete, the allocation methodologies are loaded into the DSS. There are two major sources of data input to the DSS: electronic health record/patient billing and accounting system general ledger information. These data sources are typically loaded into the DSS monthly after the general ledger has closed for the previous month. They are maintained in the system's database perpetually, enabling multiperiod, multiyear reporting.

COST ACCOUNTING REPORTS

The cost accounting system allows the organization to analyze profitability at a more detailed level than the general ledger can provide. It can also aggregate data across multiple general ledger departments for a more holistic view of financial performance such as by individual service line, by procedure type, physician, location, department, clinic, diagnoses, payer or payer types, any combination therein, or any other field captured in the DSS. It can also provide results by demographics such as patient region/zip code or age. This can provide additional insight into the organization's performance and provide additional direction to strategic focuses.

Profitability can be measured at various levels. Two of the more common levels are earnings before interest, depreciation, taxes, and amortization (EBIDTA) and net income (usually before income taxes for taxpaying hospitals). Regardless of the level of profitability selected for analysis and presentation, the following items should be reflected in the cost accounting financial reports:

- Patient Volumes (the applicable UOS–Discharges, Patient Days, Outpatient Cases, etc.)
- Profitability Components:

  + Gross Revenue

  – Revenue Deductions

  =Net Revenue

  – Variable Cost

  =Contribution Margin

  – Fixed Cost

  =Profit (EBIDTA, Net Income)

Contribution margin is an important measure of service line profitability as it presents the amount of incremental earnings a service line generates with changes in volumes and is an important measure when considering which service lines and areas to emphasize for volume growth. However, fixed costs must eventually be covered to generate an overall profit and must be considered, and measures to manage fixed costs must also be in place.

Further detail of the types of expenses within the variable and fixed cost categories are also captured, typically at the general ledger reporting account level, such as wage expense, purchased services, and supplies expense (and within this drug expense further broken out because of its materiality to pharmacy). This allows further insight into financial performance drivers.

PERFORMANCE REVIEW PROCESS

Reviewing financial performance is a multidimensional process. No single financial or metric report will provide full insight into performance, trends, and drivers. Looking at pure dollar variances does not account for changes in volume, product mix, or the other related dynamics of revenue, expenses, statistics, and metrics. Also, reviewing metrics alone without integrating them into financial performance does not provide the specific revenue, expense, and margin impacts of the metrics. It is important to review all financial and metric reports and the calculated ratios from them to assess performance.

The P&L, when paired with metrics and ratios, is one of the most important reports a leader receives. The goal of managing a P&L, metrics, and ratios is to maximize margin by increasing net revenue and/or decreasing costs to generate revenue. Volume and expense management are important parts of successful financial performance, and many are directly manageable by the department leaders. Expense reviews should not only be done on the individual line item, but also volume adjusted and per UOS and compared with similar revenue related results and metrics. By looking at what it costs to produce one unit (patient day, administration, visit, x-ray, lab test, etc.), and how that cost compares to revenue generated from it, leaders will have a much better perspective of the impact on the organization.

- Volume/UOS and expense/UOS should be reviewed for changes in relation to comparison points (such as budget, prior months, prior year). The department leader should work with the finance operations analysts to determine items such as the following. After reviewing the above, the leader should determine if there are any actions that can be taken to address any gaps or take advantage of opportunities.

- Primary driver for the volume differences (such as a reduction or increase in providers, capacity levels, low referrals, a drop in flu cases, etc.)
- Mix of services different than expected
- Is the trend expected to continue?
- How the trend compares to what is happening in the market
- What were the leading indicators?
- What will likely happen in future months with the volume

For hospital pharmacy, the largest expense category is supplies (driven by pharmaceuticals), which is also the most dynamic expense. Supplies expense as a line item will fluctuate with revenue because the more pharmaceuticals administered, the more pharmaceuticals are purchased. It is important for leaders to monitor their Cost-to-Charge ratios (Drug Purchases/Gross Drug Revenue). A $+/-2\%$ variance to budget may signify a charging error, an accounts payable posting error, or a change in drug mix and should be investigated. In addition, the pharmaceutical administration mix will also impact supplies expense, whereas higher dollar pharmaceutical therapies will not only drive higher supplies expense, but higher supplies expense per UOS. The higher supplies expense and supplies expense per UOS may not indicate an unfavorable financial performance and is an example of why integrated analysis beyond individual line item expense review should be considered. In the case of supplies expense, along with individual line item expense review, the cost per UOS and relational revenue per UOS should also be factored in. This will help account for volume increases and higher dollar therapies that may generate higher supplies expense and supplies expense per UOS but result in favorable margin generating performance.

Wage or labor expense is typically the second largest expense for pharmacy. Effectively managing productivity, overtime, and agency expenses will keep labor expenses aligned with expectations. Wage expense should be reviewed on the monthly P&L using line item wage expense and wage expense per UOS; however, this should also be managed more real time through productivity reporting. Utilizing daily productivity and staffing tools and reviewing weekly or biweekly productivity reports will help department leaders address performance results quickly. Leaders can research results and take timely actions to address. Departments that flex staffing to volume use productivity reporting to monitor if staffing is appropriately flexing to actual volume and departments that have fixed staffing use productivity reporting to monitor if staffing is at the target level. See **Table 1-8 Sample Labor Productivity Report** for a sample biweekly report that could be used.

Potential causes of productivity variances could include hours not flexing appropriately for volume changes, staffing levels above planned levels, incorrect staff charged to the department, incorrect hours floated in or out of the department, or incorrect pay codes used by staff. The department leader should focus on determining the root cause of the performance and if necessary, create actionable plans to address (to improve unfavorable or continue favorable) that include timelines and determine predicted gaps that may continue with an expected planned end.

Keep in mind that if the organization is using the accrual-based method of accounting, the monthly P&L will include a wage accrual for days in the current reporting month which do not necessarily line up with payroll specific reports that are generated based on the pay period days. This will cause some differences between the P&L wage expense and the payroll based reported expense. The accrual for hours worked but not paid is reversed at the beginning of the next month and replaced by a new end-of-month accrual.

Additional expense line items that the pharmacy leader should expect to see on their P&L report include but are not limited to the expense items listed in **Tables 1-4 and 1-5**. Many P&L reports provide the expenses at the general category level, such as "Purchased Services" but are further broken down for department leaders by more specific expense types such as "laundry services" and "lab services," so results can be further analyzed and understood.

TABLE 1-8. Sample Labor Productivity Report

Hospital Pharmacy Services	01/10/2021	01/24/2021	02/07/2021	02/21/2021	03/07/2021	03/21/2021
UOS (Volume)	8,538	8,894	8,764	8,756	8,591	9,277
Productive Hours	6,062	6,048	6,310	6,479	6,443	7,050
Actual Productive Hours per UOS (HPU)	0.7	0.7	0.7	0.7	0.8	0.8
Target Productive Hours per UOS (HPU)	0.8	0.8	0.8	0.8	0.8	0.8
Actual Productive FTE	78.5	81.3	81.7	82.9	84.8	86.7
Target Productive FTE	81.9	86.0	85.8	83.9	87.1	88.7
Productive FTE Variance	3.45	4.72	4.05	0.98	2.30	2.00
FTE Productivity Index	104.4%	105.8%	105.0%	101.2%	102.7%	102.3%
FTE Productivity Index YTD	104.4%	105.1%	105.1%	104.1%	103.8%	103.5%
Agency Hours		12.40			8.32	
Overtime (OT) Hours	375	431	389	313	451	584
OT % of Productive Hours	6.2%	7.1%	6.2%	4.8%	7.0%	8.3%
Calculations:						
Productive Hours per UOS (HPU)	Productive hours/OUS					
Actual Productive FTE	Actual productive hours/80					
Target Productive FTE	Variance departments = Target HPU					
	Fixed departments = Target productive hours/80					
Productivity Index	Target productive FTE/actual productive FTE					
	Index >100% is favorable; index <100% unfavorable					
OT % of productive hours	Overtime hours/productive hours					

Some organizations will subgroup expenses between direct expenses and indirect expenses. Direct expenses are those which occur directly in the operation of the department and include pharmaceuticals, wages, medical supplies, equipment purchases, and purchased services. Indirect expenses are those that are out of the control of the department manager, such as employee benefits (time off accrual, health insurance, retirement contributions) and payer contractual adjustments within the revenue section.

CONCLUSION

Managing the finances of an organization as large and complex as many health systems are today is a huge undertaking. While the CFO sets the overall strategy and leads the work for the organization, it is up to each leader to execute and meet performance objectives for their department. Pharmacy leaders must be intimately familiar with the details of their budget and operational performance over time. Senior executives expect the pharmacy leader to provide detailed explanations for any variances to budget as well as to accurately forecast performance for the next operational period.

The pharmacy leader's ability to analyze, understand, and communicate these variances will determine their ability to manage the department in a fiscally responsible manner. Subsequent chapters will explore many of these concepts in more detail with specific examples.

REFERENCES

1. Centers for Medicare & Medicaid Services. NHE fact sheet. December 15, 2021. **cms.gov/Research-Statistics-Data-and-Systems/Statistics-Trends-and-Reports/ NationalHealthExpendData/NHE-Fact-Sheet**. Accessed January 2, 2022.

2. American Hospital Association. Fast facts on U.S. Hospitals, 2021. **https://www.aha.org/ system/files/media/file/2021/01/Fast-Facts-2021-table-FY19-data-14jan21.pdf**. Accessed January 2, 2022.

PHARMACY BUDGET MANAGEMENT: CONTINUOUS FINANCIAL PLANNING AND FORECASTING

John A. Armitstead and Jeanette A. Alava

Pharmacy budget management requires focused financial expertise and coordination within the health system. Planning and forecasting of expenditures to provide pharmacy services to meet patient care needs is an essential component of organizational resource utilization. As part of a health system, the pharmacy budget is a significant portion of the overall healthcare spending and should reflect an accurate and dynamic financial plan.[1] There are five major components in a well-developed pharmacy budget: revenue, expense, workload, productivity, and capital expenditures.[2]

THE ANNUAL BUDGET

To ensure the effective use of resources and to meet the organization's mission, the health system develops an annual plan. Every health system must select and prioritize activities for the coming year from numerous and varied challenges and growth opportunities. Organizational, structural, and financial constraints challenge the health system leadership to select a course and to identify the means to steer the health system through the year. As a health system is a complex, highly regulated, and often financially constrained organization, the Chief Executive Officer (CEO), Chief Financial Officer (CFO), and Board of Trustees work from a strategic plan to develop goals for services, activity levels, expenditures, and revenues for the upcoming budget, and in some instances, for longer periods.

Pharmaceutical Expenditure Profile

As a major component of supplies and expenses, pharmaceuticals represent one of the largest expenditures in healthcare consumables. In fact, the pharmacy budget utilizes one of the highest supply cost to personnel cost ratio departments in the health system. **Figure 2-1** displays the overall spread of fiscal year pharmacy expenditures across five hospitals within a community healthcare system. As depicted by Figure 1, each hospital pharmacy budget consistently indicates that 75% of total expenses can be attributed to drug supply costs. The remaining expense costs usually comprise 20% salary personnel and 5% other expenses. In comparison with the pharmacy budget profile, nursing budget expenditures are usually dominated by personnel costs, while other departments, such as radiology, are dominated by capital equipment costs.

For health systems with community pharmacy operations, **Figure 2-2** displays the expenditure profiles of traditional retail or community pharmacy operation budgets. While there may be variations notable with specialty pharmacy operations, the profile remains clear in the dominance of pharmaceuticals as the major expenditure.

As part of the organizations' expenditures, the pharmacy budget is significant within most healthcare systems and can represent 8% to 10% of the overall budget funds. As pharmaceuticals

DOI 10.37573/9781585287130.002

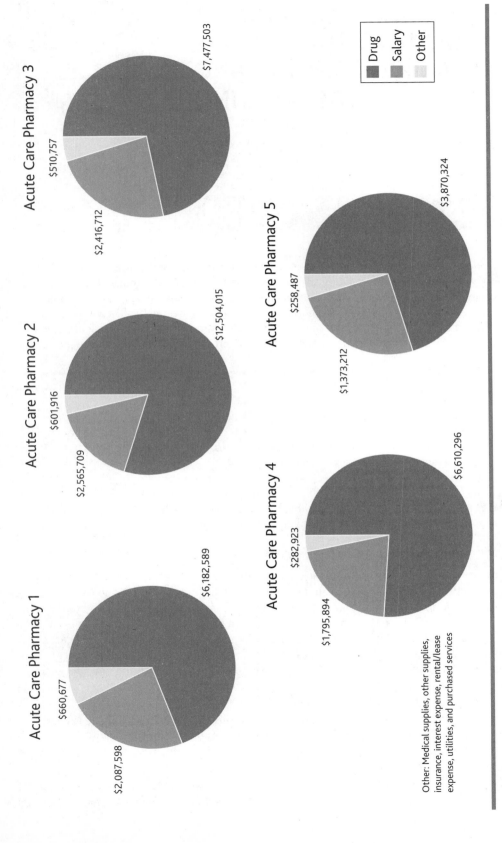

FIGURE 2-1. Fiscal year acute care pharmacy expenditures

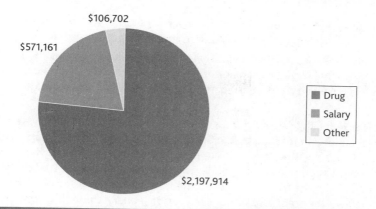

FIGURE 2-2. Fiscal year retail pharmacy expenditures

continue to play a major therapeutic role in the care of patients, this continues to demand increasing scrutiny in the budget process and require well-designed resource allocation planning. Effective financial analysis control is necessary to ensure the efficient use of organizational resources in achieving stated organizational goals. As with any form of management, financial management includes the processes of planning, organizing, directing, and controlling resources.

Initial Budget Preparation

In broad terms, a budget is an estimate of revenue or income and expenses for a set period. In health systems, traditionally annual budgets project major aspects of the overall financial plan. In essence, a health system plan for deploying and operationalizing services is revealed in the budget.

As described by Williams,[2] the budget should have several components embedded in its processes. The budget should be oriented toward goals and objectives of the services to be provided; the projections should be realistic and achievable, be implemented and monitored by the preparer, contain internal mechanisms for review and analysis, and use consistent measurement tools and reporting periods. The pharmacy budget preparation must be coordinated and authorized by financial officials in the organization.

In many cases, initiating the preparation of the new fiscal year budget will be in accordance with the governing body policy and fiscal department objectives. Since many organizations utilize incremental budgeting techniques, departmental budget preparation is often initiated based upon the past six months' performance in the existing fiscal year. Quite frequently budgeting will commence with annualizing (doubling) the first six months of the existing year to project a point of origin for the budget of the future fiscal year. Departmental budget preparation "will ensure" based upon inflationary increases and programmatic changes expected in the future fiscal year. As projections advance to the finance authority, budgetary estimates are discussed, evaluated, and negotiated. Some considerations in preparing the budget may include factors that lead to adjustments in past financial performance. These factors usually include adjustments for inflation, new drug therapies, new programs and services, or new operations. Recently we have seen that a pandemic world event can have a dramatic impact on the budgeting process. The COVID-19 pandemic demonstrated that not only adjustments to patient surges needed to be accommodated, but also drug shortage challenges and costly new pharmaceuticals can have a budget breaking effect that can influence the accuracy of the budgeting process during and after the event.[3]

In addition to dramatic events such as a pandemic, there are a number of other factors that can affect a budget. In the experience of these authors, we have observed personnel budgetary adjustments due to staffing shortages, market adjustments, significant new businesses tapping local workforce availability, overtime utilization, patient workload variations, new business provisions, and retirement incentives. The skillful financial manager should be able to forecast the changes and make adjustments or at least justify the variations in the budget performance.

Budgeting processes occur simultaneously with other departments at the same time a roll up budget of all departments within the organization is completed. Eventually a complex orchestration of adjustments to a balanced budget is prepared and advanced for the organizational governing body approval.

The budget cycle for the pharmacy must be in concert with the health system budget. A fiscal year is a financial period determined by the organization. Although fiscal years may vary, there are traditionally some fiscal year periods that are more common than others. The two most common fiscal years experienced by the authors include what could be considered traditional academic fiscal years of July through June or traditional governmental fiscal years of October through September. Some institutions use the traditional calendar year of January through December for their fiscal year. The major point is that pharmacy should be in concert with planning process of your institution and the cycle established for concerted planning and forecasting.

Budgeting Methods

There are three basic types of budgets: fixed, flexible, and zero-based. In fixed budgets the revenue and expenses are planned for the entire year without factors that will alter volume or the statistic (usually patient volume) each month. The budget is planned without an expectation of a variable statistic such as patient days or prescription volume. Although month-to-month revenue and expenses will be specified per calendar month in a fixed budget, the financial performance is generally not altered or corrected for projected volume changes. Fixed (or static) types of budgets are not elastic to the variations expected or seen in patient volumes adjustments and generally have declined in value in health systems.

In flexible budgeting, revenue and expenses are based upon the statistic of variability or "the statistic," and projected volumes of variable workload. Examples of variable workload may include: patient days, adjusted patient days, patient visits, infusions, or prescriptions. Initial budget forecasts are made based upon the projected statistic value and adjustments are made in financial monitoring based upon the actual statistic after it becomes evident. So as increased or decreased patient volumes are observed, budgetary allowance or corrections are made to reflect the actual amounts expected.

Evaluating the sample budget provided in **Table 2-1** shows an example of an Acute Care and a Retail Pharmacy budget utilizing the flexible budget process. The first section represents the Inpatient and Outpatient Statistics. In these cases, the Inpatient Statistic is Adjusted Patient Days. Adjusted Patient Days are utilized as acute care must account for the workload and utilization from not only admitted patients but from observation of patients in this setting. Acute care statistics must also account for defined outpatient patient volume such as emergency department and procedural patients that once again add to workload and utilization variances. In this case, for the outpatient statistic of the retail (or community) pharmacy the statistic is prescriptions dispensed. This is the most appropriate representative statistic for the Retail Pharmacy budget, although the pharmacy does provide some additional services which are not captured in the prescription statistic.

For the Acute Care, Retail Pharmacy, and Specialty Pharmacy, the key operational statistics are indicated in **Table 2-2**. These key performance indicators are utilized to establish the budget based upon the statistic projected for both inpatients and outpatients in the acute care environment or for the retail and specialty pharmacy environments.

The Acute Care Pharmacy statistics are based upon the adjusted patient days projected. On average, each adjusted patient day in the health system generates a posted revenue of $667.57. As many are aware, these revenue postings no longer designate actual revenue received due to implementation of payments based upon DRGs and coding of patient care. However, expenses (and more true dollar values), would include $27.74 of employee costs per adjusted patient day, $75.49 of pharmaceutical expense, and $4.60 of other expense for a total expense of $107.83.

TABLE 2-1. Example Operating Budget Hospital, Retail and Specialty Pharmacy

Department Description	Operating Budget												Total Fixed Budget
	October	November	December	January	February	March	April	May	June	July	August	September	
Statistics													
Inpatient Statistics													
HOSPITAL PHARMACY	6,643	6,671	7,272	6,698	4,984	5,482	4,936	5,198	4,694	4,784	4,742	4,673	66,777
Outpatient Statistics													
HOSPITAL PHARMACY	5,299	5,151	5,165	5,468	5,029	5,617	5,398	5,174	5,049	5,120	5,200	5,055	62,725
RETAIL PHARMACY	5,952	5,760	5,952	5,952	5,376	5,952	5,760	5,952	5,760	5,952	5,952	5,760	70,080
SPECIALTY PHARMACY	3,004	3,004	3,398	3,398	3,398	3,448	3,448	3,448	3,499	3,498	3,551	3,550	40,644
Revenues													
Inpatient Revenue													
HOSPITAL PHARMACY	5,041,907	5,063,159	5,519,306	5,083,651	3,782,759	4,160,731	3,746,328	3,945,180	3,562,654	3,630,963	3,599,085	3,546,716	50,682,439
Outpatient Revenue													
HOSPITAL PHARMACY	3,021,767	2,937,369	2,945,353	3,118,139	2,867,799	3,203,107	3,078,222	2,950,485	2,879,204	2,919,692	2,965,312	2,882,625	35,769,073
SPECIALTY PHARMACY	148	148	168	168	168	170	170	170	173	173	175	175	2,007
Other Operating Revenue													

TABLE 2-1. continued

Department Description	October	November	December	January	February	March	April	May	June	July	August	September	Budget	Total Fixed
						Operating Budget								
RETAIL PHARMACY	288,005	278,918	288,005	288,005	260,745	288,005	278,918	288,005	278,918	288,005	288,005	278,918		3,392,455
SPECIALTY PHARMACY	4,582,549	4,582,549	5,183,443	5,183,443	5,183,443	5,259,698	5,259,698	5,259,698	5,337,479	5,335,954	5,416,785	5,415,260		62,000,000
Operating Expenses														
Salaries														
HOSPITAL PHARMACY	315,476	310,974	340,812	356,247	275,363	305,308	286,664	289,249	275,904	281,358	279,733	275,647		3,592,735
RETAIL PHARMACY	53,435	51,706	55,092	56,158	49,598	54,928	53,180	54,934	53,329	55,103	54,936	53,337		645,736
SPECIALTY PHARMACY	15,437	15,036	16,294	17,057	15,053	16,343	15,904	16,338	15,969	16,385	16,437	16,014		192,267
Drug Expense														
HOSPITAL PHARMACY	879,093	870,259	915,531	895,582	737,092	817,036	760,722	763,519	717,216	729,068	731,866	716,112		9,533,097
RETAIL PHARMACY	186,672	180,650	186,672	186,672	168,607	186,672	180,650	186,672	180,650	186,672	186,672	180,650		2,197,914
SPECIALTY PHARMACY	3,652,835	3,652,835	4,131,810	4,131,810	4,122,938	4,102,564	4,102,564	4,057,546	4,117,544	4,070,665	4,132,340	4,084,548		48,360,000
Medical Supplies														
HOSPITAL PHARMACY	17,954	17,774	18,698	18,291	15,054	16,687	15,537	15,594	14,648	14,890	14,947	14,626		194,699
SPECIALTY PHARMACY	136	136	154	154	154	156	156	156	159	159	161	161		1,844
Other Supplies														

HOSPITAL PHARMACY	4,421	4,377	4,605	4,504	3,707	4,109	3,826	3,840	3,607	3,667	3,681	3,602	47,947
RETAIL PHARMACY	593	574	593	593	536	593	574	593	574	593	593	574	6,986
SPECIALTY PHARMACY	3,168	3,168	3,583	3,583	3,583	3,636	3,636	3,636	3,690	3,689	3,744	3,743	42,859
Other Expense													
HOSPITAL PHARMACY	180	240	180	180	2,055	180	180	180	210	180	180	180	4,125
SPECIALTY PHARMACY	—	—	124	358	—	—	—	—	38	—	—	—	519
Rental/Lease Expense													
HOSPITAL PHARMACY	44,951	44,951	44,951	44,951	44,951	44,951	44,951	44,951	44,951	44,951	44,951	44,951	539,412
Purchased Services													
HOSPITAL PHARMACY	9,520	3,408	3,539	3,571	5,429	3,377	3,551	3,458	3,406	5,483	3,418	3,545	51,705
RETAIL PHARMACY	8,510	8,181	7,963	8,098	8,069	7,827	7,998	7,819	8,352	8,527	8,628	8,244	98,216
SPECIALTY PHARMACY	699,900	699,900	791,466	791,469	791,576	803,086	803,296	804,821	814,939	815,818	829,280	828,295	9,473,845
FTEs													
HOSPITAL PHARMACY	41.6	42.4	43.1	42.2	39.0	39.0	37.7	36.8	35.9	35.4	35.5	35.8	38.7
RETAIL PHARMACY	8.4	8.4	8.4	8.4	8.4	8.4	8.4	8.4	8.4	8.4	8.4	8.4	8.4
SPECIALTY PHARMACY	1.9	1.9	2.0	2.0	2.1	2.0	2.0	2.0	2.0	2.0	2.0	2.1	2.0

TABLE 2-2. Pharmacy Operation Statistics

Statistic	Hospital Pharmacy	Retail Pharmacy	Specialty Pharmacy
Gross Operating Revenue per Stat	$667.57	$48.42	$1525.49
Salary Expense per Stat	$27.74	$9.21	$4.89
Supply Expense per Stat	$75.49	$31.36	$1217.05
Other Expense per Stat	$4.60	$1.41	$232.96
Labor and Purchased Service per Stat	$32.34	$10.62	$237.81
Total Operating Expense per Stat	$107.83	$42.09	$1454.90

The Retail Pharmacy statistics or financial key performance indicators are utilized to establish the Retail Pharmacy budget based upon the statistic projected for prescriptions in the community pharmacy environment. On average, each prescription in this pharmacy would indicate a revenue of $48.42. Expenses would include $9.21 of employee costs per prescription, $31.36 of pharmaceutical expense, and $1.41 of other expense for a total expense of $42.09 and a net profit of $6.33.

The Specialty Pharmacy budgeting may be substantially more complex due to the higher and more variable statistic of supply expense per stat. On average, each specialty pharmacy prescription in this pharmacy would indicate a revenue of $1525.49. Expenses would include $4.89 of employee costs per prescription, $1217.05 of pharmaceutical expense, and $232.96 of other expense for a total expense of $1454.90 and a net profit of $70.59. Nevertheless, the concepts are similar and although we are in an era of dramatic, variable, and growing specialty pharmacy financial spend and growth, the flexible budget process budget forecast may be challenging to accurately apply. Although this average drug cost per prescription is used per budgeting, the variance on an individual prescription basis can be widely divergent and filled with outlier cases.

In zero-based budgeting, the preparation of next year's budget is based upon each service projection and activity being justified on its merit as if it was a new program. Usually used for new programs or services without a revenue or expense history, all expenses and revenue are justified as if nothing existed the previous year. This means that all personnel, equipment, supplies, and other expenses must be totally valued from a base zero. Zero-based budgeting requires extensive time and effort and may not be any more accurate than the typical fixed or variable budget. Zero-based budgeting, then, is more a method for budget preparation than a budget type since once the budget is developed and approved it will be either a fixed or variable budget.

Identifying Cost Centers

Cost centers in complex organizations are useful to identify revenue and expense within identifiable business units. Some examples of business units would include hospital or community pharmacy locations. In a multihospital health system, separate cost centers would be utilized for each hospital and each community pharmacy but also for some special circumstance business units such as an infusion center, residency program, 340B contract pharmacy, corporate pharmacy, and so forth. In complex health systems, there is value in having cost centers assigned to individual directors or managers where the value of separate cost accounting provides value to management of the revenue or costs associated with its operation.

PROFESSIONAL PRACTICE STANDARDS

As the pharmacy budget process contains specific nuances unique to health system resources, hospital operations, and pharmaceutical expenditures, it is the responsibility of the pharmacy executive to effectively utilize their role in the organization to accurately plan and manage the pharmacy budget. Financial management is one of many responsibilities highlighted in ASHP's Statement on the Pharmacy Executive. In addition to being responsible for medication management across the health system, it also requires an individual to have consistent and direct communication to hospital executive leadership to ensure organizational goals and objectives are being met. This would also apply to assuring the expected financial performance of the business units.

The pharmacy executive must align departmental financial performance to the overall context of a health system.[4] Financial performance can be categorized in various methods, such as departmental metrics, revenue capture, medication expenses, and value-based reimbursements. The pharmacy executive is responsible for analyzing performance trends and applying the current healthcare environment to adjust their financial management. It is also the role of the pharmacy executive to seek new opportunities that diversify and advance pharmacy services. This advancement is best served by realizing that pharmacy is not only a cost center but also a revenue center. Revenue center opportunities exist not only in the traditional retail (or community) pharmacy venue but also in infusion center operations, population health management, health system owned pharmacy benefit management services, home infusion, nuclear pharmacy, consultative services, comprehensive medication management, and currently the highest revenue opportunity, specialty pharmacy. These services should aim to improve both patient care services and the overall financial health of the organization.

Pharmacy practice standards state that successful financial performance relies on three major components: cohesive integration of pharmacy computer systems and financial and/or administrative systems, accurate monitoring of workload metrics, and the effective management of both human and financial components of pharmacy services.[5]

As described by Hunt,[6] the pharmacy executive must demonstrate management control in regards to the budget and departmental finances. Management control may be defined as a systematic effort to (1) set performance standards, (2) design feedback systems, (3) compare actual performance with predetermined performance standards, (4) determine whether any variance in performance exists and assess its importance, and (5) take any corrective action required to ensure that all departmental resources are being used in the most effective and efficient manner to achieve departmental objectives.

In order to evaluate financial performance, hospital information systems should adequately capture all actions of the medication management process. These include, but are not limited to, computerized provider-order-entry, medication administration, inventory management, and patient billing systems. Capturing and quantifying these actions provide a means to assess effective workflow and pharmacy's financial impact to the health system.

OPERATIONAL BENCHMARKING

Operational benchmarking is an effective tool to assess department performance and success in any setting. Trending specific metrics set forth by organizational goals will help identify opportunities for cost control and improve process efficiency.[7] Despite its extensive value, pharmacy workload metrics has been a difficult topic to uniformly define for the profession.[8;9] As benchmarking is most effective when similar processes are being evaluated, significant challenges are seen when trying to collect and report data among outside organizations with underlying variations in department processes and operations.[7;10] Comparison of unreliable pharmacy metrics create an issue when correlating department workload to financial performance. Ultimately, the discrepancies in metrics can adversely impact the pharmacy practice model and hinder appropriate budget planning.

Internal and external benchmarking techniques can be utilized to address pharmacy workload metrics. External benchmarking relies on vendor systems whose productivity metrics may not represent overall quality of patient outcome.[7] There are limitations in creating meaningful comparisons between health systems due to factors such as: unclear definitions and variability of metrics, measuring total costs of care and department services, and differences in patient populations served.

External benchmarks examples include pharmacists per 100 beds, pharmacy technicians per 100 beds, drug cost per admission, and drug cost per dose. While these external benchmarks provide data on efficiency on a gross scale, they do not provide information on the quality of the services provided.

Internal benchmarking, on the other hand, compares past, current, and future pharmacy performances against each other. It is a preferred method of assessing pharmacy efficiency as it removes the inherent comparison of dissimilar health systems. Internal benchmarking allows pharmacy leadership to align pharmacy metrics to health system goals and objectives and provides a means to include department staff in creating meaningful data to report and evaluate. The formation of a clinical pharmacist productivity model comprises many steps. One method of developing internal benchmarking includes utilization of a Delphi consensus of clinical pharmacists that results in a list of clearly defined pharmacist responsibilities that contribute the most value to workload based on weighting.[11;12]

Human Resources and Personnel Management

Effective management of pharmacy human resources include ensuring the pharmacy department is adequately staffed by trained and qualified pharmacist and pharmacy technician members. A budget is established based on the needs of the organization. The patient care services provided will dictate personnel requirements. There are many considerations that must be evaluated when optimizing deployment of human resources. A robust pharmacy human resource department is the right mix of personnel verses number of full-time equivalents (FTEs). **Figure 2-3** and **Figure 2-4** depicts an

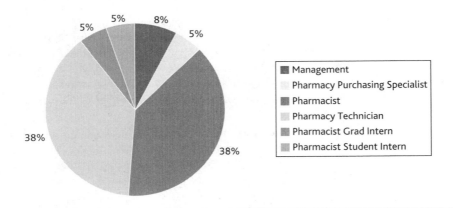

FIGURE 2-3. Acute care pharmacy FTE

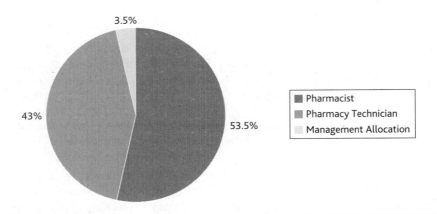

FIGURE 2-4. Retail pharmacy FTE

example of FTEs that comprise an Acute Care pharmacy and Retail Pharmacy environment, respectively. Utilizing the total fixed budget of FTEs as seen in Table 2-1, it should be noted that the spread of personnel ranges from pharmacy administration to staff. Pharmacy team members should include management (director, manager, pharmacy technician supervisor), clerical (administrative assistant), professional (pharmacists, pharmacy clinical specialists, pharmacy interns, pharmacy graduate interns), and support (pharmacy technicians, pharmacy automation technicians, purchasing specialists). It should be noted that Figure 2-4's depiction of a Retail Pharmacy includes an allocation of FTEs for pharmacy management (director and manager). The allocation per Retail Pharmacy site is attributed to the structure of the health system pharmacy model. In this case, the retail pharmacies within the health system are overseen by one System Director of Retail Pharmacy and one System Manager of Retail Pharmacy, and their respective FTEs are allocated to a separate cost center. This model provides a more cohesive structure that aids the Retail Pharmacy budgeting process.

Pharmacy leadership must certify that the entire staff meet regulatory and accrediting requirements to meet the goals of the organization. In addition, pharmacy leadership should also ensure developmental opportunities for staff growth as pharmacy services continue to expand into different patient care areas.

FINANCIAL PERFORMANCE REVIEW

Financial management is an ongoing process that includes pulling reports, analyzing data, and communicating action plans to appropriate parties. Budget reports provide pertinent information on monthly and year-to-date financial performance. These reports should be reviewed on a monthly basis to ensure variances in financial performance are being accounted for and acted upon. A budget variance is a difference between the budgeted amount and the actual amount spent within a period. Variances can be represented in absolute dollar amounts and/or percent differences.

Identifying Budget Variances

Monthly financial statements show expenses incurred each month and are compared with the budget for the current month and for the fiscal year-to-date time periods. Variances are evaluated on a monthly and fiscal year-to-date basis, and comparing these two variances helps to gauge financial performance throughout the fiscal year. Variances can be described as positive (expenses lower than forecast; revenues higher than forecast) or negative (expenses higher than forecast; revenues lower than forecast). Variances can be absolute: the total actual amount is higher irrespective of volume, or volume-adjusted, or the variance in cost cannot be explained solely by changes in activity volume.

By evaluating the financial performance of the acute care, retail, and specialty pharmacy, the monthly variance report can be evaluated. **Table 2-3** indicates an example three-month financial performance report in which statistics for all inpatient and specialty sites were exceeding the original budget and the retail site was slightly below the expected statistic.

In exploring acute care performance in Table 2-3 it is noted that the Inpatient and Outpatient Statistics were up 12.2% and 25.5% respectively. These elevated variances in this cost center lead to an increased Actual Budget expectation of revenue and although the values were adjusted/flexed, the variances did not meet the expected revenue target as calculated in the Flex Budget. Actual Salaries, although higher than the Fixed Budget, were not as high as projected by the Flex Budget and revealed a 16.3% favorable budget compared with the Flex Budget. Investigating the largest expense in Pharmacy, drug costs, it is noted that although the Actual Budget expense ($2,706,268) was higher than the Fixed Budget ($2,664,883), the drug spend was remarkably lower than the Flex Budget of $3,267,483 and revealed that this cost center was 17.2% below budget for this time period. In regards to personnel utilization, the FTE section of this report indicates that although 42.3 FTEs were budgeted, 42.6 FTEs were utilized and the flex budget was 50.9, leading to a favorable variance of 8.3 FTEs for this period.

TABLE 2-3. Example Three-Month Financial Performance Acute Care, Retail, and Specialty

Three Months – First Quarter	FYTD December 2021	FYTD December 2021	FYTD December 2021			FYTD December 2021
Department Description	Fixed Budget	Actual	Flex Budget	Variance	Variance %	Actual
Statistics						
Inpatient Statistics						
HOSPITAL PHARMACY	20,586	23,434	23,434	2,848	12.2%	23,472
Outpatient Statistics						
HOSPITAL PHARMACY	15,615	20,953	20,953	5,338	25.5%	14,003
RETAIL PHARMACY	17,664	17,615	17,615	(49)	–0.3%	17,092
SPECIALTY PHARMACY	9,406	11,758	11,758	2,353	20.0%	7,645
Inpatient Revenue						
HOSPITAL PHARMACY	15,624,372	15,213,928	17,785,948	(2,572,021)	–14.5%	18,349,988
Outpatient Revenue						
HOSPITAL PHARMACY	8,904,489	8,794,152	11,948,496	(3,154,344)	–26.4%	8,728,461
RETAIL PHARMACY	854,929	871,534	854,929	16,605	1.9%	823,486
SPECIALTY PHARMACY	14,348,542	21,669,065	14,348,542	7,320,523	51.0%	11,239,606
Salaries						
HOSPITAL PHARMACY	988,871	991,720	1,184,551	192,831	16.3%	1,044,398
RETAIL PHARMACY	164,422	170,338	164,036	(6,302)	–3.8%	145,987
SPECIALTY PHARMACY	47,716	50,419	57,408	6,989	12.2%	47,722
Drug Expense						
HOSPITAL PHARMACY	2,664,883	2,706,268	3,267,483	561,215	17.2%	3,236,417
RETAIL PHARMACY	553,995	553,672	552,458	(1,214)	–0.2%	541,635
SPECIALTY PHARMACY	11,437,480	18,496,045	14,297,451	(4,198,594)	–29.4%	9,692,066
Medical Supplies						
HOSPITAL PHARMACY	54,426	53,420	66,733	13,314	20.0%	145,250
RETAIL PHARMACY	1,941	3,823	1,994	(1,829)	–91.7%	1,800
SPECIALTY PHARMACY	427	840	534	(306)	–57.4%	384
Other Supplies						
HOSPITAL PHARMACY	13,403	14,872	16,434	1,562	9.5%	11,628
RETAIL PHARMACY	1,761	3,567	1,756	(1,812)	–103.2%	1,816
SPECIALTY PHARMACY	9,918	(4,436)	12,399	16,834	135.8%	7,248
Other Expense						
HOSPITAL PHARMACY	600	566	600	34	5.6%	630
RETAIL PHARMACY	—	—	—	—	0.0%	255
SPECIALTY PHARMACY	124	522	124	(398)	–321.5%	124

TABLE 2-3. continued

Three Months – First Quarter	FYTD December 2021	FYTD December 2021	FYTD December 2021			FYTD December 2021
Department Description	Fixed Budget	Actual	Flex Budget	Variance	Variance %	Actual
Rental/Lease Expense						
HOSPITAL PHARMACY	134,853	134,853	134,853	—	0.0%	129,876
Purchased Services						
HOSPITAL PHARMACY	16,467	17,368	16,467	(901)	−5.5%	16,484
RETAIL PHARMACY	24,654	10,402	24,654	14,253	57.8%	21,383
SPECIALTY PHARMACY	2,191,265	3,102,215	2,191,265	(910,950)	−41.6%	765,439
FTEs						
HOSPITAL PHARMACY	42.3	42.6	50.9	8.3	16.3%	45.5
RETAIL PHARMACY	8.4	8.4	8.4	(0.1)	−0.7%	8.0
SPECIALTY PHARMACY	1.9	1.6	2.3	0.8	32.3%	2.1

As the Retail Pharmacy financial performance for a three-month period is investigated in Table 2-3 it should first be noted that the statistic (prescriptions) that resulted was down 0.3% lower than expected. In this case 17,615 prescriptions were filled, compared with the fixed budget value of 117,664. As we first consider the statistic we should then consider that potentially revenue, salary, and drug costs would also be down by 0.3%. As the financial report is explored, we do find that revenue is up 1.9% (for a variance of $16,605). In addition, when exploring the salary costs we find a negative variance of 3.8%. On the other hand, drug costs did appear to be adjusted downward slightly with the decrease in the statistic and performed closely to the indicator of the statistic by having a variance of only 0.2%. In regards to personnel utilization, the FTE section of this report indicates that although 8.4 FTEs were budgeted, 8.4 FTEs were utilized and combined with a lower than expected statistic (−0.1%), leading to a negative variance of −0.7% for personnel. This is quite close to being on target with the budget.

As the Specialty Pharmacy financial performance for a three-month period is investigated in Table 2-3 note that the statistic (specialty prescriptions) that resulted was 2,353 more than budgeted (up 20.0%). In this case, 11,758 prescriptions were filled, compared with the fixed budget value of 9,406. As we first consider the statistic we should then consider that potentially revenue, salary, and drug costs would also be up by 20%. As the financial report is explored, we do find that in fact revenue is up 51% (for a variance of $7,320,523). In addition, when exploring the salary costs we find a negative variance of 12.2% most likely induced by the growing workload. On the other hand, drug costs did appear to be up $4,198,594 (29.4%).

Budget variances in expenses and revenue are expected as they are built on projections for patient volume and activity that have not yet occurred. Pharmacy leaders are expected to have a continuing and current understanding of the nature and source of budget variance. Their understanding should include their clinical therapeutics and pharmacy service operations knowledge, combined with an understanding of the business principles and practices. The regular discipline of monthly analysis provides an opportunity to understand the pharmacy's contribution to the health system.

Key Indicators

Utilizing key indicators is an essential factor in monitoring variances in financial operations over time. The pharmacy manager should be clear about the intent of each measure selected to be analyzed. They can be used to identify areas of concern, to clarify the source of cost, or to measure success of management initiatives. There are a variety of ratios that can be used. The manager should choose indicators that are most meaningful for measuring and monitoring current issues. The key indicators should be reviewed at least annually to ensure that the reports and ratios focus on the current main issues.

Measures should be chosen carefully to drive efforts and health system objectives in the correct direction. For example, additional medication costs in an outpatient retail pharmacy should generate additional revenue and improve the hospital's bottom line. The key measure for a retail pharmacy would be a margin percentage that meets or exceeds the goal. On the other hand, in the inpatient setting, additional medication costs do not usually result in additional revenue. The key measure in the inpatient setting is one that monitors drug or overall pharmacy cost.

Analyzing Budget Variances

The pharmacy manager is responsible for communicating financial results and budget variance analyses to two very different audiences. Upper management is interested in whether the variance is expected to continue and what the pharmacy manager is planning to do to help control it. Internal managers want to know how they can help control the budget variance. Upper management may ask for reports when they perceive a problem with current financial reports. Reports are often requested when variances exceed some institutionally established threshold, incorporating a dollar value, a percentage, or both. Internal managers should receive reports monthly so that they can continuously plan for and manage process improvements.

A routine monthly budget performance report should be concise yet detailed enough so that the leader is able to understand the context of the performance in regards to current events and influences. The pharmacy manager should at minimum perform the following actions within their presentation to leaders: (1) highlight significant variances, (2) explain potential factors contributing to the variances, and (3) discuss methods to improve performance.

As stated above, the threshold for significant variances varies per institution and can be defined in absolute dollar or variance percentage. Depending on the cost center and its pharmacy operation, an absolute dollar amount or variance percentage may be more appropriate. Generally, a cost center with a $100,000 variance or a 15% variance from flexed budget projections is an acceptable significant threshold to be noted in routine budget performance reports.

Pharmacy leaders must also identify and explain factors that could be contributing to the significant variances. Factors may be due to increased drug expenditures or growth in pharmacy services, such as the expansion of intensive care units, chemotherapy/oncology pharmacy growth, or specialty pharmacy growth. Significant variances can also be labor intensive in nature, such as overtime utilization, changes in FTE usage, or time spent in training new hires. In addition, pharmacy leaders should also consider current healthcare events when assessing potential causes of significant variances, eg, the COVID-19 pandemic and developing therapeutics or new biosimilars introduced into the market.

Controlling Budget Variances

Redirecting performance toward acceptable budget variances is the final piece of a routine budget performance report. While some factors cannot be controlled indefinitely, such as the impact of the COVID-19 pandemic, other factors can be handled for cost control. In the case of the COVID-19 pandemic, the cost of developing therapeutics, such as remdesivir, was unprecedented and thus exceeded significant variance thresholds immediately. Managing the utilization of remdesivir through patient specific criteria developed by infectious disease provider and pharmacist leadership was one method to control the rapidly increasing variance. On the other hand, labor-intensive factors, such as overtime utilization, can be impacted by pharmacy manager input. Pharmacy managers should identify the cause of overtime usage and address it accordingly. For example, if there is increased overtime utilization yet low pharmacy productivity based on the budget statistics, actions to address pharmacy workflow efficiency should be implemented.

CONCLUSION

Developing a strong relationship between the pharmacy and finance departments with dedicated staff working toward a common goal of producing and monitoring a pharmacy budget is critical to success. As the budget is developed, approved, executed, and monitored throughout the year, extensive dialogue and conversation is required. It is essential to understand the components of and variations from financial projections that were made as the pharmacy budget was established. A pharmacy budget is an ever-increasing significant aspect of the overall health system budget and performance.

REFERENCES

1. Wilson AL. The healthcare budget process. In: Wilson AL. *Financial management for health system pharmacists*. First Edition. Bethesda, MD: ASHP; 2008:47–62.

2. Williams RB. Preparing the operating budget. *Am J Hosp Pharm*. 1983;40(12):2181–2188. PubMed

3. Fox ER. Budgeting in the time of COVID-19. *Am J Health Syst Pharm*. 2020;77(15):1174–1175. PubMed

4. ASHP statement on the roles and responsibilities of the pharmacy executive. *Am J Health Syst Pharm*. 2016;73(5):329–332. PubMed

5. American Society of Hospital Pharmacists. ASHP guidelines: minimum standard for pharmacies in hospitals. *Am J Health Syst Pharm*. 2013;70(18):1619–1630 10.2146/sp130001. PubMed

6. Hunt ML Jr. Use of financial reports in managing pharmacies. *Am J Hosp Pharm*. 1984;41(4):709–715. PubMed

7. American Society of Health-System Pharmacists. So you want to perform internal benchmarking. Presentation series: the effective use of workload and productivity systems in health-system pharmacy. **https://www.ashp.org/-/media/assets/pharmacy-practice/resource-centers/practice-management/so-you-want-to-perform-internal-benchmarking.pptx**. Accessed January 17, 2022.

8. Rough SS, McDaniel M, Rinehart JR. Effective use of workload and productivity monitoring tools in health system pharmacy, part 1. *Am J Health Syst Pharm*. 2010;67(4):300–311. PubMed

9. Rough SS, McDaniel M, Rinehart JR. Effective use of workload and productivity monitoring tools in health system pharmacy, part 2. *Am J Health Syst Pharm*. 2010;67(5):380–388. PubMed

10. Carmichael J, Jassar G, Nguyen PA. Healthcare metrics: Where do pharmacists add value? *Am J Health Syst Pharm*. 2016;73(19):1537–1547. PubMed

11. Vest TA, Simmons A, Morbitzer KA, et al. Decision-making framework for an acute care clinical pharmacist productivity model: Part 1. *Am J Health Syst Pharm*. 2021;78(15):1402–1409. PubMed

12. Simmons A, Vest TA, Cicci J, et al. Formation and validation of an acute care clinical pharmacist productivity model: Part 2. *Am J Health Syst Pharm*. 2021;78(15):1410–1416. PubMed

340B: REGULATION, COMPLIANCE, AND OPTIMIZATION

*Chad Johnson, Christopher A. Hatwig,
and Fern Paul-Aviles*

This chapter focuses on financial management of the 340B Drug Pricing Program (340B program, 340B) for participating hospitals, the need for compliance resources, and best practices in optimizing program value.

The 340B program is a federal drug pricing program that requires drug manufacturers to provide discounted drug medications to certain eligible purchasers, known as *covered entities*. Eligible covered entities include qualifying hospitals and other organizations receiving federal funding or designations listed within the 340B statute.[1] The 340B program is administered by the Office of Pharmacy Affairs (OPA), located within the Health Resources and Services Administration (HRSA).

The importance of the 340B program for participating hospitals cannot be overstated, as it provides significant cost savings to help safety net healthcare providers improve access to affordable pharmaceutical care for their underserved and at risk patient populations. Because of the value of the 340B program and its unique compliance and operational requirements, hospitals commonly have dedicated resources for program oversight, operations, and financial management purposes. The 340B program continues to evolve and become more complex over time, so a dynamic and knowledgeable leader is important for its oversight to navigate the current and future landscape.

> **Call to action:** *Do any hospitals within your organization currently participate in 340B?*

To better understand financial management of the 340B program, it is helpful to understand what makes hospitals eligible to participate in the first place and how 340B pricing differs from other pricing available in the pharmaceutical marketplace.

Hospital Eligibility

Six types of hospitals are eligible to participate in the 340B program. Each type has its own unique requirements, but two key components of hospital eligibility include their ownership structure and amount of care provided to low-income populations. A 340B hospital's ownership classification must be one of the following:

1. Owned or operated by a state or local government.

2. Private, nonprofit entity with a contract with a state or local government to provide healthcare services to low-income patients not entitled to benefits under Medicare or Medicaid.

3. Public or private nonprofit corporation formally granted governmental powers by a state or local government.

DOI 10.37573/9781585287130.003

In addition, most hospitals are required to meet a certain threshold for care provided to low-income individuals using a calculation called the *disproportionate share adjustment percentage* (DSH percentage). The DSH percentage is a complex calculation based on the percentage of low-income Medicare or Medicaid-eligible inpatients served by the hospital versus its total hospital inpatient population.[2] Hospitals serving a higher proportion of low-income patients generally correlate with a higher DSH percentage and likelihood to meet 340B eligibility requirements; however, a hospital's uninsured inpatients do not factor into the DSH percentage calculation. DSH percentage is reported at least annually in a hospital's Medicare cost report (MCR), which contains a summary of certain financial and statistical data about a hospital.[3] The Centers for Medicare & Medicaid Services (CMS) uses the cost report for a variety of purposes, including determining whether it under or overpaid the hospital. More information on hospital eligibility and registration instructions can be obtained from the HRSA OPA website.[4]

> *Call to action:* Do you know your hospital's ownership classification (MCR worksheet S-2) and DSH percentage (MCR worksheet E, Part A)?

FIGURE 3-1. Types of hospitals eligible to participate in the 340B program

340B Pricing

The requirement to offer 340B pricing applies to manufacturers that participate in the Medicaid Drug Rebate Program (MDRP), which is administered by CMS. Drug manufacturers participate in MDRP to have their outpatient drugs covered by Medicaid. Having outpatient drugs covered by Medicaid is important to pharmaceutical manufacturers because it provides access to a large patient base. Roughly 780 manufacturers participate in MDRP.[5] In turn, they provide cost rebates to state Medicaid programs when their drugs are dispensed to Medicaid patients. Manufacturers participating in MDRP are also required to enter into pharmaceutical pricing agreements for the 340B program and the Secretary of Veterans Affairs Federal Supply Schedule, which supports the Department of Veterans Affairs and other government agencies in lowering drug costs.

Covered entities may access 340B pricing only for care provided in outpatient settings or to the extent that the drugs are for outpatient use, such as hospital discharge prescriptions. Therefore, for hospitals considering enrolling in the program, any projection of 340B benefit must consider the type and magnitude of its outpatient services. Furthermore, some categories of therapeutic agents or specific drug products may not be considered covered outpatient drugs under the 340B program (eg, vaccines, drug products whose manufacturer does not participate in MDRP) and therefore do not have 340B pricing available.

> *Did you know?* CMS publishes an exportable list of covered outpatient drugs in the Medicaid Drug Rebate Program.[6]

The 340B price calculation is called the *ceiling price* because it is the maximum price a manufacturer can charge for a drug, based on a statutory price calculation.[7] The term *340B price* often refers to the ceiling price. However, manufacturers, at their discretion, can further discount their medications below the statutory ceiling price by contracting with the 340B Prime Vendor Program (PVP), managed by Apexus, to provide pricing to all participating entities or by contracting with covered entities directly on an individual basis (or one-to-one basis).

In addition to offering 340B pricing to eligible covered entities as required by MDRP, manufacturers are also required to upload their pricing data quarterly to the 340B Office of Pharmacy Affairs Information System (340B OPAIS), in which certain authorized covered entity and manufacturer representatives can view 340B ceiling prices. Although most of this chapter focuses on 340B responsibilities of a hospital covered entity, there are considerable added operational and compliance requirements for pharmaceutical manufacturers in managing compliant 340B pricing operations. Manufacturers calculate prices and report them to government agencies (including CMS and HRSA) to ensure that accurate 340B prices are provided to covered entities.

Now that we've covered a few basic components of the 340B program, let's take a deeper dive into its financial management.

FINANCIAL MANAGEMENT

The fundamental value of the 340B program for hospitals results from the ability to purchase certain medications at a significant discount compared with other classes of trade pricing available in the market. In other words, the 340B program lowers drug acquisition costs. Hospital leaders with program and financial oversight responsibilities should focus on a few areas to appropriately monitor their 340B program and understand its value:

- Compliance: ensure that 340B drugs are provided only to eligible patients of the covered entity and adhere to all program requirements.

- Value: calculate the net financial impact and how savings are used.

- Optimization: monitor and improve 340B purchasing practices.

Compliance

All 340B covered entities are required to prevent diversion of 340B drugs to ineligible patients and prevent duplicate discounts on Medicaid prescriptions. Certain participating hospitals are prohibited from using a group purchasing organization (GPO) when purchasing covered outpatient drugs and others are affected by the orphan drug exclusion. Because this chapter is focused on financial management, a full-fledged discussion of these compliance elements is beyond the scope of this chapter. Visit the HRSA OPA and PVP websites for more information.[8]

What makes the 340B program unique over other types of marketplace drug discounts (eg, GPO contracts, individual manufacturer contracts) is the more complex compliance requirements associated with it. Being subject to the GPO prohibition has specific financial implications for settings that serve both 340B-eligible and ineligible patients (broadly, outpatients and inpatients, respectively, for a hospital) using a common inventory model called a non-GPO/wholesale acquisition cost-based (WAC) virtual replenishment inventory. This model provides a compliant way to distribute drugs to all patients from a single inventory but requires purchasing every new drug, according to National Drug Code (NDC) number, at a non-GPO/WAC price that is higher than the 340B price and may be higher than the GPO price as well. The inventory is non-GPO/WAC-based because if it were GPO-based, any products dispensed to outpatients would violate the GPO prohibition. If it were 340B-based, any products dispensed to inpatients and/or ineligible outpatients would lead to 340B diversion. A covered entity just entering the 340B program will experience a period of *higher* pharmaceutical expenses before it settles into a new pattern of purchasing covered outpatient drugs at 340B prices and continuing to purchase inpatient drugs at GPO prices. Careful management of inventory and 340B software oversight will minimize, but never eliminate, purchases at non-GPO/WAC prices. Hospitals subject to the GPO prohibition that participate in the PVP have the additional benefit of lowering their initial inventory setup costs by accessing the PVP's sub-WAC pricing portfolio on specific NDCs.

Orphan drugs are designated under section 526 of the Federal Food, Drug, and Cosmetic Act for a rare disease or condition and are classified as noncovered outpatient drugs.[9] Pharmaceutical manufacturers are not obligated to provide 340B prices on orphan drugs to hospitals subject to the orphan drug exclusion. In other words, 340B program participation for these hospitals may not result in cost savings on orphan drugs, so leaders should be aware of drug products in this category when assessing the impact of participation.

Ultimately, hospital leaders need to determine whether the benefits (or potential benefits) of the 340B program are worth the added compliance risk and need for dedicated oversight. We highlight three priorities for hospitals pertaining to compliance oversight:

- Determining oversight structure and internal resource needs.

- Ensuring that 340B drugs are provided only to eligible patients.

- Monitoring 340B OPAIS records and hospital eligibility.

Oversight Structure and Internal Resources

In addition to operational maintenance of the software and inventory management processes, it is important for the pharmacy department to have dedicated staff oversight of 340B program compliance to ensure accountability. For smaller hospitals, this could consist of one staff member with other responsibilities; for larger hospitals, it would be a team of individuals. This "340B team" is responsible for providing the compliance oversight necessary to ensure that the program is working as intended by performing routine audits, maintaining 340B policies and procedures, and ensuring adequate preparation if the covered entity is selected for a HRSA audit. For larger hospitals or health systems, it is common to have dedicated managers and/or directors over their 340B program, along with support staff.

> **Call to action:** If your organization has 340B-participating hospitals, do you know which staff members are responsible for program oversight?

The 340B team is often responsible for reporting to a 340B steering committee with multidisciplinary members (including, for example, pharmacy, compliance, finance, legal).[10] The 340B steering committee may review results of internal and external compliance audits and their corrective action plans, financial metrics, and other pertinent information to support the 340B program.[11] It also ensures that there is full organizational visibility to the program and may be crucial in communicating the value of the 340B program to senior leadership, as well as participating in strategic decision-making.

FIGURE 3-2. Assembling a 340B team

Ensuring Patient Eligibility

One of the more common day-to-day responsibilities of 340B staff is to ensure that 340B drugs are being provided only to eligible patients. This is often performed by auditing reports from the 340B software and the hospital's electronic health record.[12;13] In situations in which 340B drugs are dispensed to ineligible patients, also called *diversion*, the 340B team is responsible for identifying the full scope of the problem and following up to correct the diversion, which may include notifying HRSA[14] in the event of a material breach and will likely require repaying pharmaceutical manufacturers for obtaining a 340B discount when the patient was not eligible. Often, noncompliance is reported to the steering committee, which oversees hospital repayments to manufacturers and ensures appropriate follow-up. HRSA expects covered entities to engage with manufacturers when the manufacturers identify unexpected 340B purchases of their products and to work in good faith[15] with manufacturers to resolve all noncompliance. Some hospitals maintain a designated repayment fund budgeted annually to support repayment activities.

Call to action: If your organization has 340B-participating hospitals, what is the standard procedure for resolving noncompliance and how are repayments managed financially?

Monitoring 340B OPAIS and Hospital Eligibility

Although 340B OPAIS' function as a repository for pharmaceutical pricing information is an important one, its most common use is to serve as a public database of registered covered entities and participating manufacturers. HRSA and manufacturers both require covered entities to ensure that their 340B OPAIS record is accurate at all times,[16] so the 340B team is responsible for routinely updating the entries quarterly, or more frequently when registration changes are necessary. In addition to initial registration and routine maintenance, covered entities are required to recertify annually to remain in the 340B program.[17]

For most hospitals, closely monitoring the DSH percentage is another crucial oversight component, especially if the hospital's value is projected to be close to the threshold for 340B eligibility (> 11.75% for DSH/PED/CAN and ≥ 8% for RRC/SCH). Some hospital finance departments conduct a quarterly interim DSH calculation to ensure awareness of its proximity to the 340B DSH eligibility threshold. This ensures that there are no surprises when the MCR is filed. If a hospital slips below the eligibility threshold, it may become ineligible for the 340B program on the date the MCR is filed unless it qualifies as another hospital entity type based on its DSH percentage and designation. In situations in which eligibility criteria are met for a new hospital type, the hospital may terminate its existing registration and enroll as the new entity type on 340B OPAIS. Hospitals considering changing entity types should contact Apexus Answers, the HRSA-aligned call center, to determine appropriate steps necessary for the transition. Advance notice to the 340B team regarding impactful DSH percentage changes will ensure that the team is ready to either transition to a new entity type or terminate from the program to cease purchasing 340B products and address inventory considerations. If pharmacy leadership is not aware of its ineligibility until after the MCR is filed, such as when hospital recertification is due, it will have purchased 340B drugs for ineligible patients, which will warrant manufacturer repayments and result in negative financial implications.

Value

Because of the importance of 340B discounts to hospitals and ongoing scrutiny by regulators, government officials, manufacturers, and other stakeholders, it is important for hospital financial leaders to understand the net financial impact of their 340B participation and document 340B savings. Although not required by the 340B statute, documenting the financial benefits and costs of participation is a best practice and helps hospital leadership better understand how the 340B program expands access to care for their underserved patient populations. It can help in determining which services would be directly affected if there were a loss of program savings for any reason.[18] It may also enable the hospital to share externally how 340B savings are used to support program intent.

Call to action: If your organization has 340B-participating hospitals, how is the net financial impact calculated and distributed to senior leadership?

Hospitals often calculate 340B program value once or twice yearly, potentially just prior to the annual budgeting cycle because it can be used to support the addition of staff and other resources to ensure the operation of a compliant 340B pharmacy operation. The Prime Vendor offers a

HSRA-reviewed tool on its website to assist covered entities with these types of calculations, which is summarized by the following calculation:

340B program net financial impact = 340B benefits (drug cost savings) – compliance maintenance costs

Drug Cost Savings

Understanding the drug cost savings of the 340B program is not as straightforward as it seems. There are several scenarios that will dictate different methods for calculating drug cost savings, but in all cases, the 340B benefit should be calculated by comparing the difference between a "reference price" (the usual cost the hospital would pay for the drug if not participating in the 340B program) and the lower 340B price. To illustrate the concept of a reference price, let's say you need to complete a home repair that requires duct tape. If you want to purchase a roll of duct tape from a hardware store and have a 10% off coupon, you will want to know how much the duct tape normally costs ($5, the reference price), what your cost would be once the discount is subtracted ($4.50), and how much you saved (50¢). The purpose of 340B savings calculations is to determine the reference price (ie, non-340B cost) and how much was saved, as the pharmacy already knows its 340B cost.

Consider the following inventory model scenarios for calculating 340B drug cost savings, in ascending order of complexity:

1. A physical 340B inventory is used when 100% of the patients served are 340B-eligible ("clean sites").

2. For hospitals not subject to the GPO prohibition, a virtual replenishment inventory model is used to manage the hospital pharmacy's purchases with a two-account model: the 340B account for eligible outpatient dispenses and the non-340B (usually GPO) account for every other dispense.

3. For hospitals subject to the GPO prohibition, a virtual replenishment inventory model is used with a three-account model: the neutral "starter" account (non-GPO/WAC account); the account for inpatient dispenses (usually GPO); and the account for eligible outpatient dispenses (340B account).

Physical inventories ("clean sites")

When a hospital is evaluating the value of the 340B program in a "clean" site (or a single class of trade), it is important to calculate what its drug acquisition costs would be if it were not participating in the 340B program. For example, consider a hospital with a "closed door" retail pharmacy that dispenses only to 340B-eligible patients from a physical 340B inventory. Average acquisition costs in the pharmacy software are based on its 340B drug acquisition costs, so it may not be transparent to pharmacy leaders as to how drug acquisition costs would be affected if the hospital did not participate in 340B or what the increased costs would be if the hospital wanted to start dispensing non-340B drugs to patients who are ineligible for 340B products.

Hospitals not subject to the GPO prohibition

In hospitals not subject to the GPO prohibition, the only price other than the 340B price is typically the GPO price. Therefore, the 340B drug cost savings is a simple calculation of the difference between the GPO price and the 340B price.

Hospitals subject to the GPO prohibition

Because hospitals subject to the GPO prohibition usually manage their inventory using a virtual replenishment inventory, they must buy the first package(s) of a new NDC at a compliant, but potentially higher, non-GPO/WAC price, which they would not have to do if they were not participating in the 340B program. When the non-GPO/WAC price is higher than the GPO price, it mathematically negates some of the 340B savings benefit (called the *WAC variance*).

Purchasing on a non-GPO/WAC account, though, is not always evidence of poor management of the 340B program. For example, in the case of newly released brand-name drugs, the manufacturer may not feel compelled to negotiate a discounted price with a GPO or a hospital. In that case, the non-GPO/WAC price may be the same as the GPO price and there would be no negative financial implications to purchasing on the non-GPO/WAC account as opposed to the GPO account. Sub-WAC pricing may be available in the non-GPO/WAC account, which may create additional value for PVP participants. Because a new NDC is required to be purchased on the non-GPO/WAC account, good inventory management practices may dictate sticking with a consistent NDC number. Frequent switching of NDC numbers, which may be necessary when drugs are in short supply, can be financially detrimental and can create compliance challenges.

Calculating 340B savings over time

Acquisition costs under 340B are typically accessed by reviewing purchase history reports from a pharmacy software or wholesaler to show historical 340B account pricing and total order quantities by NDC over a given timeframe, typically one year. Once the total quantity and cost of 340B products purchased is calculated, the estimated non-340B cost of those drugs should be determined per NDC number to quantify savings from access to 340B pricing. Hospitals subject to the GPO prohibition should subtract WAC variance for purchases made on the non-GPO/WAC account when acquisition costs were higher than GPO price points.

Net drug cost savings = [(estimated non-340B acquisition cost (eg, GPO) – 340B acquisition cost) × number of units ordered] – [WAC variance × number of units ordered, if applicable]

This type of calculation should be performed in all settings in which 340B drugs are purchased, including entity-owned pharmacies providing outpatient and clinic-administered drugs, retail pharmacies, and contract pharmacies.

340B contract (retail) pharmacies

Covered entities may elect to dispense 340B drugs through a contract pharmacy, which is a contractual agreement between a retail pharmacy and 340B covered entity for the pharmacy to provide services to the entity's patients. Contract pharmacies operate using a bill-to/ship-to arrangement, under which the covered entity purchases 340B drugs and ships them to the pharmacy for eligible patients of the covered entity. Contract retail pharmacies are a special situation because the 340B drugs purchased as a result of a contract pharmacy arrangement are not drugs that would ordinarily have been purchased by the hospital. They would have been purchased by the retail pharmacy at their usual price, which the hospital cannot know and would not have incurred. Therefore, the typical methodology for calculating the net financial impact would be to subtract the 340B drug cost and any pharmacy dispensing fees and software vendor fees from the reimbursement.

Contract pharmacy 340B benefit = retail pharmacy's reimbursement – 340B drug acquisition cost – pharmacy dispensing and software vendor fees

Compliance Maintenance Costs

Although understanding the drug cost savings is the most significant part of calculating net financial impact, it does not paint the full picture. There are added costs for a hospital to participate in the program, which should be accounted for in the overall impact calculation. Consider costs for internal and external resources pertaining to program oversight and day-to-day operations. Here are a few examples:

- Internal resources: dedicated full-time equivalent (FTE) staff costs, equipment.

- External resources: 340B software costs, legal/consultant fees, external auditor fees.

> **Call to action:** *If your organization has 340B-participating hospitals, what are the added costs due to 340B program participation?*

Additional costs may be associated with 340B program participation, such as discriminatory reimbursement scenarios under which certain payers reimburse 340B hospitals less than non-340B hospitals or other pharmacies. The result can have a significant negative impact on the hospital's 340B margin or savings. These types of considerations vary by hospital and are highly influenced by the patient mix, location, and other factors. In the end, you should feel confident that the net is an accurate estimate for your hospital.

Documenting Use of Savings

It is a best practice for hospitals to share how their 340B program savings are benefiting their vulnerable and underserved patient populations. The way in which hospitals calculate savings and distribute the information varies by hospital, from being an internal document shared with senior leadership to information posted publicly on the hospital website to pamphlets shared directly with patients. The primary challenge with documenting how 340B savings are used is that it is not standard accounting practice to directly tie the funding of a program or service with savings generated from another service.[18]

> **Call to action:** *If your organization has 340B-participating hospitals, how is the use of 340B savings documented and what are the internal and external communications on use of savings?*

Hospital leaders should consider how the 340B program is directly affecting their underserved patient populations, which services are supported by 340B savings, and which services would be at risk if the hospital no longer qualified for the 340B program.[18] One way to better understand these metrics is to partner with hospital divisions of community and social impact that can best speak to community benefits provided by the hospital. There are also certain established ways that hospitals report community benefit that can be leveraged, such as reporting under MCR worksheet S10 and Schedule H, IRS Form 990.[19;20] Nonreported items that are being supported by the 340B program should also be documented. Here are a few examples:

Reported community benefit
- Schedule H (Form 990)—IRS
- Worksheet S10 (MCR)—CMS

Non-reported community benefit
- Free clinical services provided to high-risk patients.
- Free services connecting low-income patients to manufacturer drug discount programs.
- Free vaccinations.
- Prescriptions provided at no cost or for a nominal co-pay.
- Funding for new services to support low-income patients.
- Other uncompensated care.

Consider accessing templates from national hospital associations or trade groups, such as the 340B Health Impact Profile[21] or from the Prime Vendor[18] to document use of savings when creating or refining these documents. Another tactic that goes a long way is checking with other similar hospitals to see how they are calculating and documenting use of 340B savings. It is important to be able to share stories of how patients are receiving better access to care as a result of the 340B program.

4090 (Cont.)		FORM CMS-2552-10			01-22

CALCULATION OF REIMBURSEMENT SETTLEMENT		PROVIDER CCN: _____	PERIOD: FROM _____	WORKSHEET E, PART A	
		COMPONENT CCN:	TO _____		

Check applicable box:	[ ] Hospital	[ ] PARHM Demonstration		
PART A - INPATIENT HOSPITAL SERVICES UNDER IPPS				
33	Allowable disproportionate share percentage (see instructions)			33

FIGURE 3-3. Worksheet E, part A

Optimization

Once hospital leaders have a solid grasp on compliance and value of the 340B program, the next step is to look at hospital operations to determine ways to optimize their participation. Successful financial leaders often bring individuals from different hospital departments together to implement tactical strategies that support current and future state initiatives to better serve patients.

Monitor Quarterly Pricing Changes

Pharmacy purchasing staff routinely make day-to-day decisions about which products to stock in their inventory. Pharmacy leadership should work with buyers to monitor pricing closely because 340B prices change quarterly. In other words, a drug product with more favorable pricing in a prior quarter might not be the most cost-effective option in the current quarter if its 340B acquisition cost increased or another product's acquisition cost decreased. There may be additional sub-340B discounts available contracted by the Prime Vendor,[22] which also change over time, so is important to actively monitor the portfolio to create additional cost savings. Changing products is generally more straightforward in a physical "clean" 340B inventory; however, virtual replenishment inventories also benefit from close monitoring of 340B quarterly pricing to make product changes when appropriate.

Calculate Weighted Average Pricing

Because drug purchases in a virtual replenishment inventory are often made from multiple accounts (eg, 340B, GPO, non-GPO/WAC), a hospital should be aware of the weighted average pricing (or ratio of dispensing in inpatient and outpatient areas) across all accounts when determining product selection.[23] A drug with a more favorable GPO price may not be favorable overall for the hospital if the bulk of purchases are made on a 340B account for eligible patients, for one example. Alternatively, a hospital's GPO pricing for a drug that is used primarily in the inpatient setting will be a primary driver for its formulary decision compared with outpatient 340B pricing. Hospitals subject to the GPO prohibition should include optimization of sub-WAC pricing in calculations for non-GPO/WAC account purchases and track similarly to 340B and GPO pricing. Ultimately, purchasing leadership should feel confident that they are obtaining the most favorable acquisition costs for their drug inventory while following all 340B program requirements. Weighted average pricing calculations may also be helpful for leaders working to secure independent discounts from pharmaceutical manufacturers at the covered entity level by having a better understanding of current acquisition costs to determine where the manufacturer could provide added value.

> **Call to action:** If your organization has 340B-participating hospitals, what opportunities do you have to more effectively optimize 340B purchases?

340B Software Data Integrity

Software may be used to implement multiple aspects of the 340B program, such as identifying eligible claims, tracking purchasing invoices from 340B and non-340B accounts, and maintaining auditable records for compliance oversight. It is important to ensure that data feeds to and from the software are working correctly to optimize purchasing from 340B accounts and prevent diversion. Data integrity issues between the electronic health record and the 340B software could lead to under or overaccumulation of 340B products, resulting in noncompliance or underutilization of the 340B program. For example, consider a new hospital clinic that serves 340B-eligible patients and receives its drugs from a virtual replenishment inventory. If its drug administration data from the electronic health record are mistakenly omitted from an eligibility report sent to the 340B software, the software may not consider drugs administered by that clinic as eligible. Its drugs would be replenished by a non-340B account even though the clinic is serving 340B-eligible patients. Alternatively, the 340B software could mistakenly qualify unrecognized new patient types or nursing units for 340B even if they are for ineligible inpatients, leading to diversion. The 340B team should have a monthly quality assurance review to detect these types of changes and make appropriate adjustments.

Another common source of data integrity issues in 340B software is drug package-size conversion anomalies between hospital 340B software increments, such as a full vial or package, and the drug wholesaler or manufacturer package size. Inaccurate conversions may lead to under or overaccumulation. It is a best practice to audit NDCs with large positive and negative accumulations monthly, or more frequently, to identify and correct any errors in accumulations or purchasing. Small data issues can cause large problems if not monitored appropriately.

New Hospital Departments and/or Clinics

It is important to be aware of any new hospital departments that serve eligible patients of the covered entity in which 340B pricing can be used. As with monitoring the DSH percentage in the MCR, it is equally important to work closely with senior leadership to be aware of any clinics opening, closing, or being acquired by the hospital that serve 340B-eligible patients, or of changes in provider-based status. New hospital clinics with low outpatient drug use and/or prescribing may have a minimal impact on 340B purchasing, whereas others, such as new infusion clinics, may have a significant impact on 340B purchasing and necessitate additional resources and corresponding compliance oversight. Leaders should be notified months in advance to have adequate time to prepare for new clinic openings.

Forecasting 340B Pricing

From a budgeting perspective, 340B prices do not necessarily parallel the traditional pharmaceutical marketplace prices, so any pharmacy pricing forecast publications intended for the general marketplace, including GPO pricing, may not be applicable for 340B products (or market). Hospital leaders may consider other ways to attempt to forecast future 340B prices based on historical price trends for high-cost drugs driving the bulk of pharmacy expenditures while knowing that there will be some variability because the 340B price for an upcoming quarter is not known until pricing data have been submitted by the manufacturer. Generally, after several years of participation in the 340B program, pharmacy leaders tasked with drug budgeting projections do not need to try to estimate 340B purchase prices; assuming the mix of inpatient and outpatient service lines remains constant, prior years' drug expenses may be multiplied by the expected drug inflation rate plus any expected new drugs in the pipeline.

Formulary Selections

Drugs with favorable 340B acquisition costs are often preferred for hospital outpatient formularies serving eligible patients to support extending limited resources as far as possible. However, the drug with the lowest acquisition cost may not always be the best choice for the hospital's formulary if not preferred by payer reimbursement models, if there is a negative profit margin, or other therapeutic alternatives are available, such as biosimilars, that provide the best value to the patient. Hospital leaders should work closely with billing and reimbursement departments in addition to clinical staff when assessing the outpatient formulary to ensure that appropriate products are selected for the hospital's unique patient population.

Outpatient Pharmacy Opportunities

In addition to outpatient department and clinic settings, hospitals may also provide 340B drugs to eligible patients in outpatient pharmacy settings. Different types of pharmacy models, such as retail, specialty, mail order, home care, or home infusion pharmacies, may be used to provide medications for the home setting. These services can have a significant impact on 340B program value, especially for hospitals with low outpatient department/clinic dispensing but high outpatient prescribing. Consider a small critical access hospital without any outpatient clinics. A significant contributor to its 340B program value could be prescriptions issued upon patient discharge,[24] so unless the hospital has an owned or contracted outpatient pharmacy, it would lose access to 340B program savings on those prescriptions because they would be filled by a nonhospital pharmacy.

Entity-owned pharmacy

An entity-owned pharmacy is owned by, and is a legal part of, the 340B entity.[25] These pharmacies may be located within the four walls of the hospital or operate externally and may serve only 340B eligible patients of the hospital ("closed door") or be available to the public ("open door"). The 340B program provides exceptional value for entity-owned pharmacies that serve eligible patients of the hospital by lowering drug acquisition costs, supporting initiatives like drug discount programs for low-income patients, charity care, clinical pharmacist services to improve adherence, and home delivery services. Hospital leaders should consider the goals of opening an entity-owned retail pharmacy, which may include improving medication outcomes for patients being discharged from the hospital or being seen by hospital outpatient clinics, serving hospital employees, or improving medication access for the local community.

There may be hurdles to achieving profitability, such as an entity-owned pharmacy dispensing primarily low-margin primary care regimens. Despite these challenges, there are potentially other advantages to keeping prescriptions in-house:

- Strong relationships between pharmacy staff and prescribers allow for easy communication to resolve medication-related problems.

- Proximity and association with the hospital may make patients more receptive to pharmaceutical interventions expected by payers through value-based contracts, rewarding hospitals for improved health outcomes and reduced total costs of care or penalizing them for worse outcomes.

- Pharmacy staff may work more closely with prescribers to select cost-effective medication regimens and maximize patient health outcomes.

- Hospitals serving states that did not adopt Medicaid expansion as part of the Affordable Care Act may serve a large subset of uninsured patients for whom the hospital is truly the safety net provider, even for primary care medications. Because the patients are uninsured, the hospital will incur the costs of care for these patients whether they are cared for in an outpatient setting or inpatient hospitalization.

Data from the electronic health record may be used to estimate total outpatient prescriptions issued by the hospital to estimate potential value from the 340B program. Leaders should consider potential 340B value (340B savings versus non-340B acquisition costs), estimated fill rates for patients, startup/maintenance costs, and hospital services that would benefit with a close pharmacy/physician relationship to improve patient care. Once entity-owned retail pharmacies are opened, the strategy often focuses on ensuring that high-risk patients are receiving appropriate pharmaceutical care, monitoring 340B compliance, and optimizing fill rates to be able to keep providing this valuable service to the community.

Contract pharmacy relationships

Some hospitals may not have the resources or space to provide entity-owned pharmacy services, or their patients may already be filling prescriptions at an external pharmacy. Leaders may want to improve medication access for their patients by setting up contract pharmacy arrangements. Consider how contract pharmacies benefit underserved patients of the covered entity and charity care programs that they support. Ultimately, optimizing 340B program savings can support a hospital's ability to serve diverse patient populations.

One way to identify potential contract pharmacy opportunities is by reviewing data from the electronic health record to determine which pharmacies are already receiving outpatient prescriptions from the hospital. There may be a local pharmacy that is not currently serving many hospital patients but could partner with the hospital through a contract pharmacy relationship to provide clinical services or discount programs to hospital patients. Consider the types of services provided by the pharmacy (eg, low-cost medication programs, adherence counseling, medication therapy management) and categories of medications being dispensed by the pharmacy, such as retail, infusion, and/or specialty drugs. Pharmacy models evolve over time, so is important for leaders to stay attuned to emerging care models to ensure that their patients are best served by owned or contracted pharmacy services.

CONCLUSION

This chapter serves as an introduction for hospital leaders to better understand financial management of the 340B program. Additional resources are available for leaders with direct oversight of their 340B program or new leaders interested in gaining more 340B knowledge. The 340B Prime Vendor Program, managed by Apexus, offers 340B University with in-person and virtual learning opportunities available.[8] It is also recommended to read the *340B Program Handbook: Integrating 340B into the Health system Pharmacy Supply Chain* by Andrew L. Wilson to obtain a detailed perspective on the 340B program.

REFERENCES

1. Health Resources & Services Adminisration. Section 340B, Public Health Service Act (Pub. L. 102-585). **https://www.hrsa.gov/sites/default/files/opa/programrequirements/phsactsection340b.pdf**. Accessed March 15, 2022.

2. Centers for Medicare & Medicaid Services. Disproportionate share hospital (DSH). **https://www.cms.gov/Medicare/Medicare-Fee-for-Service-Payment/AcuteInpatientPPS/dsh**. Accessed March 15, 2022.

3. Asper F. Introduction to Medicare cost reports. *Research Data Assistance Center*. **https://resdac.org/sites/datadocumentation.resdac.org/files/Introduction%20to%20Medicare%20Cost%20Reports%20%28Slides%29_0.pdf**. Accessed March 15, 2022.

4. Health Resources & Services Administration. 340B program hospital registration instructions. Updated February 11, 2019. **https://www.hrsa.gov/sites/default/files/hrsa/opa/hospital-registration-instruction-details.pdf**. Accessed March 15, 2022.

5. Medicaid.gov. Medicaid Drug Rebate Program (MDRP). Updated November 8, 2021. **https://www.medicaid.gov/medicaid/prescription-drugs/medicaid-drug-rebate-program/index.html**. Accessed March 15, 2022.

6. Data.Medicaid.gov. Drug products in the Medicaid Drug Rebate Program. Updated March 11, 2022. **https://data.medicaid.gov/dataset/0ad65fe5-3ad3-5d79-a3f9-7893ded7963a**. Accessed March 15, 2022.

7. Department of Health and Human Services. 340B drug pricing program ceiling price and manufacturer civil monetary penalties regulation. 42 CFR Part 10. Fed. Reg. Vol. 82 No. 3, January 5, 2017. **https://www.govinfo.gov/content/pkg/FR-2017-01-05/pdf/2016-31935. pdf**. Accessed March 15, 2022.

8. 340B Prime Vendor Program. 340B university: essential education for all stakeholders. **https://www.340bpvp.com/340b-university**. Accessed March 15, 2022.

9. Health Resources & Services Administration. Orphan drugs. Updated October 2021. **https:// www.hrsa.gov/opa/program-requirements/orphan-drug-exclusion/index.html#about**. Accessed March 15, 2022.

10. Peek GK, Williams AM. 340B oversight: interdisciplinary approach ensures continuous compliance. *Pharmacy Times*, November 30, 2017. **https://www.pharmacytimes.com/ view/340b-oversight-interdisciplinary-approach-ensures-continuous-compliance**. Accessed March 15, 2022.

11. 340B Prime Vendor Program. 340B oversight best practices dashboard. Updated April 30, 2019. **https://www.340bpvp.com/Documents/Public/340B%20Tools/340B-oversight-best-practices-dashboard.docx**. Accessed March 15, 2022.

12. 340B Prime Vendor Program. Self-audit: prevention of diversion and GPO violation, GPO prohibition hospitals. Updated February 13, 2020. **https://www.340bpvp.com/Documents/ Public/340B%20Tools/gpo-prohibition-hospitals-self-audit-prevention-of-diversion-and-gpo-violation.docx**. Accessed March 15, 2022.

13. 340B Prime Vendor Program. Self-audit: prevention of diversion, rural hospitals. Updated February 13, 2020. **https://www.340bpvp.com/Documents/Public/340B%20Tools/rural-hospitals-self-audit-prevention-of-diversion.docx**. Accessed March 15, 2022.

14. Health Resources & Services Administration. Entity self-disclosures. Updated August 2018. **https://www.hrsa.gov/opa/self-disclosures/self-disclosure.html**. Accessed March 15, 2022.

15. Health Resources & Services Administration. 340B administrative dispute resolution (ADR). Updated January 2021. **https://www.hrsa.gov/opa/340b-administrative-dispute-resolution**. Accessed March 15, 2022.

16. Health Resources & Services Administration. Program requirements. Updated March 2020. **https://www.hrsa.gov/opa/program-requirements/index.html**. Accessed March 15, 2022.

17. Health Resources & Services Administration. Annual recertification. Updated September 2017. **https://www.hrsa.gov/opa/recertification/recertification.html**. Accessed March 15, 2022.

18. 340B Prime Vendor Program. Calculating 340B net financial impact and use of savings. Updated April 22, 2019. **https://www.340bpvp.com/Documents/Public/340B%20Tools/ calculating-340b-net-financial-impact-and-use-of-savings.docx**. Accessed March 15, 2022.

19. Internal Revenue Service. About Schedule H (Form 990), hospitals. Updated June 10, 2021. **https://www.irs.gov/forms-pubs/about-schedule-h-form-990**. Accessed March 15, 2022.

20. Centers for Medicare & Medicaid Services. Reviews of cost report worksheet S-10. Updated December 1, 2021. **https://www.cms.gov/Medicare/Compliance-and-Audits/Part-A-Cost-Report-Audit-and-Reimbursement/Reviews-of-Cost-Report-Worksheet-S-10**. Accessed March 15, 2022.

21. 340B Health. Impact profiles. **https://www.340bhealth.org/members/advocacy-tools/ impact-profiles/profile-page**. Accessed March 15, 2022.

22. 340B Prime Vendor Program. PVP entity enrollment. **https://www.340bpvp.com/covered-entities/pvp-entity-enrollment**. Accessed March 15, 2022.

23. 340B Prime Vendor Program. WAC account purchasing strategies, GPO prohibition hospitals. Updated September 18, 2019. **https://www.340bpvp.com/Documents/Public/340B%20 Tools/wac-account-purchasing-strategies.docx**. Accessed March 15, 2022.

24. 340B Prime Vendor Program. HRSA FAQ 1563. **https://www.340bpvp.com/hrsa-faqs/faq-search?Ntt=1563**. Accessed March 15, 2022.

25. 340B Prime Vendor Program. HRSA FAQ 1364. **https://www.340bpvp.com/hrsa-faqs/faq-search?Ntt=1364**. Accessed March 15, 2022.

DATA ANALYTICS AND INSIGHT: DRIVING VALUE, OPTIMIZING UTILIZATION, AND IMPROVING OVERALL PERFORMANCE

*Seth Hartman, Randall Knoebel,
Ravi Patel, and Mark Siska*

The deployment of electronic health records, advanced clinical systems, and supporting automation combined with more sophisticated data management capabilities have transformed how data are generated, processed, analyzed, and visualized. Progress in the techniques used for analyzing large quantities of data while leveraging analytics has created significant opportunities for health systems to drive value, optimize utilization, and improve overall business and practice performance. As pharmacy department leaders continue to improve the process and workflow integration issues created by the deployment of core medication management supporting technologies, they must set their sights on the era of big data, analytics, and use of artificial intelligence for deriving insight, remaining competitive, and advancing the practice. This chapter intends to provide pharmacy leaders a framework for forging a data-centric department while playing a leadership role in managing data and optimizing its use.[1–3]

TERMINOLOGIES, DEFINITIONS, AND METAPHORS

A fundamental understanding of big data terms, metaphors, and definitions (**Table 4-1**) is essential for the pharmacy executive to effectively participate in internal and external discussions involving data uses and how it may benefit the practice.[1] The knowledge can also serve as a quick start guide when preparing for that next strategy meeting with the Chief Digital or Data Officer.

CHALLENGES

The very nature of big data in healthcare is cumbersome given its:

- Formats
- Definitions
- Structure
- Source
- Regulation
- Complexity[6]

DOI 10.37573/9781585287130.004

TABLE 4-1. Terms and Definitions

Term	Definition
Big Data	A broadly used term to describe ways very large and complex datasets are systematically mined and analyzed for acquiring information and new knowledge.
Data Literacy	Focuses on building competencies to evaluate, construct, and communicate meaning with data.
Data Fluency	Enables people to express ideas about data in a shared language and connects employees across roles through a set of standards, processes and tools, and terms.
Artificial Intelligence	Experts define AI as the use of computer systems to analyze large quantities of data, then applying the results of those analyses programmatically to better inform decisions.
Business Intelligence (BI) versus Business Analytics (BA)[2;4]	Business intelligence focuses on descriptive and diagnostic analytics which provides a summary of historical and present data primarily visualized through static reports. These reports help identify what and why something has happened so you can replicate what works and change what does not. Business analytics focuses on predictive and prescriptive analytics, which uses data mining, modeling, and machine learning to determine the likelihood of future outcomes. BA helps identify what may happen and how one can make something happen and can be used as a forecasting tool to remain competitive and drive future decisions.
Data Scientist	A data scientist utilizes several advanced skills including mathematics, statistics, behavioral sciences, business, and technology to mine and then analyze stores of big data for trends and patterns while interpreting the data to discover solutions and opportunities.
Data Visualization	Data visualization tools render data and information in a user friendly and accessible way using charts, graphs, scorecards, dashboards. These tools allow end users to better understand trends, outliers, and patterns in the data and can also help when it comes to validating data.
Machine Learning	Sometimes referred to as enhanced processing automation given its ability to process unstructured data and recognize patterns. In practice, machine learning is capable of augmenting human judgment, and can make decisions based on learning from processed data.
Data Characteristics (The big Vs of data)	See **Table 4-2**[5]
Data Warehouse	A system that stores data to analyze and process it in the future. The source of data can vary, depending on its purpose. A data warehouse collects data from various sources, whether internal or external, and optimizes the data for retrieval for business purposes. The data are usually structured, often from relational databases, but it can be unstructured too.
Data Lake	A data lake is a place that stores a large amount of structured and unstructured data in its original format. It is also a method for organizing large volumes of highly diverse data from a variety of sources.
Data Mining	Data mining is the process of analyzing large sets of data primarily through the use of analytics to determine trends and patterns. It allows businesses and industries to learn customer tendencies, better identify their opportunities, and remain competitive.
Data Cleansing	Data cleansing is the process of preparing data for analysis by correcting, removing, or modifying data that is incorrect or wrongly formatted.
Metadata	Metadata is data about data and is often intended to make finding, working, or understanding instances of the data easier. Examples include timestamps or creators of data.

TABLE 4-2. Big Data Characteristics[5]

Data Characteristics	Definition
Volume	The amount of data needing to be processed at a given time.
Velocity	Refers to the speed at which data are being generated, produced, created, or refreshed.
Variety	Refers to heterogeneous data sources that need to be identified and normalized before computation can occur.
Veracity	Refers to the reliability of the data source, its context, and how meaningful it is to the analysis based on it.
Value	Includes understanding your customers better, targeting them accordingly, optimizing processes, and improving machine or business performance.
Visualization	Refers to how challenging it is to visualize big data. Current tools face technical challenges due to limitations of technology and poor scalability, functionality, and response time.
Viscosity	Measures the resistance to flow in the volume of data. Resistance can come from different data sources, conflict from integration flow rates, and processing required to turn the data into insight.
Virality	**Measures how quickly data are spread, conveyed,** and passed on quickly.

This has required healthcare organizations to take a closer look at their approach for processing and transforming the data including how they are gathered, stored, analyzed, and distributed. The primary big data characteristic (big V) challenges in healthcare include volume, velocity, and variety. These all pose significant technology, data validity, and privacy risks to healthcare systems seeking to leverage big data.

The volume of data presents several technological challenges not only from a storage perspective but also from the availability of tools to analyze large quantities of data. The issue of velocity is not about the speed at which data are being generated, produced, created, or refreshed, but more about the timeliness in which analytics are performed in relation to the real-time need. Physicians, pharmacists, and all healthcare workers rely on real-time, actionable information to make urgent decisions that improve quality while ensuring value.

Data validity and integrity pose significant big data challenges and use of analytics for the healthcare industry. The medication data and coding systems incorporated into the multitude of medication management supporting applications creates significant variation and complexity. The data are often represented in a variety of proprietary formats and different conceptual models using different terminologies that adds to the ongoing challenges. Pharmacy departments and their leaders play a key role for ensuring the appropriate level of expertise is allocated to maintain data, information, and knowledge assets across all medication management supporting technologies within the health system. Their role must include validating data quality and safety, minimizing data quality risks, and affirming medication-related data, information, and knowledge management best practices. Patient privacy and confidentiality challenges are an additional impediment for deploying analytic and big data solutions. Keeping a patient's information safe while utilizing big data tools, which often require patient-identifiable information, can ultimately lead to significant healthcare system risk. Strict protocols must be used to manage personal identifiers prior to data release. Despite *Health Insurance Portability and Accountability Act* (HIPAA) protections, there is still the risk, particularly if datasets are merged with other information.[6–10] Other big data challenges include:

- Capture
- Cleaning
- Storage

- Stewardship
- Querying
- Reporting
- Visualization
- Sharing[6]

LITERACY, GOVERNANCE, AND SUPPORTING STRUCTURES

Literacy

Data literacy is the ability to recognize, evaluate, work with, communicate, and apply data in the context of practice priorities and outcomes. Much like learning a foreign language, data literacy requires learning shared vocabulary and being able to translate, speak, interpret, and become fluent in the language of data. Simply democratizing data to nontechnical users will likely not translate to success. End user data literacy that includes understanding the context of the data will create tool proficiency and a better chance of communicating value. Health system pharmacy leaders will need to invest in education and training given self-service tools will not always translate to self-sufficiency.

Data literacy is foundational to becoming a data-centric organization. Rapid changes in technology and greater access to data have changed the way we communicate, engage, build relationships, track progress, and make decisions. Adopting the essentials of data literacy (**Table 4-3**) [7] will bridge the gap and ensure effective translation amid such change while empowering health systems to drive value and transform healthcare. By leading the language of data and growing a data skilled workforce, the pharmacy healthcare system leader will be in a better position to drive value across the medication use process. (**Table 4-4**) [7–9]

TABLE 4-3. Data Literacy Essentials[7]

Data Literacy Essentials	
Processes and outcomes	Analytics
Metrics and key performance indicators	Rules based process automation
Diversity of data sources and types	Augmented human judgment
Data predisposition	Augmented human intelligence
Data context, source, and assumptions	Instinct versus data-driven decisions
Data quality	Data security and privacy

TABLE 4-4. Medication Management Big Data Value[9]

Medication Management Big Data Value	
Operational performance, resource demand, and capacity management	Formulary compliance
Cost of care and treatment outcomes	Safety and quality
Prior authorization management	Compliance with medication use and treatment guidelines
Pharmaceutical expenses	Medication adherence and utilization
Drug shortage forecasting and inventory management; waste reduction	Medication diversion

Governance

Data governance is foundational to building a successful data literacy program. Data governance provides a framework to guide and connect members of the data community: those who create or provide the data (data producers), those who need the data (data consumers), and those who know or interpret the data (data stewards). More importantly it provides the structure including the people, process, and technology to ensure that high value data are defined within proper context and available at an Enterprise level. Pharmacy health system leaders must build a medication-related data governance program aligned with the broader institutional program aimed to[10-12]:

- Provide a framework for decision rights and streamline decision making regarding the care and use of data assets;

- Ensure data assets are defined and created with sufficient quality, standards, and business rules to maximize value and repurposing; and

- Grow and foster stewardship, data literacy, and trust in data.

The role of data governance is to establish the structure, policies, and procedures for governing data, while data management implements or enacts the rules that will enable:

- Best practices and operational workflows for consistent data creation and collection;

- Standard tools for data capture, data maintenance, data quality and cleansing, data integration, and replication;

- Processes for data maintenance, syndication, audit trails, and lifecycle management;

- Efficient data collection, storage, and error correction; and

- Increased access to trusted data while protecting the privacy of individuals.[10-12]

Structures

As pharmacy healthcare system leaders set their sights on becoming more data and performance driven, they will require a highly skilled supporting structure that can effectively leverage data and information.

They must embrace a data-centric culture within their departments that recognizes medication management data and information as foundational assets for providing patient care, quality improvement, research, and education. The structure must encompass the enterprise, allowing for consistent and comprehensive historical, concurrent, and prospective insight into medication use within the health system. It must include:

- Data architecture and design strategy

- Data quality management, oversight, and best practices

- Governance

- Collaboration and coordination across all health system disciplines

- The corporate vision of analytics

- Flexibility and alignment with individual business units

- A program anchored by pharmacy informatics[13-15]

Pharmacy health system leaders must recognize the importance of building a highly skilled and accountable pharmacy informatics team in maintaining the data, information, and knowledge assets across all systems that support medication management. They will be important in ensuring data

TABLE 4-5. Data and Information Best Practices

Data and Information Best Practices	
Providing the appropriate level of data governance and stewardship.	Ensuring that data, information, and knowledge assets are validated, integrated, normalized, consolidated, and routinely optimized.
Adopting standard human and machine interpretable formats.	Developing infrastructure for knowledge, metadata, and terminology management.
Utilizing controlled terminology for integration and interoperability.	Ensuring that information is readily and rapidly understood and accessed within the workflow.
Ensuring that data are accurate, accessible, complete, consistent, current, timely, and precise at appropriate level.	Ensuring that information and knowledge are centrally managed, collaboratively developed, and easily disseminated and maintained.
Ensuring consistent use of maps to internal and external standards and reference data.	Ensuring that information and knowledge are platform independent.
Ensuring that system architecture supports data interchange.	Developing tools to effectively maintain and manage data, information, and knowledge while ensuring it's audited, measured, and evaluated for effectiveness.

quality and safety, minimizing data quality risks, and affirming medication-related data, information, and knowledge management best practices **(Table 4-5)**.[13–15]

STRATEGY

A clearly articulated data strategy constructed within the framework of a fundamental cultural change will enable an integrated, creative, and holistic approach to building a pipeline that unlocks the knowledge within medication-derived data assets. Creating a trusted flow of packaged, curated, and trusted medication management-related data for widespread use is a winning strategy to advance medication management and reimagine the pharmacy practice.

A high-value pharmacy data management strategy begins with a commitment from pharmacy leadership to focus on answering the right questions. They must understand their priorities, practice model, departmental and resource gaps, and goals. Core strategic tenets should include[16–22]:

- Cultivating a data-centric culture

- Embedding data in every decision, interaction, and process

- Building a data literacy program and advancing analytical experience across the department

- Promoting a data-centric culture

- Processing and delivering data in real time while making derived information and knowledge actionable

- Creating and supporting flexible data stores that enable ready to use data

- Supporting both data producers and data consumers by creating an integrated, collaborative data ecosystem to serve business, customer, and practice needs across sites, departments, and projects

- Acquiring the right talent and ensuring that those individuals have access to the right data and are supported by the right technology

- Utilizing descriptive, diagnostic, predictive, or prescriptive analytics to deliver needed insight for effective decision making
- Coupling analytical systems with end user friendly data visualization tools will provide the infrastructure to:
  - Routinely utilize ad hoc query tools for exploratory analysis
  - Drive operational and clinical best practices and outcomes using comparative data
  - Effectively support continuous quality improvement efforts
  - Promote financial accountability and transparency
  - Maintain competitiveness and develop winning strategies
- Executing the data strategy, which requires:
  - Dedicated, empowered, agile teams
  - Streamlined data governance and data stewardship
  - Active engagement for all sites, practice, education, research, and platforms
  - Trusted data products, services, and support readily available
  - Searchable catalog of available data products to promote exploration and reuse of current assets
  - New technologies, capabilities, and services supported within a transformed data architecture
  - Learning and education resources to build data literacy and advanced analytics maturity across the enterprise[16-22]

Executing on the pharmacy departments strategy will:

a. Translate medication management related data into the language of medicine, derive new insights, support decision making, and improve meaningful outcomes.
b. Ensure competitive advantage and drive higher enterprise performance.
c. Help solve business challenges and inspire creative solutions that lead to new opportunities.
d. Improve operational efficiencies through automation and augmentation, reuse, waste reduction, and transparency and visibility of data assets.
e. Safeguard and enhance trust in our critical data assets.

Summary: Sections I-V

A comprehensive data centric strategic plan where decisions at all levels are compelled by data, rather than by intuition, feeling, or personal experience will assist pharmacy health system leaders in advancing the practice and driving transformative change. To accomplish this strategy, pharmacy departments should no longer consider data a "by-product" of their operations but rather a core part of their products and services. Data must be treated as an appreciating organizational asset that will open entire new revenue/value channels, products, services, platforms, and practice models. More importantly by building technologies, processes, and structure around the data-centric pharmacy operating model departmental, leaders will play an influential role in deploying and developing an improved practice. These key steps will assist pharmacy leaders in developing the needed framework to drive a cultural change centered around data:

1. Become a data-centric organization in which data are a core part of its strategic products and services.

2. Data Literacy.

3. Successful execution requires a skilled workforce who recognizes, evaluates, and effectively communicates with data—in short, is data literate.

4. To effectively process and transform medication management data, utilize highly skilled resources deeply rooted within pharmacy informatics.

5. Build a pharmacy data-centric structure that can play a leadership role around medication data governance and analytics across the Enterprise.

6. Develop an Enterprise-wide multidisciplinary medication management analytics program that targets and prioritizes medication use quality, safety, utilization, and outcome initiatives.[16–22]

PROBLEM TO SOLUTION

To capitalize on efforts to build a data-centric organization, the pharmacy executive must be familiar with the basics of analytics to determine the best use of the available data within the structures in play at their organization. Following these six steps will ensure that the pharmacy executive will be efficient in their requests and ensure optimal analytics to work to solve the business and clinical problems they will face. These six steps are[23]:

- Recognize the problem or question

- Review previous findings

- Model the solution and select the variables

- Collect the data

- Analyze the data

- Present and act on the results

The first thing any executive must do is to establish what problem or question is attempting to be solved. Are you attempting to reduce clinical variability within a service line to decrease length of stay? Are you attempting to identify medications that can have their utilization reduced to lower the overall cost of care? Are you evaluating a new service line and making a determination of how to staff it? These are all interesting questions, but ensuring that you are asking the right question to address the right problem will ensure you identify the correct data/metrics you need to proceed and find success.

To identify this, you must clearly articulate to yourself and others the problem or question you need to answer. This must be exacting in its specificity otherwise you may find the data returned may not match your need. For instance, if you are attempting to address late deliveries from your pharmacy to the ICU, there are a lot of moving parts to consider in the workflow and thus in the data requested for review. A problem that consists of late deliveries may have many etiologies; however, a question that asks where in the process from order to administration do we have the largest variability in time and the largest average duration among the steps of order, verification, preparation/dispense, product check, and administration would be better to identify areas that could be improved upon. A pharmacy leader should challenge themselves and others around them for exacting specificity in not only their problem recognition but also the questions they are asking about the problem to help to identify a solution.

The second piece to consider when choosing the correct problem or question is where this will fit into the story related to the item in question. In the example of the late deliveries, understanding one's operations and common challenges is helpful in marrying the data to a story of reason for why this may exist, but perhaps it is not a compelling story for pushing for change within the department. Consider what you may need in terms of qualitative data rather than solely quantitative that can be added to the story from event reports or other sources to help provide the emotional connection from the recognized problem to choosing to modify one's actions toward a solution. Change is hard for everyone, and if your need from your data at the end of the day is to help to drive toward a new solution, ensure you are connecting the emotional need for change to something you and your staff care about, often patient experiences, that can help tie the operations data and desire for change together.

Finally, the last piece in properly identifying your problem and/or question you need data for is related to your audience and how you will reach them. Your audience may vary from simply being yourself as you work to identify areas for improvement within workflows in your department or assessing improvements already made, or your audience may be your executive suite or your staff. Considering your audience and your method of communication is important to ensure you obtain the data necessary to address their questions and concerns. If in the ICU delivery delay example you identify your audience as nursing and pharmacy leadership, then you need to choose when/where you will deliver the results of your findings to finalize your ask. If you have a monthly meeting then perhaps you will be creating slides to share results; if you are amid an email exchange or will have in person communication on the fly, perhaps you need to create a bulleted list for better communication. Knowing this will allow you to decide what the end use of the data will be and will allow you to ensure you consider factors that are relevant to each method and display type.

Next you should proceed to review previous findings. This may be obvious and yet it is often overlooked. When you have finally set your problem in as much detail as possible and you understand your delivery method and audience, you need to pause and identify whether you already have this data or if you already have information related to this issue that can provide insight prior to requesting or obtaining more. If you do not have data, quickly ask or search for others who have approached a similar or same issue, identify their approach, and ask the questions: what data did they gather; did it assist in answering their questions; what were their results? These questions will help save you valuable time in assessing your approach and keep you from repeating mistakes or issues others have uncovered in the process. Once you have completed this you will either have gathered new information to further enhance your request, or you will land on the knowledge that you have a novel idea or question that is being assessed and can proceed with this new knowledge to further your work.

Once you have identified any learnings that can be found from previous work in the problem area, select the model you will use to address your problem or question. This can be as simple as calculating average times between the steps from order to administration as in the issue above or it can be a more complex statistical analysis, perhaps looking into the area under the curve for the fit of a new machine learning algorithm to clinical care. Regardless of the method, you need to identify the model that fits the needs of your identified issue and then proceed to set your hypothesis and null hypothesis so that you can begin your evaluation. This seemingly innocuous step is quite important in ensuring that you have a data-driven mindset and will react appropriately to the results of your analysis. If our hypothesis in our ICU example is that there is a significant workflow barrier or staffing shortage leading to a lengthy preparation/dispensation time in the process, then we need to seek data to support or disprove that hypothesis. This data supporting this inquiry could be turnaround time for each step in the process and some average or mean calculation to derive insight into where to look for improvements. Now if we review these data and do not see a large variance within a step and do not see an excess of time spent in one area, we should not attempt to interpret this data to indicate anything other than what it tells us: there is no significant issue in the process and our null hypothesis is true. If we were to jump to a conclusion that the first due time in the order when signed is too near the time of signing and does not allow enough time to prepare the dose and distribute it, we would be incorrect to do so as our data does not include the relevant points to draw that con-clusion. We would need to form a new hypothesis and identify new data that would be relevant to answering that question prior to asserting that answer.

Once your hypothesis and null hypothesis are set and you have identified the relevant data to assess these hypotheses, to address your problem/question you should then move forward to col-lecting the data. At this point it is again important to reflect on your audience and delivery method as you need to pull in your primary data that addresses the specific hypothesis, but you may also want to pull in secondary data that can help to further assess and add context to your analysis. In the ICU delivery delay example, this may be as simple as getting the date and time of day for each step of the process alongside the time differences between the steps. This could be used to analyze your data around the 24 hour cycle and assess for weekend versus weekday variance. This could be important as many pharmacies are not staffed equally 24/7/365 and this would allow us to measure and quantify shift differences (another secondary data point would be shift times) based on staffing.

Once you have your data be sure to follow the steps from above to ensure the data are com-plete, accurate, and free from common errors.[23] Then begin your analysis. Again this may be applying a statistical model to the data or performing some more simple analytics to identify trends. Be cer-tain to reevaluate the fit of the model once you apply it to the data you have in hand. If the results of the analysis can be improved upon by different methods of analysis, attempt multiple and assess the results of each compared with the hypothesis you have set and identify which is the best fit for the current analysis. When you have identified the best fit, step away and come back with a fresh mind to challenge your assumptions of this fit. It can be helpful at this point to ask a trusted colleague to step in and challenge the data to identify if there are ways to improve your analysis in order to get to a deeper understanding of the issue at hand. Once you have completed these steps and are certain you have the right model with the right data to support or deny the hypothesis that will provide insight into your overall problem or question, then you are ready to present and act on your results.

Now you must go back to your qualitative analysis of the issue and insert your data and find-ings into your story and method of communication. Ask yourself the question: does this data fit my story and is there a better way to communicate this now that I have my results? You may find you need to pivot from previous uninformed conclusions about your methods to build a better overall tool to help provide the initiative for change. Create your action plan from this and then deliver. You will most likely incur additional questions at this stage or during your presentation. This is when you begin the process anew to clarify the problem or question and work through obtaining your results needed to continue to iterate and improve upon your business.

STRATEGIC DATA CHOICES

Understanding the journey from idea to answer is highly important, and along the way you are going to need to begin to identify which data are relevant and how much data you need continu-ously versus once in order to move your business forward. Often, identifying the correct data to identify a problem will contribute to a continuous need for that data to measure the improvements to the issue. When doing so it is important to consider four types of metrics and which you may need to address your issue. These four types are process metrics, outcome metrics, balance metrics, and proxy metrics.

Process metrics are data that measure something you can directly or nearly directly affect through small or large changes in your business. These metrics are often at the worker or automa-tion level and will be relevant to a single step within a process that you are trying to improve or hold steady. An example following our ICU delivery delay example would be the average or mean prepa-ration time for IV products in the clean room. Adding staff or smoothing inputs is likely to have a direct effect on the average preparation time and this metric would be a good direct measure of the impact of those changes. Process metrics are often measured daily or weekly so that small adjustments and iterative improvements to the process itself can be measured and instituted.

Outcome metrics are data that measure something that is relevant to the business or business unit. These metrics are at a higher organization level and often lack work unit changes and have many variables that may directly or indirectly impact them. In our ICU delivery delay example this may be the number of late administrations per 1000 patient days for our ICU. Our changes in the clean room processes may influence this metric, but this metric may be heavily influenced by nurse staffing, patient acuity, medication administration time schedules, and other factors. This isn't to say that this metric is unimportant—in fact this is likely the main reason we are looking at our process—but we should not have the expectation that this metric will change abruptly because of our process changes. Often outcome metrics are measured monthly or quarterly and serve as an indicator of multiple process metric changes making improvements at the same time.

Balance metrics are data that measure something that may be indirectly affected by our process changes. These metrics are often at a process metric level but may not appear to be directly related to the outcome metric we are measuring. In our ICU delivery delay example we may opt to measure a balance metric of sterile process compliance, expecting that as we measure the turnaround time for preparation we may be incentivizing our staff to work at a faster rate. This in turn may increase the urge to cut corners in order to improve the speed at which products are prepared. So we could measure the compliance with our sterile preparation procedures to ensure we do not reduce that process compliance along the way to improving another. Often balance metrics are measured at the same frequency as the process metric they are supporting.

Proxy metrics are data that indirectly measure something related to our outcome or process when the outcome or process is challenging to measure. These metrics can be challenging to identify and typically have a cause and effect relationship with the metric they are a proxy to. In our ICU delivery delay example it may be challenging to directly measure our balance metric of sterile process compliance. Our proxy metric for that balance metric may be to look at individual staff throughput in the clean room and then perform spot checks for staff that have the highest throughput to evaluate for gaps in their technique. So while this isn't assessing overall compliance, this is still likely to help us arrive to the same conclusion by measuring something that is much simpler to obtain.

Once you have set your metrics for your analysis you will need to determine how much data you will need. To do this you should review your goal once again to ensure you are matching the right metric to the goal. Then identify what you already know; this will be data you already have or that you do not need to obtain since you already know the answer. Then identify what you don't know and rank these unknowns using a chart such as the one below and obtain as much as necessary. Then analyze your data for your goal and work through the steps above.[23]

It is important to avoid common pitfalls in your analytical process. One such area to avoid is stopping your data collection or experiment when you have your first positive result. There is natural variation in all things and if you avoid running the full course of your analysis you may simply be reacting to this variation without identifying or addressing the issue. Second, avoid using too many metrics. Often one or two process metrics related to one outcome with a balance metric is more than enough data to assess your changes. Selecting too many metrics can make it confusing for you and your staff on where to put their efforts and will create a more challenging environment to make change. Third, be certain to retest and recertify your results. For process related changes, as you move on to new processes to improve, you will often transfer your last improvement to a balance metric for a period to ensure you don't have slippage in the improvements you have made.[24] Finally, avoid making spurious correlations or drawing conclusions from data that are not related to one another. This may seem obvious, but our minds are great at matching similar patterns, and it can be easy to draw a conclusion without the correct data or relationship of your cause and effect within it. For instance, in the ICU delivery delay example, perhaps another project has collected data about staff call offs and staffing issues for our department. It may be easy to assume that staff shortages are to blame for the delivery delays, but without assessing the turnaround times and throughput of the individual processes we have no actual relationship between staffing and delivery delays for which to base this on. Spurious correlations are something our minds love to do, so always be certain that there is a cause and effect relationship between the problem/goal you are addressing and the data you are analyzing to draw your conclusions to avoid making big missteps in your improvement or analytical processes.

CASE STUDY

The reduction of low-value care is critical to ensuring patient safety, reducing costs, and promotion of a sustainable healthcare system.[25] Low-value can harm patients either directly, by downstream effects, or by over-testing or over-treatment.[25] In addition to harm, it has been estimated that 30% of healthcare dollars in the United States is spent on harmful or wasteful practices.[26] When put into the context, if nearly 18% of the United States gross domestic product is tied to healthcare expenditures without incremental gains in life expectancy there are real societal costs.[27] Furthermore, reducing low-value care can allow resources to be redirected toward care that provides higher value.

Low-value care can be tests, medications, and/or procedures in any healthcare setting which have been deemed, through evidence, to be ineffective, harmful, or unnecessary. Overuse, a form of low-value care, has been defined as the delivery of interventions that provide little to no clinical benefit, are unlikely to have an effect on clinical decisions, increase healthcare spending without improving healthcare outcomes, or risk patient harm in excess of potential benefits.[28] Simply put, value is defined as patient outcomes divided by cost over time.[29]

So How Can You Identify Potential Areas of Waste?

While it is easy to identify high cost items, framing waste as only a problem of cost or resource utilization only ignores the impact that intervention might have on outcomes and will not move clinicians or patients in any meaningful way.[25] Despite this, we observe administrators within our own health systems putting downward pressure on providers to lower costs, with providers pushing back with a desire to optimize patient outcomes. While these conversations can (and have) gone badly, they also have the potential (when framed appropriately) to result in something very good: selective pressure to weed out low-value care. To make selective pressure productive we require a method of measuring variation in cost and outcomes and tying that variation to discrete differences in clinical practice that can be changed.[30]

There are, generally speaking, three approaches to identifying areas of potential waste or inappropriate care variation. (1) the vertical approach being a disease specific top-down approach, (2) the horizontal approach being a resource specific cross-cutting approach, and (3) the "just do it" approach being a specific disease-intervention specific approach.

Starting with the vertical approach, your desired outcome is the development of standardized care pathways for condition, diagnosis, or specific care processes to reduce the variability in decision making. An example of this might be heart failure stewardship. You might through your quality measures discover a low rate of adherence to and prescribing of guideline directed therapy in this patient population. While the initiation of heart failure medications in the hospital is likely more expensive from a pharmacy perspective, starting these drugs in the hospital increases the chances of that patient continuing therapy outpatient which reduces readmissions, reduces mortality, improves reputation with external rating organizations (U.S. News, AHA Get with the Guidelines), increases prescription capture, and improves performance in value-based care organizations (managed Medicare or Medicaid populations).

With the horizontal approach, your desired outcome is to reduce inappropriate utilization of a specific resource, usually through the development of criteria for use. An example of this might be intravenous immune globulin (IVIG) stewardship. The goal here is to reduce total spend and control how IVIG is used, making it easy to do the right thing and hard to do the wrong thing. Generally, you are working with clinical experts to conduct a rapid review of the evidence that will inform the recommendations for preapproved usage criteria that accounts for most use cases in addition to a process for exceptions.

The "just do it" approach is the identification of individual services that are, under specified circumstances, deemed wasteful. The best known of these types of recommendations come from the Choosing Wisely campaign, under which more than 70 national organizations representing medical professionals have identified nearly 500 tests, procedures, and other services commonly used in their field whose necessity should be questioned and discussed. This could also be something like adjusting a billing unit mismatch in your 340B splitting software that was driving WAC expenditure.

The choice of approach depends on what you are trying to accomplish, who your stakeholders are, and the drivers behind waste. As a result the approach tends to evolve.

For example, let's say that you want to reduce your total spend on dexmedetomidine, a sedative agent, that accounts for ~6% of your inpatient drug spend. Using the value-oriented approach, the first step is to find out if this is potentially wasteful spending (ie, use not translating into improved outcomes). First, conduct external benchmarking at the hospital level and compare your use of this drug to other similar organizations in order to get a signal of potentially inappropriate care variation. If at that level your utilization is higher than what would be expected at a similar organization, then you would drill into which diagnosis related groups (DRG) are driving this spend. Consider the Pareto Principle,[31] whereby 80% of the potential opportunity comes from 20% of the cases. This will help in focusing your attention. After you have identified the one to two DRGs you then might benchmark those DRGs to peer institutions to determine if that DRG is high spend in addition to comparing outcomes such as LOS, readmission, complications, mortality, etc. If that DRG is high spend or has worse outcomes, this might signal that the approach should evolve from a horizontal to vertical approach in order to identify other potential areas of waste. Additionally, you might consider evaluating other sedative drugs for that DRG to see how their use compares to other organizations. In this case for example, you might demonstrate that the use of propofol is lower and dexmedetomidine is higher compared with peer organizations for mechanically ventilated patients.

This example highlights a few important considerations:

1. Utilize a value-oriented approach—costs alone should not be the driver for change.

2. Conduct your analysis hierarchically—start broad (hospital-level) and narrow to the issue (DRG or ICD10 or Discharge Service).

3. The approach should be contextual based on similar conditions and because of this will evolve based on identified drivers of the variation.

How Can I Create Action from My Data?
Turning Data Into Stories

The next step is to turn this data into insights. It is not just enough to analyze your data and share a bunch of spreadsheets; you need to know how to communicate the story in a clear, compelling manner—a skill called data storytelling. Data storytelling is a structured approach for communicating insights from your data and generally involves three (probably four) key elements: data, visualizations, narrative, and context.[32]

Seldom are great stories created by a single individual. You must first identify who your target audience is and begin to learn what their motivations are, what they care about, what they know about the problem, and how best to align with their goals. Once you understand your audience's motivations you can start to evaluate the data through a different perspective. Once you've identified the data that truly matters you can start to outline your story arc and start to explore some of the possibilities. Let's go back to the sedation stewardship example. After meeting with the ICU clinical pharmacists to learn more about their perceptions around sedation management, you learn that they spend a significant amount of time training the medical staff as they rotate in through the unit. However, when they are not there the use of dexmedetomidine is increased and generally harder to discontinue once initiated. These are important insights that will help you develop your story arc—especially around the potential temporal relationships between dexmedetomidine use and time of day or time of year.

From there you should start to create your visualizations—the key here is to keep it simple. Visualizations should be able to speak for themselves (or with very little explanation). Lastly, you will then use your narrative to weave the data and visualizations together to frame the story to context. After you have your story, reflect on your assumptions or bias. These can sometimes be referred to as your blind spots. The best way to do this is to share your presentation with a trusted colleague, or even better, a person who identifies with your audience. Utilize their feedback to further refine and polish your presentation before delivering it to the larger audience. The best stories stimulate dialogue, and you should expect to receive more feedback. In the end you'll have hopefully created engagement and action around the topic.

All data stories should have a beginning, a middle, and an end. A data story will often always begin with you setting the scene: what is the background on the current situation, why did you start this analysis, who are the characters, and what's the hook. The next section of the story then provides rising insights. These should be hierarchically ordered by importance and what's contributing or influencing the variation, followed by additional supportive insights to further reinforce your main point. At this point, if you have told an effective story, your audience should then be able to connect your insights to the current situation to arrive at the "aha moment." This is also referred to as the burning platform, and this is what creates the engagement for change. Lastly, you end with solutions or proposed next steps. Sometimes you might not have all of the solutions but rather a list of questions to stimulate discussion.

LOOKING FORWARD

Pharmacy often faces a challenge or motivating influences from topics that drive healthcare during a specific time frame. Past examples of how healthcare needs drive pharmacy considerations include the priorities of patient safety surrounding the reports of quality gaps, waste in healthcare, and detrimental risks to patient health.[33] This framework of patient safety in the *To Err is Human* report motivated changes in individual, clinic, institutional, and national standards. Analytics are novel in their rapid evolution. This constant technology iteration creates a leading indicator that outpaces the lagging indicator in clinical utilization. This challenge to bring together the potential of technology and the value it offers clinical settings is ongoing and complicated by operational, fiscal, ethical, and clinical friction. Data-driven improvement in healthcare systems is reflected in frameworks like The Institute of Medicine and their advocacy of the "continuously learning healthcare system." This concept aims to constantly bring together leading indicators in science and the application in clinical settings.[35] With this reframing of priorities across different time frames, leaders in pharmacy health systems can recognize the resources and initiatives that complement either the introduction or ongoing leverage of data and analytics in their work.

Business frameworks look to characterize the continual shift of technologies and the progress of their implementations. Examples include consulting firm Gartner and their hype cycle research methodology. This cycle describes how the perceived values of technologies, analytic or otherwise, evolve over time. These stages of the hype cycle include an innovation trigger, peak expectation, a trough of disillusionment, and a slope of enlightenment.[34] This framework, while not a prescription for every pathway of technology, offers insight on potential challenges of the value of analytics to pharmacy. The profession will, if not already, face expectations of data beyond what clinical settings can currently realize. As initial cases of success are more common and more visible, the value of analytics will face the challenge of distrust or under realized potential. The key skills of building data stories will be complemented through the narrative of which methods were selected and why that process impacted the eventual actions made possible through data. Eventually, analytics will find meaningful incorporation at multiple different levels of implementation as the scalable use cases, sustainable resources, and human capital align.

Leaders in pharmacy will have to balance the role of data alongside business cases that it must support in order to pair them with very qualitative, human-centered concerns that influence the adoption of technology. The promise of data to deliver automated reporting or decision support is often contrasted by the user's willingness to leverage these data derived recommendations over the clinical human intuition.[39] Conflating these challenges is the balance between business needs and operational output across multiple settings. The expectation and needs of institutions will have to be aligned with the potential and marketing that comes from the vendors and parties responsible for developing these advanced data analytics.[44] The evolving field of analytics looks to refine not only its methods and its applications, but its financial sustainability as data-oriented products and platforms. As early iterations of these quantitative methods look to find technical feasibility, the eventual clinical relevance is often focused on a combination of these data-driven approach's feasibility, business sustainability, and clinical contexts.[45] Further definitions of this gray area that exists between technical feasibility and real-world implementation is an area ripe for the skill set of pharmacists to develop, translate, and implement changes in practice based on advances in science.

The value that a health system generates from its analytics will be driven through multiple perspectives of observation, utilization, and standardization. As previously described, the opportunity and challenge to align problems and solutions is an ongoing cycle of problem identification, solution implementation, and outcome evaluation. Many similar principles still apply to anticipated technologies. Starting with a pilot project can demonstrate clear value and constraints of technology. With small wins, there is an opportunity to minimize the complexity of data variance and the opportunity to pilot the vendor assessment and contracting pathway. This approach toward value definition with new advanced analytics also builds the role of both a value-oriented approach and the due diligence required of novel technical approaches to data analysis. Small pilots with data analysis approaches can find analogs related to the essential questions in taking action and communication frameworks for outcomes with leadership. Selecting appropriate approaches and scale with an ongoing technological shift in advanced analytics will drive the adoption of these technologies across the profession.

Innovation in technology is a richly studied area that often finds limited exploration or highly affected uptake in the application to healthcare.[42;46] In these theories of diffusion, questions address the variations between institutions or individuals and how there are different influences for adoption at different stages of the process. Translating these theories to the burden of the real world challenges the value that technologies must be able to demonstrate. In practice, it is a challenging position to be either the first user or the last user of a new technology. Understanding what factors contribute to these adoption metrics with analytics will come from the factors discussed earlier in this chapter, including but not limited to governance, budget, team, and other local culture. Factors that will define the gap between the early adopters and the laggards of these technologies may not come in the form of the technology itself but rather the human capital that helped make technology not just feasible, but also relevant to care. Completing a cycle of the human-based creation of data and human-based application of data will help drive adoption across organizations. These human components are often siloed in approaches to data. Bridging these silos will address the use of data across an entire life cycle of framing questions, dealing with challenges, iterative analysis, and contextualization and communication of results.[36]

Change in the generation and use of data has led to many questions about the future of these technologies in practice. The translation of machine learning and artificial intelligence is presently framed in research or developmental contexts. Using datasets from limited settings or with a significant resource requirement to obtain, explore, and clean can be restrictive for many settings. How and when these broader implementations of quantitative methods will translate from developmental perspectives to daily practice are key questions guiding both technology development and practice. The use of these algorithmic methods in other consumer or commercial contexts may face less stringent performance standards compared with needs in clinical practice. Clinical decision support systems may be one entry point for future implementations of advanced analytic in practice. Clinicians and patients have expressed that appraisal of these systems alongside ethical and regulatory consideration should be a part of the evaluation of these technologies in the process of implementing them.[37;43] Aligning the function of artificial intelligence and machine learning in clinical practice will require a balance of the technical implementation and the users' acceptance of their role in practice.

The promise of these technologies are balanced with their limitations. The potential insight that advanced analytics uncover are still limited to the contexts in which they were generated. Even if low-value care is identified, the opportunity for improvement comes from the clinicians, staff, and leadership involved. In the process of discharge through identification of readmission potential, data and analytics alone are powerless to enact the changes to improve counseling at the time of discharge. An alignment of value, resources, and implementation will drive the changes to clinical practice at the front line, and improvement will be reflected in later analysis and evaluation. The layer of data in a health system alone will not suffice to bring forth the potential for data. Additionally, there are significant limitations in the data quality required for descriptive, predictive, and prescriptive data analyses. Many health systems face fragmented data systems, lack governance infrastructure, and have limited staff support of the data pipelines essential for meaningful engagement with data. As individual institutions overcome these barriers to deploy algorithmic techniques, the methods and outcomes for such projects can be highly limited to the institution of origin.[41] While scaling algorithms to other institutions presents a major limitation to translation of these methods across multiple settings, it provides an optimistic goal which multiple institutions can strive for together. As more institutions adopt these approaches and are able to share outcomes from their algorithmic approaches, standards and comparisons of value-based care can help shape national and local understanding and approaches.

In addition to these human capital related limitations and resources, external factors such as regulatory constraints and pathways will direct the future of the role of analytics in healthcare. Advanced analytic approaches with machine learning and artificial intelligence uncover insights from data to inform descriptive and predictive needs in healthcare. These methods are iterative in their technical means and are especially valuable as they can be repeated and refined according to the datasets which inform them. Amid all of these valuable adaptations, the United States Food and Drug Administration (FDA) is faced with a significant challenge related to safety and efficacy. In 2018, the FDA had cleared its first quantitative based software for use in screening for diabetic retinopathy. Even with this approval and many others that followed, however, there is still an unclear future for pathways of quantitative methods either in practice or with review by the FDA. Challenges to these regulatory approaches are found in the iterative approach of these quantitative methods. If algorithms improve through machine learning and artificial intelligence improves through continually adding new data to train the algorithms, then there remains a question of whether the FDA approval is sustained with new iterations. Currently there's a focus on evidence for safety and efficacy at the time of application as a regulatory milestone. The future of regulatory challenges will be, in part, characterized by the role of transparency in the data used to derive these methods as well as the transparency of the regulatory bodies review of safety and efficacy. The replication of quantitative methods are a key benefit of the potential they hold, but the local customization required to highlight relevance to a health system will be challenged by the need to define safety and efficacy of these iterative algorithms.

As the regulation of these technologies find more definition and nuance, leaders within health systems will need to understand the regulations, clinician trust, data quality transformation, and many other factors that surround use of data to make the most of the present technology and to anticipate the future of this ever changing field.

REFERENCES

1. Potanski T. Big data terms every manager should know: simple and advanced technical and big data terms. July 12, 2020. **https://devsdata.com/big-data-terms-every-manager-should-know/**. Accessed April 15, 2022.

2. Davenport TH, Harris JG. *Competing on Analytics, The New Science of Winning*. 1st ed. Boston, MA: Harvard Business Review Press; 2007: 8.

3. Yi WM, Bernstein A, Vest MH, et al. Role of pharmacy analytics in creating a data-driven culture for frontline management. *Hosp Pharm*. 2021;56(5):495–500. 101177/0018578720920799. PubMed

4. Tableau. Business intelligence vs. business analytics: what's the difference? **https://www.tableau.com/learn/articles/business-intelligence/bi-business-analytics**. Accessed April 5, 2022.

5. M-Brain. Big data technology with 8v's. **https://www.m-brain.com/technology/**. Accessed April 5, 2022.

6. LeSuer D. 5 reasons healthcare data is unique and difficult to measure. Published July, 3,2018. **https://www.healthcatalyst.com/insights/5-reasons-healthcare-data-is-difficult-to-measure**. Accessed April 6, 2022.

7. Logan V. Data literacy vs. data fluency: whats in a name? *The Data Lodge*. Published August 23, 2022. **https://www.thedatalodge.com/blog/data-literacy-vs-data-fluency-whats-in-a-name**. Accessed April 8, 2022.

8. Bersin J., Zao-Sanders M. Boost your team's data literacy. February 12, 2020. **https://hbr.org/2020/02/boost-your-teams-data-literacy**. Accessed April 7, 2022.

9. Ma C, Smith HW, Chu C, et al. Big data in pharmacy practice: current use, challenges, and the future. *Integr Pharm Res Pract*. 2015;4:91–99. 10.2147/IPRP.S55862. PubMed

10. Olavsrud T. Data governance: a best practices framework for managing data assets. CIO. Published March 18, 2021. **https://www.cio.com/article/202183/what-is-data-governance-a-best-practices-framework-for-managing-data-assets.html**. Accessed April 8, 2022.

11. Foote K. How to become a data governance lead. Dataversity. March 2, 2022. **https://www.dataversity.net/how-to-become-a-data-governance-lead/**. Published March 2, 2022. Accessed April 3, 2022.

12. Dennis AL. Establishing data governance as a service. Dataversity. January 6, 2022. **https://www.dataversity.net/establishing-data-governance-as-a-service/**. Accessed April 10, 2022.

13. Wolfe A, Hess L, La MK, et al. Strategy for pharmacy data management. *Am J Health Syst Pharm*. 2017;74(2):79–85. 10.2146/ajhp150694. PubMed

14. Chalmers J, Siska M, Le T, Knoer S. Pharmacy informatics in multihospital health systems: Opportunities and challenges. *Am J Health Syst Pharm*. 2018;75(7):457–464. 10.2146/ajhp170580. PubMed

15. ASHP. ASHP Statement on the pharmacist's role in clinical informatics. *Am J Health Syst Pharm*. 2016;73(6):410–413. 10.2146/ajhp150540. PubMed

16. Flynn AJ, Fortier C, Maehlen H, et al. A strategic approach to improving pharmacy enterprise automation: Development and initial application of the Autonomous Pharmacy Framework. *Am J Health Syst Pharm*. 2021;78(7):636–645. 10.1093/ajhp/zxab001. PubMed

17. Hernandez I, Zhang Y. Using predictive analytics and big data to optimize pharmaceutical outcomes. *Am J Health Syst Pharm*. 2017;74(18):1494–1500. 10.2146/ajhp161011. PubMed

18. DiPiro JT, Fox ER, Kesselheim AS, et al. ASHP foundation pharmacy forecast 2021: strategic planning advice for pharmacy departments in hospitals and health systems. *Am J Health Syst Pharm*. 2021;78(6):472–497. 10.1093/ajhp/zxaa429. PubMed

19. Dash S, Shakyawar SK, Sharma M, et al. Big data in healthcare: management, analysis, and future prospects. *J Big Data*. 2019;6:54.

20. McKinsey & Company. The Data-Driven Enterprise of 2025. **https://www.mckinsey.com. br/capabilities/quantumblack/our-insights/the-data-driven-enterprise-of-2025**. Updated January 28, 2022. Accessed April 2, 2022.

21. Widjaja JT. How analytics maturity models are stunting data science teams. January 28, 2020. **https://towardsdatascience.com/how-analytics-maturity-models-are-stunting-data-science-teams-962e3c62d749**. Accessed April 3, 2022.

22. Dash S, Shakyawar SK, Sharma M, et al. Big data in healthcare: management, analysis and future prospects. J Big Data. 2019;6(54). **https://doi.org/10.1186/s40537-019-0217-0**. Accessed April 3, 2022.

23. Davenport T. Keep up with your quants. In: *HBR Guide to Data Analytics Basics for Managers*. Boston, MA: Harvard Business Review Press; 2018:13–24.

24. Gallo A. The fundamentals of A/B testing. In: *HBR Guide to Data Analytics Basics for Managers*. Boston, MA: Harvard Business Review Press; 2018:68–69.

25. Brownlee SM, Korenstein D. Better understanding the downsides of low value healthcare could reduce harm. *BMJ*. 2021;372:n117. 10.1136/bmj.n117. PubMed

26. Berwick DM, Hackbarth AD. Eliminating waste in US health care. *JAMA*. 2012;307(14): 1513–1516. 10.1001/JAMA.2012.362. PubMed

27. Skinner J, Cahan E, Fuchs VR. Stabilizing healthcare's share of the GDP. *N Engl J Med*. 2022;386:709–711. 10.1056/NEJMP2114227. Accessed April 3, 2022.

28. MacLeod S, Musich S, Hawkins K, et al. Highlighting a common quality of care delivery problem: overuse of low-value healthcare services. *J Healthc Qual*. 2018;40(4): 201–208. 10.1097/JHQ.0000000000000095. PubMed

29. Scheurer D, Crabtree E, Cawley PJ, et al. The value equation: enhancing patient outcomes while constraining costs. *Am J Med Sci*. 2016;351(1):44–51. 10.1016/J.AMJMS.2015.10.013. PubMed

30. Stowell C, Robicsek A. Endless forms most beautiful: evolving toward higher-value care. *NEJM Catal*. July 26, 2018. **https://catalyst.nejm.org/doi/full/10.1056/CAT.18.0126**. Accessed February 22, 2022.

31. Mind Tools. Pareto analysis: choosing the solution with the most impact. **https://www. mindtools.com/pages/article/newTED_01.htm**. Accessed March 14, 2022.

32. Dykes B. Data storytelling: the essential data science skill everyone needs. Forbes. March 31, 2016. **https://www.forbes.com/sites/brentdykes/2016/03/31/data-storytelling-the-essential-data-science-skill-everyone-needs/?sh=483d6e9952ad**. Accessed March 22, 2022.

33. Baker A. Crossing the quality chasm: a new health system for the 21st century. *BMJ Clinical Research*. 2001;323(7322). doi: 10.17226/10027. Accessed April 3, 2022.

34. Car J, Sheikh A, Wicks P, Williams MS. Beyond the hype of big data and artificial intelligence: building foundations for knowledge and wisdom. *BMC Med*. 2019;17(1):143. PubMed

35. Smith M, Saunders R, Stuckhardt L, et al, eds. *Best care at lower cost: the path to continuously learning health care in America*. Washington (DC): National Academies Press; 2013.

36. Dolezel D, McLeod A. Big data analytics in healthcare: investigating the diffusion of innovation. *Perspect Health Inf Manag*. 2019;16(Summer):1a. PubMed

37. Esmaeilzadeh P. Use of AI-based tools for healthcare purposes: a survey study from consumers' perspectives. *BMC Med Inform Decis Mak*. 2020;20(1):170. 10.1186/s12911-020-01191-1. PubMed

38. Hwang TJ, Kesselheim AS, Vokinger KN. Lifecycle regulation of artificial intelligence- and machine learning-based software devices in medicine. *JAMA*. 2019;322(23):2285-2286.

39. Lee MK, Rich K. "Who is included in human perceptions of AI?: Trust and perceived fairness around healthcare AI and cultural mistrust." *CHI '21: Proceedings of the 2021 CHI Conference on Human Factors in Computing Systems*. 2021;138:1-14. doi: 10.1145/3411764.3445570. Accessed April 3, 2022.

40. Ng A. How to choose your first AI project. *Harv Bus Rev*. 2019; Feb 06:1–6.

41. Panch T, Mattie H, Celi LA. The "inconvenient truth" about AI in healthcare. *NPJ Digit Med*. 2019;2(1):77. 10.1038/s41746-019-0155-4. PubMed

42. Rogers EM. *Diffusion of Innovations*. New York, NY: Simon and Schuster; 2010.

43. Romero-Brufau S, Wyatt KD, Boyum P, et al. A lesson in implementation: A pre-post study of providers' experience with artificial intelligence-based clinical decision support. *Int J Med Inform*. 2020;137:104072. PubMed

44. Shah ND, Steyerberg EW, Kent DM. Big data and predictive analytics: recalibrating expectations. *JAMA*. 2018;320(1):27–28. PubMed

45. Van Hartskamp M, Consoli S, Verhaegh W, et al. "Artificial intelligence in clinical health care applications." *Interact J Med Res*. 2019; Apr 5;8(2): e12100.

46. Ward R. The application of technology acceptance and diffusion of innovation models in healthcare informatics. *Health Policy and Technology* 2.4 (2013): 222–228.

FINANCIAL PLANNING AND ASSESSMENT FOR PHARMACY EDUCATION AND RESEARCH PROGRAMS

Stephen F. Eckel and Kelly M. Smith

The Accreditation Council of Pharmacy Education (ACPE) sets the accreditation requirements that all doctor of pharmacy programs in the United States must meet. Of importance to health system pharmacists are the expectations surrounding experiential education. According to ACPE Standards 2016, Introductory Pharmacy Practice Experiences (IPPEs) and Advanced Pharmacy Practice Experiences (APPEs) are required to be a part of the curriculum. IPPEs need to be no less than 300 hours, with a minimum of 150 hours in community and health system settings, while APPEs are no less than 1,440 hours (36 weeks), with 160 hours each in community, ambulatory care, health system pharmacy, and inpatient general medicine.[1] Because of these expectations, colleges of pharmacy must engage with practice sites to secure these experiences as they need external partners for precepting. While different types of practice sites could be used to accomplish these requirements, health systems can provide a vast majority of them.

Many health systems view their role with academia as mainly a place for precepting IPPEs and APPEs. This is a limiting view because there are many benefits they can receive when collaborating. The traditional transactional relationship is the result following a contractual negotiation that occurs between the health system and school of pharmacy. For a health system to utilize its pharmacists for precepting these students and having access to its patients and electronic health record, there must be some benefit to the organization for providing these services. This benefit is usually viewed as a dollar amount, and a negotiation occurs to ensure fairness is achieved. The result is that a hospital will charge or expect a certain amount of money per rotation offered and will negotiate with the college to increase that number. The pharmacy school is required to offer experiential education as a condition of accreditation, so they need to find sites that are willing to take students. This is the genesis of most relationships between hospitals and academia.

If a hospital has access to students from different institutions because there are multiple schools in the region, they can use this to negotiate against each college to extract the maximal amount. Depending on the financial situation of the school, this could be a significant financial barrier. In response to this, a school may identify numerous potential sites to negotiate more favorable rates. A third option, albeit rare and not optimal, is the school could place the responsibility on the student to find and fund their rotations, completely absolving the school of this burden. The student would have to contact places to find the needed IPPEs and APPEs for graduation. In the end, each of these models reduce the students to a financial dollar amount and does not recognize any valuable contributions students have to patient care services as a part of their rotation or a potential future employee who wants to work at the organization. A better model is to develop a

DOI 10.37573/9781585287130.005

synergistic partnership, whereby the benefits that derive for both organizations is greater than what either contributes.

To develop a partnership with a college of pharmacy, one must have a better understanding of the financial drivers of academia, the financial assets they have available, and the potential overlapping needs both organizations have. This can help transition these transactional negotiations to value-building opportunities.

FINANCIAL ECONOMICS OF ACADEMIA

Health system pharmacists know well of the revenue opportunities that exist, as well as the major cost drivers that can impact a budget. Pharmacy leaders will alter their charging model for drugs if they need to increase drug revenue, and will optimize dispensing efficiency, inventory management, purchasing, or a variety of strategies if they are trying to minimize expenses.

Higher education financing is structured much differently than that of health systems. There are three common types of institutional budget models in academia: incremental, incentive-based, and Responsibility Center Management (RCM). The incremental model relies upon annual funding allocation from a central resource (the larger university, for instance), with the potential for minor changes in the allocation based upon individual requests from the unit (eg, the school that is part of the larger university), or capacity for additional or lesser funds based upon any overall change in the institution's collective fiscal resources. In this model, some units are subsidizing others that do not generate much revenue. Thus, the incentive for highly efficient or well-performing units to increase their financial performance is diminished, as they are unlikely to be rewarded for any changes. A hybrid approach to incremental budgeting is using incentives or performance measures to drive adjustments in resource allocation. Targets are set (eg, volume of teaching conducted collectively by faculty within a school, graduation rates) and funds are awarded in a subsequent year for goal attainment. These goal-driven funds are provided in addition to the unit's base budget. On the other end of the spectrum is the RCM model, in which the unit and its performance approaches a self-sustaining model. In an RCM model, the unit (school) retains a share of revenue it generates, while having responsibility for paying many of the costs necessary for operations (eg, space occupancy fees, utility fees, information technology service access and use), in addition to liability for fixed costs, like personnel support. Fundamentally, the RCM model is predicated upon revenue growth and cost control at the local level. The unit assumes greater risk, but has the potential of greater reward.

Academic Revenue Streams

Regardless of the institutional budget model in use, a school of pharmacy typically has four major types of revenue streams, as aligned with its institutional mission and focus:

1. Tuition—each doctor of pharmacy student pays tuition for attending classes at a school. Public universities will segment students based upon their residency, whether they are in-state vs. out-of-state students. In-state students will pay lower tuition costs than out of state, because the state government usually subsidizes the tuition for its citizens. While state regulations vary, it may take a student at least 12 months to establish residence in a new state and then be eligible for in-state tuition. International students many times will need to pay out of state tuition for all four years, as they are not able to complete all of the activities required for in-state tuition. Private institutions will have a flat tuition model in which all enrollees pay the same rate. Strategies to maximize tuition as a revenue stream include:

   a. Increase the class size—pharmacy has experienced several years of consistent declines in the applicant pool size, with recent rates of roughly one applicant for every available slot.[2] Finding quality applicants to fill the current existing seats is challenging, so thinking that one can easily increase the number of students per class will make recruitment all that more difficult. In addition, there is no guarantee that there are employment opportunities for these students once they graduate years later. Finally, each student that is added requires a minimum of 11 more months (1,740 hours) of IPPE and APPE placements at hospital and community pharmacies, which might not be easy to identify.[3]

b.   Alter class composition—if the college has a tuition differential between in-state and out-of-state students, one could preferentially favor out-of-state or international students. While this might increase revenue for the time students are paying the increased rate, public institutions could find this balance unappealing. Public universities often have an institutional commitment to educating the citizens of their states. Valued stakeholders, including state legislators and university governing bodies, may tie state appropriations or other parameters to maintaining a minimum threshold of state residents in the student body. Thus, matriculating a disproportionate share of nonresidents could put the organization in disfavor with key constituents. Institutions also have a commitment to educating the local or regional workforce. This may be challenging to achieve, as nonresident graduating students may not desire to enter the workforce in the catchment area of the school or university. Educating a large cohort of individuals who do not contribute to the state's economy or healthcare workforce becomes a difficult proposition, given the large number of external stakeholders with significant financial influence on a school or college. Similarly, a health system's ongoing interest or investment in precepting may wane as they are not able to recruit qualified pharmacists to work in their organization following the student's training.

c.   Increase tuition rates—while this could be an attractive option for school leadership, this means that students will have to pay more for their degree. This increased expense could incentivize students to identify careers other than pharmacy or to pursue enrollment at another institution that has a lower tuition rate. A tactic used by some public institutions is to offer tuition discount programs to students who reside out of state but in proximal regions, thus shrinking the larger price tag for out-of-state tuition yet increasing the potential to matriculate more students. A parallel student recruitment approach may be used by many private institutions to award financial aid packages to offset portions of the higher tuition rates generally associated with private schools. Amid this backdrop is the continuing increase in pharmacy student debt loads nationally, whereby the average students graduated with $173,000 of student loans in 2021.[4] Further raising the tuition will only increase the amount of loans that a student has, reducing the overall interest people have in becoming a pharmacist because of changing the debt to salary ratio.

d.   Offer additional degree programs—undergraduate degree and some graduate degree programs (eg, master's) also charge tuition for students to enroll. Schools can diversify their instructional revenue streams by offering these types of tuition-generating degree programs, in addition to other types of credentials (eg, certificate programs).

2.   Research grants—in many schools, faculty must also conduct scholarship in areas in which they are experts. Obtaining external funds to support this research is a means of offsetting fixed costs incurred by the college. External funding, commonly known as grants and contracts, is typically predicated upon a structured project budget that accounts for the expenses incurred by conducting the research activity. This includes all personnel time and supplies that are part of the study. If a faculty member spends 10% of their time for three months conducting the research project, then that is a known expense amount. Determining all the personnel time, supply costs, and travel are added up to determine the direct cost of the study. Federal grants will also include an option for indirect costs, sometimes referred to as facilities and administrative costs (F&A) or overhead. These "charges" to the agency or group that provides the grant funding offset the costs of the school's resources

used to conduct or administer the grant—the depreciation for existing research equipment, use of computers and technology, payroll and human resource services, facility occupancy, etc. Each university rate will slightly differ but could be 25% to 33% of the total budget of a grant.[5] The total grant award will be the summation of direct and indirect costs.

The expenses associated with grants will be costs that tuition does not need to cover. However, grants are extremely competitive. In 2021, there was a 19% funding rate for research project grants submitted to the National Institutes of Health.[6] Focusing faculty time more on research and grant submissions could allow for a reduction in tuition because the overhead will cover costs that tuition has, but there is no guarantee of successful funding. A faculty member will need to submit numerous grants to increase their chances of success, but each submission takes significant time that could be devoted to other activities, like teaching or providing clinical services in a practice site. When they are successful, they will have limited time for anything but the grant and planning their future submissions so they can remain funded. Because of the need for devoted time to conduct research, a college might need to hire other faculty to teach the classes successful researchers are not able to teach. However, having successful researchers does increase the reputation of the school.

3. Gifts—schools solicit financial donations from those with affinity for the organization, often alumni, local or regional corporations or foundations, or others who may have stakes in the success of the school. These donations can be used to provide scholarships to students, offset some costs of constructing or renovating the buildings, or provide flexibility for school leadership to apply to areas of need. These gifts, while generous tokens from alumni, are difficult to obtain and require time on the part of school leadership to cultivate. They might not be consistent in nature and hard to dependably count on an annual basis. Some may also be narrowly focused in their applicability to support areas of the school's mission. Thus, a school that is overly reliant upon funds in its endowment runs the risk of exhausting a source that is not guaranteed in the future and must withstand changes in the investment market to generate spendable income at a predictable rate.

4. Other potential revenue sources—colleges of pharmacy might have continuing education programs, royalties received from licensing the intellectual property of its faculty, manage on-campus pharmacies, conduct contract research for external companies, or provide consulting services. While small, each of them can contribute revenue to the school's operations. Some schools are aligning themselves more closely with health systems, much like colleges of medicine do in academic medical centers, to become integrated in the care delivery model and the flow of funds that may result.

Academic Expenses

Balancing these revenues are various expenses that academia has:

1. Faculty salaries—the major expense for pharmacy schools is its personnel. Expenses that are not offset by grants or gifts need to be supported by dollars generated by tuition. While faculty salaries are known to be less than in practice settings, schools need to be competitive in their financial package to maintain quality education through faculty retention.[7;8] As faculty expenses increase, tuition needs to cover these costs as there are limited sustainable funding alternatives.

2. Support personnel—besides faculty, each college has infrastructure responsible for supporting its teaching and research missions. Employees in these roles might not be directly involved in teaching or research but are critical for their success. They will need to be covered by tuition or grant overhead.

3. Facilities—depending on the school, its relationship to the larger university, and the university's budget model, a school may have payments for building maintenance, upgrades,

remaining loan repayment for past construction projects, groundskeeping, computing/technology infrastructure, housekeeping, room occupancy, teaching and research equipment, and even utility costs.

4.   Experiential partnerships—any contractual relationships that the school makes with its partners will be an expense that it needs to cover. Whether this is negotiated as a per student fee, fixed amount, or potential salary support for a pharmacist, these expenses must be accounted for. If a partner site negotiates with the college for a higher amount, the college does not have the option to stop all experiential rotations. While they could minimize the number of students placed at that hospital, experiential education is a condition for accreditation. Therefore, the school needs to identify revenue to cover this increased expense, and this usually results in increasing the pharmacy class size and/or tuition adjustments.

5.   Other—a host of other expenses may be incurred, including costs to solicit gifts and support alumni and student events; student recruitment and marketing costs; travel funds to support the professional development and research engagement of faculty, staff, and students; annual fees for accreditation and institutional-level memberships, and other mission-critical costs. A component of expenses that crosses expense types is typically referred to as start-up costs—dollars allocated to faculty upon their hiring to support the success of their research or teaching assignments. Those dollars can be applied to make equipment or supply purchases for research laboratories, underwrite the salaries of research personnel or doctoral students, yield access to large-scale databases or statistical consulting services, support travel to professional conferences, or a host of other applications. Faculty in several scientific domains within pharmacy schools, notably those requiring heavy chemistry or related laboratories for their research programs, often command start-up packages in excess of $1.5 million.

Value of a School–Hospital Partnership

While the relationship between a health system and academia can just be transactional, having a true partnership can add value to both organizations. While it will take time to invest in relationship-building and to align incentives, the outcome should be well worth it. Understanding the financial elements shaping higher education can guide a health system pharmacist to cultivate greater value with an academic partner.

The value proposition for academia includes:

1.   Consistent student placements—schools are reliant upon the opportunity to partner with practice sites for experiential education placement for their students. Thus, having a limited number of stable relationships with health system pharmacies is preferable to seeking to maintain more numerous connections. While there is more risk if a partner drops out, developing codependencies should minimize this risk. Many students also prefer the housing and transportation cost stability that results from being placed in a single or only few practice sites. The school can also invest more quality time in preceptor development and other training needs of health system pharmacists when there are a limited number of partners. Serving as a consistent host for student rotations is often associated with greater familiarity with and commitment to providing a quality educational experience for the students the site hosts, minimizing the challenges the school must manage to ensure quality of its experiential education placements.

2.   Access to high quality practitioners—there is no better education than that provided by the real-world. Faculty without active practice sites could become stale in their clinical knowledge. Instead of gaining knowledge from patient presentations and discussions on rounds, they must rely upon learning from the literature. Being able to have current practitioners

teach students from their experience will help them gain the potential clinical knowledge which will assist them on their clerkships and preparation for licensure exams. This teaching can occur in the classroom, through the design of curricular concepts, and in the precepting of students in the delivery of patient care. Residents also can provide valued teaching through layered learning in both the practice and classroom settings.[9;10]

3. Research collaborations—hospitals generate a significant amount of data in the ongoing patient care process. Health system pharmacists do not have the time and expertise to conduct research and publish on all that information. Faculty, on the other hand, are trained and incentivized to conduct scholarship in their interest area, yet gaining access to quality data can sometimes hamper their research pursuits. Developing research collaborations with the practice site can support faculty in their research missions, develop meaningful collaborations between faculty and practitioners, increase the brand recognition of the pharmacy department as they are included in publications, and generate revenue if the pharmacists are written into the grant budget.

The value proposition for health system pharmacy departments includes:

1. Extended patient care capacity—if a department can rely upon a consistent number of student placements, then it can creatively think about what services might get completed. Students, residents, and faculty who are then placed in the patient care setting can now be relied upon, and that becomes an additional patient care resource the department can build into its practice model. For example, a rotation that focuses on medication reconciliation, admission medication histories, transitions of care, or discharge counseling could help the pharmacy department meet its institutional goals. A pharmacy department does not have to identify new or existing resources to cover these services, instead they can train and deploy these students for this task. This extends the capacity of the department to provide a broader array of services. Not only is this helpful to the department, but it's also excellent for student training. Having the opportunity to engage directly with patients will develop their skills and a commitment to patient care.[9]

2. Mitigating a workforce shortage—given the challenges in recruiting and retaining a qualified technician workforce, employing students in meaningful roles can assist the department in activities often delivered by technicians. The students could work on a weekend rotation, on evenings, holidays, and over the summer. Departments can also formalize student roles through internship programs, which provide deeper contributions to the department, allow students to advance in practice-based opportunities, and can serve as a pipeline for recruitment of future employees.[11;12]

3. Revenue stream—while minimal compared with drug revenue, precepting pharmacy students can generate additional resources for the pharmacy department. Besides the opportunity to be written into research grants, pharmacy schools also utilize split-funded faculty positions. These individuals balance their time between the practice site, where they precept and provide patient care, and academia, where they teach and publish. While more complicated to manage across both entities, these positions are attractive because no partner needs to fund an entire position. The other revenue that can come from precepting is a per student fee. These dollars can be applied to supplement the travel to conferences or cover preceptor costs like maintaining licensure and board certification. Since these resources are difficult to fund on the hospital side, having access to these from the college as a direct result of precepting can be valuable.

4. Other—students, residents, and faculty provide a pool of individuals who can support quality measures in the patient care setting, both through providing actual care and in conducting analyses to ensure measures are met. The extra capacity brought by these same individuals can be applied to piloting new practices or roles (eg, one-year funding to establish

a PGY2 residency program), building business cases for new services, or other projects that can best benefit from external resources that are not readily deployable from a health system budget. Pharmacy departments also benefit from the commitment to innovation and change that academic partners bring. These benefits may result in enhanced recruiting of pharmacists, brand name and recognition for the institution, a pipeline of well-trained future practitioners, or related elements.[10;12]

To create and maintain mutually beneficial partnerships, there needs to be ongoing discussions as one develops trust at the highest levels of both organizations. Inherent in this is the cultivation of the relationship between leaders on both sides of the partnership. For instance, if the dean and chief pharmacist can meet and develop a positive relationship, it will be easier for faculty and health-system pharmacists to agree and execute on the partnership. Deepening the relationship beyond those two individuals is equally as important, though, as the occupants of or focus of positions may change over time. Thus, the relationship should be cultivated at both the institutional and individual levels.

To foster these collaborative relationships, it is important that the following are idealized[9]:

- Focus on the outcomes and not the individual transactions

- Codify the partnership through a memorandum of understanding that both administrative leaders sign

- Review the agreement annually by administrative leaders (eg, dean, pharmacy practice department chair, chief pharmacy officer, pharmacy director)

- Recognize that both entities have significant pressures and will require flexibility periodically within the daily operations of the relationship

- Review the outcomes each year so that both entities are receiving equitable and mutual benefits in correspondence with their investments

- Celebrate the collaboration frequently so that all members of the organization understand its importance, and all are involved in its operation

- These types of relationships are special and should be initiated selectively by either entity

CONCLUSION

Understanding the financial models of academia are important, as they are different from health system pharmacy. There are various expenses that a school of pharmacy must balance against limited options for increasing revenue. Experiential education is required to maintain a college's accreditation, so there is an imperative for academia to cultivate relationships with health systems. Focusing on developing a mutually beneficial, sustained partnership is more ideal than having a transactional relationship. In this situation, both parties will gain more when they approach it in this manner.

REFERENCES

1. Accreditation Council for Pharmacy Education. PharmD program accreditation. 2016. **https://www.acpe-accredit.org/pharmd-program-accreditation/#tab-Standards**. Accessed April 1, 2022.

2. Brown DL. Years of rampant expansion have imposed Darwinian survival-of-the-fittest conditions on US pharmacy schools. *Am J Pharm Educ*. 2020;84(10):ajpe8136 10.5688/ajpe8136. 10.5688/ajpe8136. PubMed

3. Education. Acredditation standards and key elements for the professional program in pharmacy leading to the doctor of pharmacy degree, ("standards 2016"). Febraury 2, 2015. **https://www.acpe-accredit.org/pdf/Standards2016FINAL2022.pdf**. Accessed April 1, 2022.

4. American Association of Colleges of Pharmacy and Office of Institutional Research & Effectiveness. American Association of Colleges of Pharmacy graduating student survey, 2021 national summary report. July 2021. **https://www.aacp.org/sites/default/files/2021-07/2021-gss-national-summary-report.pdf**. Accessed April 1, 2022.

5. The Association of American Universities. Frequently asked questions about facilities and administrative (F&A) costs of federally sponsored university research. **https://www.aau.edu/key-issues/frequently-asked-questions-about-facilities-and-administrative-fa-costs-federally**. Accessed April 1, 2022.

6. National Institutes of Health. Success rates: R01-equivalent and research project grants. Accessed May 19, 2022.

7. Chisholm-Burns MA, Gatwood J, Spivey CA, Dickey SE. Net income of pharmacy faculty compared to community and hospital pharmacists. *Am J Pharm Educ*. 2016;80(7):117. 10.5688/ajpe807117. PubMed

8. Murawski MM, King BJ. Influence of salary on faculty recruitment and retention: current pharmacy faculty salaries relative to past faculty, community practitioners, and new hires. *Curr Pharm Teach Learn*. 2011;3(4):267–282.

9. Pinelli NR, Eckel SF, Vu MB, et al. The layered learning practice model: Lessons learned from implementation. *Am J Health Syst Pharm*. 2016;73(24):2077–2082. PubMed

10. Smith KM, Phelps PK, Mazur JE, May JR. Relationships between colleges of pharmacy and academic medical centers. *Am J Health Syst Pharm*. 2008;65(18):1750–1754. PubMed

11. Nisly SA, Brennan LF, Verbosky L, et al. Creating a pharmacy internship: a toolbox for success. *Innov Pharm*. 2018;9(4):11. PubMed

12. Skledar SJ, Martinelli B, Wasicek K, et al. Training and recruiting future pharmacists through a hospital-based student internship program. *Am J Health Syst Pharm*. 2009;66(17):1560–1564. PubMed

BENCHMARKING AND PRODUCTIVITY ANALYSIS

Kristin Tiry, David Hager, and Steve Rough

Benchmarking and productivity analysis continue to be a leadership topic that frequently recurs within the pharmacy profession. When times are lean financially this can become a major focus of a pharmacy leader. This chapter provides an overview of benchmarking, an introduction to its use in healthcare, and an overview of the data utilized by commercially available vendors. This chapter will additionally compare external benchmarking to internal benchmarking and key considerations for the use of each. Further, this chapter aims to provide pharmacy leaders with an understanding of internal productivity monitoring, the benefits of its use, and tools for the creation of productivity models to assess department workload.

KEY DEFINITIONS IN PHARMACY BENCHMARKING AND PRODUCTIVITY

- *External benchmarking* is the continuous process of measuring products, services, and practices against the company's toughest competitors or those companies renowned as industry leaders in order to find and implement best practice.[1]

- *Productivity* is the rate of output per unit of input, or the effectiveness of a productive effort.

- *Productivity benchmarking* is the use of a vendor-managed financial and operational comparative database to determine comparative productivity against a defined comparison (or peer) group.

- *Internal benchmarking* (eg, internal productivity monitoring) is a process of comparing one's performance in current state against past performance.

- *Full-time equivalent (FTE)* is an employee's scheduled hours divided by the employer's hours for a full-time workweek. When an employer has a 40 hour workweek, employees who are scheduled to work 40 hours per week are 1.0 FTEs.

DOI 10.37573/9781585287130.006

- *Case mix index (CMI)* is the average relative diagnosis related group weight of a hospital's inpatient discharges, calculated by summing the Medicare Severity-Diagnosis Related Group (MS-DRG) weight for each discharge and dividing the total by the number of discharges.[2]

- *Pharmacy intensity score* is a pharmacy specific assessment of intensity based on weights assigned to DRGs, using median drug cost across all hospitals, normalized to a 100-point scale (or weight).[1]

EXTERNAL BENCHMARKING

Key Definitions in External Benchmarking

- *Characteristic* is a feature or aspect of service provided by a department that helps to describe a distinguishable mark or trait.[1]

- *Characteristic survey* is a profile of characteristic questions designed to identify characteristics of each participating department and hospital in order to assist departments in identifying a meaningful peer or compare group for benchmarking purposes.

- *Peer group* is a grouping of similar hospitals or departments.

- *Element* is a reported metric (eg, volume statistic, expense, revenue) within a productivity monitoring system.

- *Percentile* is a relative ranking of how one is performing versus a comparison (or peer) group.

- *Acuity* is a measure of severity of illness.

- *Revenue adjustment* is a ratio of pharmacy department gross revenue/pharmacy department inpatient revenue. This adjustment is used in external benchmarking because most commercially-available vendor software systems require that organizations report inpatient pharmacy expenses in the same benchmarking department as expenses that are incurred in ambulatory clinics, infusion centers, and procedure areas. This adjustment provides an approximation of actual inpatient pharmacy expense since the actual inpatient expense is not reported separately into the system.

- *Normalization* is a movement or transfer of reported costs, volumes, and/or FTE from one cost-center to another for the purposes of ensuring that these data are reported and compared in consistent fashion by each participating hospital.

Use of External Benchmarking in Health Systems

Used appropriately, external benchmarking can drive improved department performance. The goal of external benchmarking is to enable comparison of departmental operational and financial performance in comparison with peer organizations.[1] This provides a platform for transparent benchmarking against an organization's defined group of peers or "best-in-class" organizations. External benchmarking made its first appearance in healthcare in the 1990s when The Joint Commission (JC) defined it as a practice measurement tool for monitoring the impact of governance, management, clinical, and logistical functions.[3] External benchmarking should be used to gather data, or elements, in order to identify those who are best in class or to identify areas where further investigation is warranted by department leadership. This should trigger performance improvement activities to monitor progress toward best-in-class performance. Through effective benchmarking, pharmacy departments should be able to identify opportunities for improving workflow efficiency, patient care services, and financial performance, thereby improving the department's overall value to the organization. One limitation is that external benchmarking in healthcare often lacks a qualitative evaluation, an approach that has been successful in other industries. This hinders adequate comparison or best practice sharing.

Use of external benchmarking in healthcare continues to increase, despite many longstanding limitations. Use of external and internal productivity monitoring systems continue to gain popularity among hospital administrators looking to understand pharmacy performance and determine the value they are achieving for the organization's investment of resources.[1;4] As such, many pharmacy departments are asked to incorporate external and internal benchmarking data into their pharmacy budgeting and continuous quality improvement processes. The inability to effectively measure workload and productivity have been persistent problems for health system pharmacy. A standard set of metrics or best practices for how to measure health system pharmacy productivity does not yet exist. A new goal of measuring value—not only measuring cost, but also determining quality as a function of cost—is even earlier in its development. The American Society of Health-System Pharmacists (ASHP) is contributing to this goal through the Pharmacy Accountability Measures (PAM) work group, which seeks to identify and develop consensus quality measures that can be used on a national scale to demonstrate health system pharmacist accountability and improve clinical outcomes.[5] However, these quality measures have yet to be incorporated into external benchmarking systems. Software used for external benchmarking purposes remains available through a limited number of commercial vendors and incompletely describes departmental operations, clinical services, and overall performance.

External benchmarking needs to be carefully applied to avoid unintended consequences. Benchmarking works well when the process being compared is essentially the same with little variation in quality and includes large numbers of comparison departments with high degrees of transparency. For example, processes that are very consistent may be useful to compare, such as the cost of producing a unit dose packaged medication or processing time for a benefits claim. Benchmarking is not informative when it is used to compare fundamentally different processes or products. For example, the time it takes to complete an inpatient admission from a pharmacy perspective could vary widely based on pharmacist and technician roles in admission medication reconciliation, benefit investigation, drug therapy monitoring, clinical pharmacist scope of practice, and many other factors. Benchmarking of departments that do not offer similar levels of service and quality to customers will result in inaccurate comparisons. Due to the complexities and variability of services provided by pharmacy departments, external benchmarking struggles to provide accurate comparisons across organizations.

Commercially Available Vendors

Commercially available vendors pose another challenge when armed with external benchmarking tools.[1;4] Commercial vendors and consultant groups, often without contemporary expertise in identifying and measuring pharmacy practices, sell and purchase crude benchmarking metrics that ultimately result in the downsizing of pharmacy departments. Commercially available systems are excessively rigid and not reflective of contemporary health system pharmacy practice. They usually focus on productivity, and are rarely able to measure quality or value. They produce productivity ratios, are highly focused on a very limited number of available operational metrics (doses dispensed, prescriptions filled, etc.), and fail to capture clinical workload. They rarely, if ever, assess the overall impact of pharmacy services on patient outcomes and total cost of care; therefore, they are unable to measure value. Rather, it is common for consulting firms that specialize in external benchmarking to assess pharmacy department effectiveness by comparing staffing or workload ratios based solely on measures of operational workload or high-level comparisons of expenses. These external benchmarking metrics are inappropriately used by health system administrators within the budgeting process, or by consultants to recommend or mandate reductions in pharmacy staffing.

When labor productivity ratios are rigidly applied, without adequate comparison of the services provided or identification of a peer group, incorrect decisions could be made and force a department to move away from their own established best practices. Pharmacy department leadership should be highly engaged in any external benchmarking activities before decisions on future budgeting and workforce planning are finalized.

In an attempt to create an accurate comparison, commercial vendors utilize a reference manual that dictates the costs, labor, and services that should be included into each section of the database. Pharmacy leaders must master the reference manual to identify the strengths and weaknesses of the comparison being generated. A healthy professional relationship with your hospital's data coordinator is strongly suggested so pharmacy leadership can understand how their data are being entered at a granular level. Working with one's data coordinator to make sure expenses are reported accurately is strongly advised. Departments must also pay particular attention to the costs and labor that fall into their accounting unit and assure normalizations are reported as instructed in the vendor's reference manual instructions.

Characteristic Surveys and Data Reported

Commercial vendors provide characteristic surveys to assist organizations in the determination of their external peer group.[1,4] These characteristic surveys include a series of questions related to the reporting organization's size, services provided, technologies used, and types of patient care provided. Characteristic questions are often not granular enough to distinguish meaningful differences between peer groups. It is recommended to limit this peer group to a set of 10 to 30 similar organizations to enable an effective understanding of each of the individual organizations included in the group. The first step a pharmacy leader should take is researching each of the potential peer hospital services. This is most efficiently completed by connecting with leadership at the peer organizations to understand their services provided, the types of patients they serve, and how their own organization uses the data from the commercial vendor. It is very important to understand the extent to which peer departments have implemented best practices for achieving quality and safety and lowering total cost of care.

Elements reported into commercial vendor productivity monitoring software systems provide the foundation for data reporting. Frequently reported elements are listed in **Table 6-1**. Data are reported from several areas of the organization such as the general ledger (eg, supply expenses), payroll system (eg, paid hours, worked hours), charge master (eg, procedure and other workload volumes), monthly financial reports (eg, revenues), manual statistics supplied from departments (eg, orders processed, clinical interventions), and billing and coding data (eg, revenues). Comparison reports of these data elements are provided on a standard cadence to health system leaders. In external benchmarking, percentiles are often used as a basis for comparison. They range from 0% to 100% and better performance is signified with a lower percentile ranking. For example, if you ranked at the 25th percentile, that means that you are performing better than 75% of your compare group and worse than 25% in that category of performance. A ranking of 50th percentile indicates that you are the average performer, with half performing better and half performing worse than your organization. A ranking of 75th percentile indicates that you are better than only 25% of your compare group.

In addition to a comparison of the data elements included in Table 6-1, commercial vendors report a variety of productivity ratios. These productivity ratios always include a measure of volume or activity (eg, hours worked, admissions, discharges). They frequently also include an acuity weighting such as case-mix index (CMI) or pharmacy intensity score (PIS) as a means to approximate patient complexity, as well as a revenue adjustment as a means to approximate inpatient comparisons across organizations reporting data in a heterogeneous manner. Take time to understand the definitions and mathematical formulas behind each productivity ratio. Understand

TABLE 6-1. Examples of Frequently Reported Pharmacy Data Elements

Staffing configuration
- Paid FTEs
- Paid hours
- Worked hours
- Overtime hours
- Skill mix: % pharmacist
- Skill mix: % management
- Skill mix: % technicians
- Skill mix: % other
- Number of pharmacy residents

Facility information
- Admissions
- ED visits
- Ambulatory visits
- Total beds and staffed beds
- Patient days
- Case mix index
- Pharmacy intensity score – Inpatient and Outpatient
- Discharges

Operating statistics
- Gross drug charges
- Clinical service workload units
- Drug expense (can be broken down by drug classes and reported in aggregate)
- Orders processed
- Doses administered
- Doses dispensed
- Labor expense
- Supply expense
- Overall operating expense
- Inpatient gross drug charges
- Outpatient gross drug charges
- Gross charges
- Retail pharmacy revenue
- Retail pharmacy prescription volume
- Ambulatory infusion revenue
- Hours devoted to learners
- Investigational drug studies open

which metrics represent one's department favorably or unfavorably, and understand the root causes behind these explanations. Examples of commonly used productivity ratios are included in Table 6-2.

Tips for Getting Started and Deriving Value from External Benchmarking

- Understand how your health system is monitoring and benchmarking productivity and what vendors or consultants are utilized

- Ask questions around how productivity measured performance is factored into budgeting decisions

- Know the details of any external benchmarking commercial vendor's reference manual

- Develop a strong relationship with your organization's data coordinator or whoever manages your peer group, and ensure they report information accurately according to the vendor's most recent reference manual

TABLE 6-2. Examples of Frequently Used Pharmacy Productivity Ratios[a]

Cost-Based Productivity Ratios
- Total pharmacy cost per (PIS or CMI weighted) (adjusted) discharge*
- Drug cost per (PIS or CMI weighted) (adjusted) discharge*
- Labor cost per (PIS or CMI weighted) (adjusted) discharge*
- Total pharmacy cost per (PIS or CMI weighted) (adjusted) patient day
- Drug cost per (PIS or CMI weighted) (adjusted) patient day
- Labor cost per (PIS or CMI weighted) (adjusted) patient day
- Total pharmacy cost per 100 orders processed
- Drug cost per 100 orders processed
- Labor cost per 100 orders processed
- Labor cost per ambulatory patient visit supported
- Drug cost per ambulatory patient visit supported
- Total pharmacy cost per prescription processed
- Labor cost per prescription processed

Labor Productivity Ratios
- Hours worked per (PIS or CMI weighted) (adjusted) discharge*
- Hours paid per (PIS or CMI weighted) (adjusted) discharge*
- Hours worked per (PIS or CMI weighted) (adjusted) patient day
- Hours paid per (PIS or CMI weighted) (adjusted) patient day
- Hours worked per 100 admissions
- Hours worked (paid) per 100 orders processed
- Hours worked per dose dispensed
- FTEs per order processed
- FTEs per staffed bed
- FTEs per dose dispensed
- FTEs per adjusted patient day
- Prescriptions processed per day
- Hours worked per prescription processed
- Hours paid per prescription processed

[a] Oftentimes, productivity ratios are weighted for acuity using a CMI-weighted index or PIS, and adjusted using a pharmacy revenue factor adjustment when non-inpatient expenses are included in the inpatient department. Such weighting may occur for any productivity ratio.

[b] Preferred inpatient pharmacy metrics are indicated by an asterisk (*)

- Be involved in submitting the data reported, evaluate the details of each data element to ensure accuracy

- Choose your peer group wisely and be involved in these discussions with your data coordinator and health system leadership

- Evaluate the differences between your organization's services and those of your peer group and understand how these differences may impact your success

- Advocate for the use of appropriate productivity ratios that more closely reflect contemporary pharmacy services

- Be able to explain why these ratios are a good measure of pharmacy services and where they fail to reflect the bigger picture—when possible, push toward internal productivity benchmarking and quantifying value for services provided

- Never benchmark solely on the basis of labor productivity metrics (eg, hours worked per adjusted discharge), always insist upon accompanying financial metrics (eg, total pharmacy cost per adjusted discharge, drug cost per adjusted discharge, labor cost per adjusted discharge). This can demonstrate that more FTE with a more favorable skill mix or more labor expense and less overall cost due to better control of medication spend is valuable in hard dollars back to the organization.

INTERNAL BENCHMARKING

Key Definitions in Internal Benchmarking

- *Internal benchmarking* (eg, internal productivity monitoring) is a process of comparing one's performance in current state against past performance.[1]

- *Productivity* is used to evaluate efficiency and is equal to outputs divided by inputs.[6]

- *Productivity index* is present productivity divided by base period productivity. It measures the total percent change from a base period and represents the relationship between budgeted and actual productivity.

- *Productivity ratio* is a measure of productivity (output/input).[1]

  - *Example labor productivity ratios:*

    - Hours worked or paid per unit of output

    - Hours worked per 100 orders processed

    - Doses dispensed per hour worked

  - *Example cost-based productivity ratios:*

    - Expense per unit of output

    - Drug cost per 100 orders processed

    - Total pharmacy cost per patient discharge

- *Time standard* is the mean time required to perform a task.[4]

- *Volume indicator* is the mean frequency of a reported task.

- *Relative value unit (RVU)* is the weighted workload, time standard or volume indicator standardized to a common unit.[6]

- *A Delphi process* involves a facilitator presenting panel members with a series of specific questions in which responses are collected anonymously and then averaged.[7]

Comparison of Internal Benchmarking to External Benchmarking

Internal benchmarking, comparing one's performance in current state against past performance, is a preferable way to monitor departmental productivity and performance.[1,4] It is preferred to the use of external benchmarking as it allows for more control of the data utilized and eliminates the challenges of comparing one's self to another organization with dissimilar services. Having internal productivity targets and positive productivity trends is helpful when working with administrators to maintain or expand pharmacy labor resources. It allows leadership to responsibly explain budget variances, demonstrate need for resources when volumes change, and give support to requesting additional pharmacy FTEs as a result of workload increases. In some cases, this data and productivity assessment may allow pharmacy leadership to predict the workload associated with new initiatives or expansion of patient care services. In contrast to external benchmarking, internal benchmarking allows organizations to focus on the specific activities their staff complete that most significantly represent the contributions of the pharmacy department to the organization's success.

Methods for Measuring Internal Productivity

Despite attempts to identify a gold standard for pharmacy department internal productivity monitoring, none has been established. There have been a number of reasons as to why the profession has been unsuccessful, including advances in practice, differences in clinical practice throughout the country, expansion of services to include ambulatory care, and inability to measure nonproduct dispensing related work.[1;4;7] Without a defined standard, pharmacy departments must work to identify metrics that accurately reflect the workload and demonstrated efficiency of their departments. The key is to strive for metrics that are validated, fairly accurate, automated, and applied consistently over time.[1;4]

Given the volume of activities within a pharmacy department, it can be intimidating to develop an internal benchmarking system. With more metrics that can be utilized, the up-front and ongoing commitment required to maintain the system of measure is significant. It has taken some organizations multiple years to develop a method that accurately reflects their department's productivity.[6;7] When starting, it is essential to begin with the core activities of a department as these generally drive most workload (eg, medication order volume, doses dispensed, patient admissions and discharges, orders verified, infusions prepared, ambulatory encounters). Identify a few key pharmacist and technician activities that you want to measure. Then, strive to add in additional activities over time—this is particularly important when new services and new positions are added to ensure productivity ratios remain positive.

With the growth in use of technology in pharmacy practice, measuring productivity has largely trended toward the use of data derived from automated systems.[8–12] When it is possible to obtain productivity data from an automated source (eg, electronic health record, inventory management systems, financial software) it is preferred to manual work sampling methods. Recent literature has highlighted the effectiveness of using electronic data sources as it allows for real-time analysis, is automated, and is applied consistently over time. If electronic data points are unavailable for the activity you are trying to measure, manual methods can be utilized. Examples of these methods include direct observation, self-reporting, work sampling, time-motion studies, a Delphi approach, or utilizing a time study from a similar organization.[1;4;6;7] Whether you are utilizing an automated system or a manual method, it is important to define the cadence at which you will validate the accuracy of your model. This ensures you capture any changes in workload associated with a task over time.

Development and Application of Time Standards and Volume Indicators

The first step to understanding the workload associated with a task is to develop a time standard.[1;4] Once the time standard for the task is developed, it will be multiplied by a volume indicator to provide the total effort for the task over a given volume defined time period. Volume indicators are often obtained in an automated fashion from various electronic data sources (eg, electronic health record, inventory management systems, financial software). However, in some instances, volume indicators may need to be obtained via self-reporting, particularly for knowledge-based work that does not interact with the electronic health record, such as time spent rounding. Once time standards and volume indicators are established for the majority of tasks that drive workload, then the total time requirement can be determined. **Table 6-3** lists some volume indicators that have been used in work measurement for pharmacy departments in recent years. These metrics may be valuable to consider as you develop your own productivity model.

Given the lack of quick insight that can be gained by a singular productivity number, it needs to be standardized to something more useful. When measuring productivity over time, many health systems will represent productivity as a percentage.[13] If your productivity=100%, this means your efficiency is as expected when compared with historical data. When productivity is >100%, this

TABLE 6-3. Commonly Used Volume Indicators in Pharmacy Productivity Monitoring

- Clinical Workload[6;7;9;10;12]
  - Patient profile reviews completed
  - Notes written by a pharmacist
  - Pharmacist consults completed
  - Orders verified
  - Pharmacist initiated orders
  - Admission medication reconciliations completed
  - Discharge medication reconciliations completed
  - Patients counseled
  - Student cosigned notes by a pharmacist
  - Pharmacy student notes completed
  - Codes attended
- Inpatient Volume Indicators[9;10;12]
  - Orders or doses dispensed
  - Medications distributed
  - Number of returns sorted/restocked
  - Phone calls answered
  - Automated dispensing cabinets stocked
  - Intravenous medications prepared
- Outpatient Infusion Clinic Volume Indicators[8;11]
  - Orders verified
  - Clinical reviews completed
  - Outpatient infusions dispensed
  - Intravenous compounds prepared
  - Number of medications distributed
  - Number of each CPT code for intravenous infusions billed
- Ambulatory Pharmacy[14]
  - Pharmacist interventions completed (addition of medication, dose change, patient education, etc.)
  - Number of benefits investigation completed

means you are producing more output than expected (conversely a productivity less than 100% means you are producing less than expected—which could be the product of overstaffing or reduced volume). Pharmacy departments should strive to achieve a productivity of 100% or greater.

Standardized Comparisons within Internal Benchmarking Systems

With the integration of health systems, many health systems now include multiple hospitals and pressure will exist to utilize the same internal productivity measures across dissimilar areas (eg, acute care, retail, infusion clinics). Before this is undertaken, it is important to ensure that the characteristics within each area are roughly equivalent or you will mischaracterize productivity based on differences in service or practice. One way to account for differences in productivity is to standardize workload to a common unit. Standardizing either the inputs or outputs of a productivity ratio can be useful when incorporating multiple activities or tasks of varying complexities into one workload indicator.

Recently developed outpatient infusion-based productivity models highlight the value of standardizing workload to a common unit.[8;11] These productivity models have standardized their workload to a relative value unit (RVU). RVUs are currently used in measuring the work performed by physicians in the United States in order to calculate reimbursement.[15] In physician reimbursement, current procedural terminology (CPT) codes are assigned a RVU that represents the expected workload for the billable CPT. A similar approach can be applied to various activities in pharmacy practice. For example, in outpatient infusion-based pharmacy practice, CPT codes can be used to designate volumes and types of medication orders.[11] In one productivity model, CPT codes were categorized into groups of differing workload requirements (eg, hydration, chemotherapy, therapeutic injection). The required activities for pharmacists and technicians for each category were identified and time standards were assigned to these activities. The total time standard was then assigned for each CPT category. This productivity model accounts for differing complexities of services provided but simplifies the analysis by categorizing the data.

An additional example of quantifying outpatient workload includes using RVUs to represent workload that is normalized to a common unit of one hour (one RVU=one hour).[8] In this productivity model, RVUs were assigned to multiple pharmacist and technician tasks (eg, clinical review, verification, reconstitution, admixing, delivery). These time standards and associated RVUs were obtained from data within the electronic health record for each medication dispensed. Through the use of automated data points and a robust workload assessment for each medication dispensed, this model could be utilized for daily analysis of productivity. Additionally, this model could be applied to other outpatient infusion sites by updating the time standards to be reflective of workload and efficiency at each site. This concept, standardizing workload to a common unit, is an effective way to minimize the ongoing commitment to maintaining an internal productivity model when applying it across multiple acute care hospitals, ambulatory clinics, or infusion services within a health system.

Tips for Getting Started with Internal Benchmarking

- When identifying activities to include within internal productivity monitoring systems, consider the audience. How will the data be used?

- Choose metrics and data that are available real time and are automated. Determine the cadence at which you will validate the data on an ongoing basis to ensure it remains reflective of current workload.

- Start small and start with the core activities of the department; grow the number of elements over time so a robust model can be developed.

- Modify your model over time in order to be reflective of the contemporary services provided by your department.

- Consider standardizing your activities to a common unit, this allows one unit of service to account for multiple tasks or for the productivity model to be applied across multiple sites. Additionally, this standardized unit of service may minimize the time spent explaining multiple models to nonpharmacy leadership as a justification for expansion of services or increases in pharmacy staff.

REFERENCES

1. Rough SS, McDaniel M, Rinehart JR. Effective use of workload and productivity monitoring tools in health system pharmacy, part 1. *Am J Health Syst Pharm*. 2010;67(4):300–311. PubMed

2. Centers for Medicare & Medicaid Services. MS-DRG classifications and software. **https://www.cms.gov/Medicare/Medicare-Fee-for-Service-Payment/AcuteInpatientPPS/MS-DRG-Classifications-and-Software**. Accessed April 24, 2022.

3. Ettorchi-Tardy A, Levif M, Michel P. Benchmarking: a method for continuous quality improvement in health. *Healthc Policy*. 2012;7(4):e101–e119. PubMed

4. Rough SS, McDaniel M, Rinehart JR. Effective use of workload and productivity monitoring tools in health system pharmacy, part 2. *Am J Health Syst Pharm*. 2010;67(5):380–388. PubMed

5. Andrawis M, Carmichael J, Collins CD, et al. Improving patient care and demonstrating value during a global pandemic: Recommendations from leaders of the Pharmacy Accountability Measures Work Group. *Am J Health Syst Pharm*. 2020;77(23):2003–2005. PubMed

6. Simmons A, Vest TA, Cicci J, et al. Formation and validation of an acute care clinical pharmacist productivity model: Part 2. *Am J Health Syst Pharm*. 2021;78(15):1410–1416. PubMed

7. Vest TA, Simmons A, Morbitzer KA, et al. Decision-making framework for an acute care clinical pharmacist productivity model: Part 1. *Am J Health Syst Pharm*. 2021;78(15):1402–1409. PubMed

8. Achey TS, Riffle AR, Rose RM, Earl M. Development of an operational productivity tool within a cancer treatment center pharmacy. *Am J Health Syst Pharm*. 2018;75(21):1736–1741. PubMed

9. Naseman RW, Lopez BR, Forrey RA, et al. Development of an inpatient operational pharmacy productivity model. *Am J Health Syst Pharm*. 2015;72(3):206–211. PubMed

10. Pawloski P, Cusick D, Amborn L. Development of clinical pharmacy productivity metrics. *Am J Health Syst Pharm*. 2012;69(1):49–54. PubMed

11. Reichard JS, Garbarz DM, Teachey AL, et al. Pharmacy workload benchmarking: Establishing a health system outpatient infusion productivity metric. *J Oncol Pharm Pract*. 2019;25(1): 172–178. PubMed

12. Gupta SR, Wojtynek JE, Walton SM, et al. Monitoring of pharmacy staffing, workload, and productivity in community hospitals. *Am J Health Syst Pharm*. 2006;63(18):1728–1734. PubMed

13. Vest TA, Gazda NP. Develop pharmacy productivity metrics. *Pharmacy Purchasing and Products*. 2019;16(11):34–39.

14. Schmidt L, Klink C, Iglar A, Sharpe N. Implementation of performance metrics to assess pharmacists' activities in ambulatory care clinics. *Am J Health Syst Pharm*. 2017;74(1):e76–e82. PubMed

15. Baadh A, Peterkin Y, Wegener M, et al. The relative value unit: history, current use, and controversies. *Curr Probl Diagn Radiol*. 2016;45(2):128–132. PubMed

FINANCIAL ASPECTS OF PHARMACEUTICAL CONTRACTS AND SUPPLY CHAIN MANAGEMENT

*Wayne Russell, Steven Lucio,
and Gretchen Brummel*

The COVID-19 pandemic and resulting societal impact reverberated across healthcare, including in the supply chain, labor market, and care delivery—and pharmacy is no exception. In some cases, the pandemic has identified the need for completely novel and/or expanded access points to care (eg, telepharmacy, increased home care availability, hospital-at-home programs). In other respects, it has focused attention on critical supply chain infrastructure as evidenced by the shortages we have seen in everything from nasal swabs to personal protective equipment (PPE) to ventilators and pharmaceuticals.[1] As a result of this experience, there is a greater recognition of the essential nature of the supply chain—its quality, reliability, and security. It is at this critical nexus where group purchasing organizations (GPOs) reside.

GPOs are the entities that partner with healthcare organizations, providers (eg, hospitals, health systems, nursing homes, home health agencies), and manufacturers of healthcare products to lower the cost, improve the quality, and increase sustainability of the healthcare supply chain by aggregating their members' purchasing volume. GPOs use this aggregated volume to negotiate discounts with manufacturers, distributors, and other vendors that enable provider organizations to manage the growth of healthcare costs.[2] By pooling or aggregating purchasing volume of their member organizations and individual providers, GPOs can negotiate product availability and pricing by bringing committed volume and sustainable contractual agreements to suppliers and manufacturers.

While participation in a GPO is completely voluntary and member organizations may choose to negotiate selected targeted contracts on their own, GPOs bring systematic efficiencies by minimizing the extent to which individual providers must devote resources to contract negotiation and management and the degree to which suppliers must negotiate with each provider separately.

According to the Healthcare Supply Chain Association (HSCA), over 100 national, regional, and local GPOs and other regional cooperatives provide group purchasing services across the U.S. Examples of GPOs include the Children's Hospital Association (CHA), HealthTrust, Innovatix, Intersectta, Premier, Inc., Provista, and Vizient®.[3] While an important responsibility of GPOs is to work with manufacturers and suppliers to provide goods and services (ie, aggregated contracting and sourcing functions) to healthcare members, the functions provided by GPOs continue to expand to meet the evolving needs of healthcare providers. We will cover the broadening scope of GPO-related services in this chapter.

DOI 10.37573/9781585287130.007

GPO SERVICES OVERVIEW

As part of their sourcing function, GPO membership covers health systems, individual hospitals, clinics, infusion centers, home care, hospital-at-home, retail pharmacies, long-term care practices, physician's offices, and other extended care settings. Diverse membership calls for broad product and services coverage including pharmaceuticals, medical and surgical supplies, laboratory supplies and equipment, food, and capital equipment. Services contracted outside of product contracts include consultative services, risk insurance, educational services, technology, software, clinical decision support, safety programs, and comparative data to assist organizations in benchmarking and performance improvement strategies. Some GPOs also offer private label programs, whereby they contract with a manufacturer to provide products that have the GPO's label/branding on them. Novaplus, one of the largest private label programs, is offered by Vizient and provides hundreds of products, ranging from pharmaceuticals to medical supplies. Premier offers two private label programs, PremierProRx, which covers pharmaceuticals, and PremierPro, which is commodity medical surgical supply items.

Participation in a GPO is voluntary and multiple factors influence this decision, including the type of organization requiring sourcing support, the environment it serves, and the complexity of services it provides among other considerations.[4] In addition, member organizations can and do choose to negotiate certain agreements on their own depending on specific needs. For the work they provide, there are typically two mechanisms by which GPOs are funded. One is a membership fee paid by members to belong to the GPO and to access GPO contracts offered. The other is an administrative fee from product manufacturers or suppliers, which typically range from 1% to 3% of the product purchase price. The Social Security Act, amended in 1986, allows GPOs to collect administrative fees from those suppliers with whom the GPO has developed a contractual relationship.

Administrative fees must be disclosed in an agreement between the GPO and each participating member. The agreement must state that the fees are 3% or less of the purchase price of the product.[5] If the fees are higher, the amount each vendor will pay must be disclosed in writing at least annually, along with the amount received by each vendor from purchases made by the member. Most GPOs subtract operating expenses from the administrative fees and return the remainder of the fees to their membership each year. The percentage returned to the member hospitals varies among GPOs. These monies are called patronage or share back fees.

GPO membership can vary depending on the type of GPO (nonprofit or for-profit) and primary type of member served. Many nonprofit GPOs have owner hospitals that are shareholders of the GPO. They can also have regional group affiliate members, which are smaller regional GPOs that can access the larger GPOs contracts, and affiliate hospital members that are sponsored by owners or regional groups. GPOs, while traditionally focused on acute care, now offer contracts to providers outside of hospitals, including outpatient health system practices, physician offices, retail pharmacies (including specialty pharmacies), clinics, other nonacute care sites, long-term care facilities, home care agencies, and other alternate sites of care. Some large health systems have also created GPOs with the health system being the anchor and with other smaller hospitals or health systems as members. Thus, you have traditional large national GPOs like Vizient, Premier, Inc., HealthTrust, and smaller health system based GPOs that also access the larger national GPO contracts or services in addition to their own locally negotiated contracts.

GPO CONTRACTING

Several studies have examined the benefits of GPOs on product costs. A recent analysis suggests GPOs reduced healthcare costs by $55 billion annually and up to $864 billion over 10 years—and that hospitals save 10% to 18% by buying through GPOs.[6,7] A critically important way GPOs provide value is through helping providers minimize and manage increasing costs by utilizing aggregated purchasing power to negotiate better pricing. In turn, the suppliers working with GPOs receive additional volume commitment, which provides more accurate demand signaling, predictable revenue and the long-term planning of manufacturing and supply.

A typical GPO pharmaceutical portfolio contains over 15,000 individual items and represents contracts with more than 250 suppliers. Contracts represent products and prices used in the acute care setting as well as nonacute (long-term care, managed care, home care, physician office, and retail pharmacy). With the Medicare Modernization Act of 2003, GPOs also contract for disproportionate share hospitals on inpatient-priced products. These hospitals use 340B pricing for their outpatient purchases.[8] The inpatient portfolio is called "Disproportionate Share Hospital (DSH) inpatient" to differentiate from the acute care pricing or 340B outpatient pricing. Please see chapter X of this reference for more information on the 340B program.

When looking at portfolio pricing, GPOs monitor the market and refresh their pricing accordingly throughout the contract lifecycle. Some GPOs conduct periodic bids for categories of pharmaceuticals to refresh pricing. Contract lengths vary among GPOs from yearly to six years or so. GPOs take a comprehensive approach to purchasing that considers not only the competitive price offered by suppliers, but also the quality of the manufacturer, product, and the reliability and stability of supply. Nonfinancial attributes critical to determining a supplier contract award include the presence of barcodes, unit dose packaging, latex-free packaging, alcohol free solutions, preservative free products, ready to use formulations, and more. Given the history of drug shortages, assessing suppliers' resiliency to disruption has become an even more critical consideration when determining the suppliers with whom to contract. This can include evaluating quality records, redundancy of supply sources, vertical integration, location of manufacturing of active pharmaceutical ingredients and final product, fill rates, manufacturing capabilities, and communications transparency prior to making an award. Other critical items such as contract terms and conditions must be negotiated in the bid process, which in some cases take additional time and effort. Negotiations also vary depending on the degree of competition for a product. For example, sole-source product manufacturers typically submit a price, but because their product lacks direct competition, there is less ability to negotiate additional financial value as compared with generic and biosimilar products.

However, sole-source manufacturer contracts may contain other features, such as firm pricing for a specified period, limitations on the extent and/or frequency of price increases, market share considerations for performance-based programs, and other benefits. In the generic market, more direct competition and product pricing occurs. As a result, the product attributes described above can play a bigger role in determining which pharmaceuticals are preferred.

GPOs must also consider the extent to which a manufacturer is able to supply the market, especially in the generic and biosimilar marketplace. A "market competitive" clause often exists in generic contracts that allows for price reductions if competitors within the generic class offer a sustainable lower price to GPO members. In some circumstances a manufacturer may offer a low price, but only for a brief time frame. If the price is not sustainable and/or the related supply cannot meet member demand, such pricing may not result in a change by the incumbent supplier. A GPO must have a mechanism for monitoring pricing in the marketplace, which is often done by analysis of pharmacy wholesaler data representing the GPO members' purchases through contract, noncontract, and off-contract. Noncontract purchases occur when neither the GPO nor the member has a contract. Off-contract purchases occur when the member does not purchase through the GPO agreement, but through an individual contract with the supplier or another GPO or distributor agreement with the supplier.

Various contracting strategies exist as part of the bid process. A GPO typically seeks originator, sole-source manufacturer products on contract, but such coverage may be challenging as these agents lack direct competition (eg, oncology and other specialized drugs). In some cases, while direct generic competition is lacking, certain products may have competition within a related therapeutic class. Selecting one product within a therapeutic class to have on contract at the exclusion of all other products within the same category is very difficult, especially for the larger GPOs that represent a large number of hospitals, each with their own Pharmacy and Therapeutics committees, and clinicians with a wide spectrum of opinions. Thus, a GPO will typically seek to contract for all sole-source manufacturer products within a therapeutic class, such as injectable iron agents, insulins, and cholesterol lowering agents, to allow their members to choose which products represent the clinical needs of that particular organization and its patient population. The introduction of biosimilars has created a related landscape where GPOs work to secure agreements for the originator biologic and biosimilar competitors and allow members to select the product(s) that best suits their needs.

This strategy does not usually hold true for generic products where products are defined by the Food and Drug Administration (FDA) as equivalent. The number of generic products within a category can be limited to increase contract compliance with the supplier product on agreement. However, GPOs can also contract for multiple generic products with the same chemical entity, particularly if there are concerns about the ability to supply.

Contract compliance and volume are critical factors to a generic supplier and can result in better pricing for GPO members. In this case, volume, market share, and contract compliance with the supplier(s) on contract can be enhanced to benefit both the GPO member and the manufacturer. Several GPOs, including Vizient and Premier, Inc., have private label programs with suppliers that aim to drive contract compliance toward the contracted product, which in turn yields additional value to members who purchase the private label product through better up-front pricing or rebates. Some GPOs have auto substitution programs that allow the contracted product to be ordered at the wholesale level, even if another similar generic product was initially selected. The contracted product is "automatically substituted" for any noncontracted generic. The GPO member must agree to participate in this program by signing a letter of commitment, and the member can select a percentage of products in the auto substitution portfolio that they do not want substituted for clinical or safety reasons.

The Bid Process in Detail

The GPO bid process can occur on various timelines. It may encompass the entire pharmaceutical portfolio or a specific segment within the portfolio separated into subcategories and then bid over time. However, during the course of each year "minibids" for specific items are conducted if the awarded supplier decides they cannot continue to be price competitive on a specific generic drug or contract. The GPO will conduct a minibid for the generic product and guide product suppliers through a process that takes, on average, one month to determine a new contract awardee that is market competitive. This process can also occur if the contract awardee cannot supply product to the GPO membership and the membership must obtain a competitor product off-contract. The GPO will conduct a minibid if continued or prolonged product supply or quality issues cannot be resolved in a timely manner (usually stipulated in the terms and conditions of the contract). These opportunities have now extended to biosimilars as these agents have opened doors for competition in the biologics' space. Other contract strategies include negotiations (no bid), which frequently occur with proprietary sole-source manufacturer products that do not have a competitor in the marketplace.

Another historical contracting strategy is a reverse auction. However, this approach is not optimal. This process has been employed in other industries (automotive, chemical, lumber) in which multiple suppliers bid for a contract through an electronic auction process. Three or more suppliers must participate so that although the suppliers can see the prices submitted by their competitors, they cannot determine which competitor represents any given price. The price is driven down through the auction process (hence the term reverse auction) rather than driven up. However, this approach creates concerns about the impact on drug shortages. Auction rules include the stipulation that the competitors must be able to supply the marketplace for a given length of time and not drive down the price without the intention to continue operating in the market at the auction price. This allows the product to be launched on contract in the market very quickly. Large GPOs generally do not utilize this strategy given the need to ensure that both the pricing and the ability to supply the market are more rigorously evaluated. The focus now is on manufacturer attributes such as FDA track record regarding quality, active pharmaceutical ingredients (APIs), and finished product production sites, vertical integration, and product formulation, among others. While some smaller GPOs might still employ strategy of reverse auctions, especially for generic drugs, it is not the optimal mechanism to support value and reliability of supply.

GPOs also use a variety of electronic tools to conduct bids. A major challenge in the bid process is negotiating contract terms and conditions—and ensuring that the product and price data submitted by the manufacturer are accurate so that when the contracts are awarded, the process of notifying the pharmacy wholesalers and members can be accomplished in a timely manner. Wholesalers typically need 30 to 45 days to accurately load a new pharmacy portfolio and to change existing pharmaceutical stock in their distribution centers to accommodate the GPO membership. Usage data and communication with pharmacy distributors and suppliers is essential to a smooth transition from the existing portfolio to the new GPO portfolio. If the portfolio transition process is not managed well, the installation of the new contract portfolio contract will be prolonged and membership will be dissatisfied because of the charge-backs and rebills associated with incorrect products and pricing.

Contract Types

GPOs encounter a variety of contract types with the pharmaceutical industry, including:

- Base contract: product and price (eg, price without commitment or tiers)

- Base contract with rebate

- Contract families: commitment to multiple products to achieve the value

- Performance contract: based on market share, total units purchased, or total dollars purchased with or without a rebate

- Committed agreements: member commits to a certain volume of product at a specific price in a take-or-pay model

Supply chain and GPOs have their own unique terms and language. Two critical terms that are essential for understanding are class of trade (COT) and cost of goods (eg, cost plus or cost minus). Both terms have a substantial impact on the actual price paid for a medication.

A member's COT is the category to which they belong that determines prices (and discounts) to which they are eligible.[9] Common classes of trade include acute care, nonacute settings, home infusion, long-term care, and retail pharmacy. A pharmaceutical company may for example offer more favorable pricing in the physician office COT as compared to that for the acute care setting. Such variations usually are associated with sole-source manufacturer products.

Contracts include simple base contract pricing, whereby the products and prices are listed for each COT. However, with generic drugs and the expanding market of biosimilars, the pricing is usually the same across all COTs given the direct competition for these products. Still, the net price paid by a provider is further affected by their terms with their wholesaler, either a markup (cost plus) or markdown (cost minus). In today's environment, most hospitals and health systems receive a markdown from the wholesaler for GPO-contracted products excluding specialty products whereby each major wholesaler creates their individualized list of defined products that fit into the "specialty" category and offer less of a discount based upon their fee structure with manufacturers. In other words, they pay the price of the drug minus a certain percentage (eg, contract price minus 2%). The pharmacy distributor markup or markdown is often based on the amount of purchases per month in total dollars, the payment terms, and the number of deliveries per day or per week to the facility. The overall mix of drugs purchased by the hospital or healthsystem has also become increasingly important in determining the cost structure of pharmaceuticals sold through the wholesaler channel. This is due to the various fee structure negotiated by the wholesaler with manufacturers and the pricing differential between the contract price and wholesaler acquisition cost (WAC) in addition to the other factors mentioned above. The more purchases per month, the fewer deliveries per week, and the more timely the payment terms results in a better cost of goods through the pharmacy distributor.

Many generic suppliers now offer a base price contract with additional rebate opportunities for members that are paid either quarterly, semiannually, or annually. The rebate is a percentage of the total purchase cost of the product. Rebates are discounts and encourage commitment to a product, allowing for greater predictive demand and long-term resilience of supply. Pharmacy distributors also have their own generic product lines (initially in the retail market and now increasingly in the hospital setting). This proliferation of portfolios can increase the complexity of pricing and value evaluation as well as the forecasting of demand. Given these dynamics, it is necessary for close working relationships and consistent use of analytics to monitor performance by all parties supporting a GPO member organization's supply needs.

Contract families are contracts for multiple products produced by a single manufacturer. If a pharmaceutical manufacturer wants to encourage contracts for multiple products with the GPO to maximize their production runs and to minimize manufacturing costs, they will offer lower pricing for one or more products if the GPO contracts for a certain grouping of products. This type of contract is usually anchored by a key product in a competitive market, along with several other products for which the manufacturer has competition from other suppliers. However, not all GPOs have contract family awards.

Performance agreements have historically been used by proprietary manufacturers for sole-source manufacturer products in defined therapeutic categories. Examples have included drugs such as iron replacement products, certain antifungals, and even some biologic drugs, like the erythropoietins. However, many of these drugs have come to the end of their exclusivity periods and as the market has shifted to biologic therapies, fewer of these opportunities now exist. Still, when available, performance agreements typically have multiple tiers, each of which is associated with a product price. Tiers are differentiated based on a market share percentage scale, total number of units purchased, total dollars spent, or a combination of these attributes. The price a member pays for a contracted product decreases as the market share percentage for the product increases, the total units purchased increases, or the total dollars spent increases. Another variable used in some performance agreements (typically antibiotics) is days of therapy. Performance agreement calculation of market share is usually based on a market basket of competitive products, whereby the contracted product usage is divided by overall usage of all other products in the market basket. This calculation can be complex when products are not dosed at the same frequency and/or provided in the same strength, thus leading to conversions necessary to compare actual product utilization.

Recently, a new type of contractual agreement has emerged whereby hospitals commit to a specific amount of product that they will buy over an annualized basis. The genesis of these programs is primarily due to drug shortages. These programs offer the manufacturer a committed volume of sales of specific products as the healthcare organization enters into a "take or pay" arrangement. This type of model brings stability to the supplier by ensuring manufactured product will be sold, thus improving availability of products prone to drug shortages.

Sometimes the comparison is based on dollars purchased, and to equilibrate the calculation, the actual cost of goods is not used. Instead, wholesale acquisition cost (WAC) is compared among products within a given therapeutic class. Many performance-based contracts are created to incent the provider to use the manufacturer's product the majority of the time (ie, high market share percentage). If a member falls below a certain market share percentage by using multiple products within the defined therapeutic class or market basket, the WAC discount will be a very small percentage. These programs, by definition, are designed to reward contract compliance and performance.

Many performance programs have letters of commitment (LOCs) that the pharmaceutical supplier requires the provider to sign in order to access the program for pricing of a specific drug.

These LOCs may be managed by the GPO to track membership enrollment in the program or by the pharmaceutical supplier, in which case the GPO may not be able to reliably track which members have enrolled in the program. This latter situation can lead to members not receiving the pricing agreed to by the program because of a communication breakdown between the manufacturer and the pharmacy distributor regarding the assignment of the tier (pricing) to the hospital member. Many GPO agreements require that the GPO manage any performance-based agreement in which a LOC is required so that the GPO can assist the members in determining if they are receiving the correct pricing based on the tier assignment and also in notifying the member when they are close to achieving the next tier (better pricing). GPOs have developed analytic tools to allow members to determine contract performance so appropriate decisions can be made regarding procurement, formulary status, and clinical utilization of specific products.

A newer development is that many wholesalers, manufacturers, and some GPOs are now supporting blockchain technology that notifies the GPO and manufacturer when a member's price is loaded incorrectly and thus the member (customer) is paying an incorrect price. This technology will spread as more manufacturers support it since it minimizes credit/rebills through the wholesalers and enhances correct pricing at the member (customer) level.

Other Contracts and Engagement Opportunities

GPOs contract for other types of products and services used in health system pharmacy departments. Examples of these contracts are service agreements with pharmaceutical distributors; reverse distribution agreements; auditing services; specialty distributor agreements; agreements for pharmacy technology and equipment such as sterile product hoods, medication administration cabinets, robotics, and carousels; as well as contracts for consulting services that focus on operational design and improved medication usage and standardization. Other typical areas for consulting services include sterile compounding, diversion prevention of controlled substances, antimicrobial stewardship, expansion of pharmacy services to nonacute areas, and supporting compliant 340B programs. Sometimes consulting services are agreed to "at risk" or "success-based," meaning that an agreed upon savings target is built into the contract. If the consultant's assistance does not result in the hospital or health system achieving the agreed upon savings, then the GPO will reimburse the facility the difference between the actual amount saved and the target amount in the contract.

Most GPOs have advisory committees comprised of provider membership that assist in product and supplier selection and in other strategic initiatives and goal setting. In the pharmacy area, a national committee also usually implements a strategy and sets goals. Other advisory committees might include a contracting committee to assist with the bid process and individual contract and product decisions; a clinical committee to assist in setting practice guidelines and sharing best practices among members; a safety committee to monitor adverse events and share knowledge related to safe medication practices; and an advocacy committee to work on issues related to advancing the profession of pharmacy, pharmaceutical pricing, reimbursement, revenue cycle management, and other issues that could affect overall product pricing, availability, and usage. Multidisciplinary committees assist in contract negotiations for products used throughout the healthcare system such as IV fluids, pumps and sets, medication administration cabinets, bedside barcode technology, and so forth.

Providers expect much more today from their GPOs than in the past, when GPOs primarily provided contracts for goods and services. Although contracting is still a foundational role of GPOs, many provide services to differentiate themselves to suppliers in the marketplace and to provide the additional value their membership expects. Hospitals, health systems, and other members expect the following from GPOs:

- Contracts that cover the breadth of products and services a member organization would need and contracts that are competitive and representative of different facets of the overall membership

- Price competitive goods and services that are consistently available during all operating conditions (normal situations and during crises, natural disasters, etc.)

- Price protection on contracts for specified lengths of time, especially in commodity markets

- Contract coverage that addresses financial needs across all COTs, not just acute care

- Supporting members in enabling efficiencies and performance improvement and driving costs out of their systems through improved contracting and resource usage

- Supply chain and performance improvement technology to drive organizational decision-making, standardize care, and eliminate variation

- Information that allows for benchmarking capabilities against other organizations of similar characteristics

- Consulting services (whether fee based or in-kind) to assist in contract pull through as well as standardization and best practice initiatives

- Finance and budget tools to forecast pharmaceutical cost increases year-over-year—allowing individual hospital pharmacy departments to plan for projections and find cost savings

- Greater resiliency measures—including innovative strategies, creative partnership, and technology and data—to help mitigate supply chain disruptions and drive stable supply

- Advocacy support to advance priority legislative and regulatory needs to lower costs, bolster pharmaceutical supply chain resiliency, support patient access to care, and advance the pharmacy profession

For their part, suppliers expect GPOs to assist them with uptake after a product(s) is added to the contract and in member education on any operational, clinical, and safety issues related to their products. GPOs can serve as an avenue to certain markets and in the case of generic products and biosimilars, support additional competition for specific molecules and/or dosage forms. In these areas, GPOs can assist suppliers with enrollment of members into their performance programs. Additionally, purchasing data are also important to suppliers in competitive markets, and GPOs are often asked to provide purchase data at the aggregate level to calculate market share for performance agreements and to provide this data to the manufacturer.

EVOLUTION OF THE GPO

As healthcare has changed, so have GPO responsibilities and areas of focus. Examples of changes that have affected the expansion and enhancement of GPO services include:

- The ongoing challenge of drug shortages and supply chain resiliency

- Shift in product pipeline to specialty drugs and biologics (including biosimilars)

- The continued migration of care outside the hospital to multiple nonacute settings

Building a Truly Resilient Supply Chain

COVID-19 has focused the nation's attention on the risks associated with complex, global supply chains, particularly related to healthcare products and prescription drugs. Drug shortages have been pervasive for two decades—well before COVID-19's onset—and particularly with respect to generic injectables. At the time of writing this chapter, more than 115 medications are listed by the Food and Drug Administration (FDA) as being in shortage.[10] The American Society of Health-System Pharmacists (ASHP) list, which extends beyond the FDA's definition of medically necessary drugs, notes over 240 drugs in short supply at the end of 2021.[11] A 2019 survey by Vizient estimated that the annual labor cost to the U.S. health system to manage drug shortages prepandemic was nearly $360 million.[12] A recent Premier survey of 150 health system pharmacy leaders and frontline staff revealed that 94% of respondents have been impacted by interruptions in their pharmaceutical supply in the past 18 plus months. To meaningfully address these challenges, GPOs are bringing forward innovative strategies to drive diversification, commitment, predictive data, advocacy, and market-based strategies.

Over the last several years, we have also seen regulatory and legislative activity focused on the challenges faced by manufacturers and providers due to drug shortages:

- The FDA has fast-tracked approvals of drugs in the shortage categories

- The FDA began publishing a list of drugs that are off patent but lack significant competition[13]

- The FDA created a 180 day exclusivity pathway for manufacturers who receive generic drug approval through the Competitive Generics Therapy Designation as an incentive to promote competition[14]

The COVID-19 pandemic has further accelerated these actions to prevent drug shortages and supply chain disruption:

- The Coronavirus Aid, Relief, and Economic Security (CARES Act) included powers to enhance the FDA's visibility into drug supply chains.[15]

- In October 2020, the FDA published a list of 227 drugs and biologicals considered essential.[16] In January 2020, Vizient published a list of essential medications, which it continues to update quarterly.[17]

- Premier, Vizient, and 55 other organizations supported the MEDS Act which granted additional authority to the FDA for priority review, manufacturing incentives, reporting requirements, interagency coordination, consumer notification, and national security risk assessment due to drug shortages.[18]

- GPOs worked with manufacturers and the DEA to ensure adequate quotas of raw materials were available for the Schedule II drugs used in the treatment of mechanically ventilated, COVID-19 ICU patients.[18; 19]

- In January 2022, Premier and Vizient urged Congress to pass the Drug Shortages Shelf Life Extension Act which allows the FDA to grant temporary shelf life extensions of expiration dating for drug shortage products.[18; 20]

In addition, many GPOs have partnered with suppliers to develop private label medications and expand these programs to include more medications as a way to build additional inventory in the event of unanticipated supply disruptions. GPOs work closely with manufacturers to articulate both current and anticipated demand so suppliers can better predict the requirements for their supply channels. They also coordinate with distributors, and of course, directly with members to locate needed supply to avoid patient harm.

Example: Vizient Novaplus and Novaplus Enhanced Supply

Subsequent to the cost survey on drug shortages, Vizient, along with its members, began the work of identifying the drugs where supply disruptions represent the greatest threat to patient care and therefore deserved the greatest attention from a strategic sourcing perspective. This "essential medications" list, which was initially published in January 2020, paved the way for Vizient to extend the function of its long standing Novaplus private label to what is now known as the Novaplus Enhanced Supply (NES) strategy. Through NES, Vizient works with suppliers to create an additional four to six months of essential medication inventory. As of January 2022, NES now consists of over 100 million domestically housed units of essential medications, representing 79 different molecules. During the initial peak of the first COVID-19 outbreak, this strategy delivered an additional

676,000 units of essential medication propofol to members.[19] Vizient continues to expand NES as well as revise its essential medications reference quarterly.

Example: Premier's ProvideGx Program

With more than 1,000 hospital members, ProvideGx® was created to expand strategic relationships with select pharmaceutical manufacturers to increase market competition, resolve drug shortages, reduce waste, and mitigate irrational pricing. Premier and its members work together to identify and prioritize critical at risk drugs and together incentivize manufacturers to increase supply, invest in redundancies, enter or reenter markets, and explore new therapeutic categories for innovation. ProvideGx® uses long-term contracts to establish both consensus demand forecasting as well as minimum requirements on manufacturers to retain an average of three to six months of APIs and finished dose products. The program also has a dedicated supply channel through FFF Enterprises with the ability to dynamically allocate product to members based on clinical need rather than by purchase history alone. Since this program began in 2019, Premier successfully resolved 14 drug shortages, resulting in their official delisting from the FDA shortage list. At the same time, the program also helped prevent new shortages from occurring, as contracted products have not fallen into shortage drugs despite 150% demand spikes during COVID-19.

Recommendations that should be considered to create stronger, more resilient pharmaceutical markets and supply chains include the following:

- Sustainable contracts with suppliers who focus on quality and consistent supply to allow for improved manufacturing forecasting and production

- Education of stakeholders regarding the need to move beyond a price conversation to a combined cost, quality, and consistent supply discussion

- Increased transparency in the supply chain so manufacturing production schedules can be matched with market demand

- Increased transparency of manufacturing to understand what level of economic investment is required for manufacturers to provide sustainable, high-quality medications

- Incentives to encourage greater domestic manufacturing, thus decreasing reliance on foreign manufacturing and mitigating global supply chain challenges

- Changes in the pharmaceutical wholesaler cost minus financial model for hospitals, which is funded by fees charged to generic manufacturers

- Technology and data investments and capabilities for greater supply chain visibility, risk mitigation, and preparedness

- Close monitoring of market dynamics to ensure continued investment in high-quality manufacturing by multiple suppliers to avoid unanticipated consolidation in the supply

U.S. regulators, manufacturers, distributors, purchasing groups, and providers must collaborate to resolve drug shortages. These stakeholders must work together to create a transparent model that aligns need and commitment. This strategy allows manufacturers a committed volume for an extended period of time and to negotiate for the raw materials needed in the manufacturing of key products. We need greater transparency into the supply chain, including manufacturing locations for both the final product and the APIs so that vulnerabilities can be determined if there is overreliance on one supplier. All stakeholders need to understand that high-quality products, consistent supply, and a reasonable cost structure should be the mantra for generic injectable drugs. And lastly, we need to consider the number of manufacturers producing a product—too few or too many can create a vulnerable supply chain.

The Growth of Biologics and Specialty Pharmaceuticals

Many of the largest GPOs initially began as hospital-centric organizations given the characteristics of their members. Over time, most hospitals have not only become part of larger integrated healthcare systems, but they have also expanded their footprints to encompass dimensions of nonacute care from outpatient clinics and physicians' offices to home infusion practices, retail pharmacies, and specialty pharmacies. As a result, GPOs have evolved to meet the changing needs of their members and to account for changes in the drug development pipeline. Increasingly, new medications approved for use are drugs for chronic, highly specialized conditions. As such, GPOs have expanded their sourcing, analytics, and consulting services to address the growth in use and expense of these novel, highly preferred medications. Unlike small molecule medications used for inpatient care where the introduction of lower cost generics offers direct, well accepted competition, many of these specialized products, particularly biologics, have not previously been subject to competition. In addition, these drugs are used in the outpatient setting where medications can be separately payable, creating an entirely different methodology for value consideration. One example of GPOs' leadership in this area has been through the introduction and adoption of biosimilars.

Prior to 2010, no mechanism existed by which the FDA could approve competing versions of biologics, which are complex medications derived from living organisms.[20] As these products are not appropriate for generic development, pharmaceutical manufacturers were able to implement indefinite price increases for these sole-sourced medications. With the increasing availability of biosimilar competition, GPOs have worked to secure contract coverage for these products and promote the opportunity for savings to members and the patients they serve. Many of the contract structures described above, including the opportunity for increased discounts related to higher market share, have been utilized for biosimilars. While biosimilars uptake has been relatively strong, GPOs continue to work to promote greater use, especially as we approach the 2023 timeline for competition for adalimumab.[21]

Supply Chain and the Impact of Payers

Increasing drug costs are not only a concern of providers but they are also a critical concern for both public and private payers, and many payers have enacted strategies to limit their exposure to growing drug expenditures. One area where we have seen these issues is when payers select a biologic preferred agent, either an originator biologic or a single biosimilar, but not all biosimilars. Another area of influence has been the way in which high cost, provider-administered drugs are acquired and billed.

In 2021, Vizient conducted a survey regarding the impact of "white bagging," the process by which a payer requires a provider to administer an infused medication dispensed by a third-party specialty pharmacy rather than acquiring the medication directly. This process, while intended to lower drug costs, actually creates patient care disruptions, additional expense, and can potentially introduce medication safety issues. Based on the survey responses, it is estimated that white bagging requirements cost the U.S. health system providers an additional $310 million annually in terms of workload to locate white bagged drugs, coordinate patient care, manage changes in therapy, and deal with delays in the delivery of medications.[22] This information has been used to support several state legislative acts to limit this practice along with information from other professional practice organizations like the American Society of Health-System Pharmacists. In addition, Vizient, Premier and HealthTrust have been working together with ASHP to address the "white-bagging" issue with our member health systems and collectively have developed strategies which are now being deployed nationally and at the state level.

We anticipate that such challenges will continue as different stakeholders continue to limit their exposure to higher drug costs. Therefore, members should work with their GPOs to partner on new solutions and strategies.

GETTING THE MOST FROM YOUR GPO RELATIONSHIP

Pharmacy distributors work closely with GPOs to provide purchase data and to stock appropriate quantities of product under GPO contracts. GPOs also contract separately with pharmacy distributors to offer price matrices that allow members competitive pricing on contract and noncontracted purchases. Pharmacy distributors expect the GPO to assist them in inventory management at the distribution center level by assisting with member communications on estimated supply and demand reports. Pharmacy distributors also work with GPOs to provide repackaged products, in which the manufacturer only supplies the product in bulk quantities. Hospitals need unit dose and barcoded products, and GPOs contract with subsidiaries of the pharmacy distributors to provide these products. Additionally, GPOs contract with pharmacy distributors to provide technology such as robotics, medication administration cabinets, and so forth, so the relationship between GPOs and pharmacy distributors crosses many product lines and services.

Chief pharmacy officers, pharmacy directors, and managers must maximize the value of their GPO relationship, and pharmacy management should consider the following areas of focus regarding contract pricing:

- Develop communications with the pharmacy staff at GPO corporate offices. A pharmacy manager can do this by meeting with GPO pharmacy staff at national meetings or by participating on pharmacy advisory committees. Consider scheduling time to visit the corporate or regional office.

- Volunteer to serve on pharmacy advisory committees. Committees devoted to pharmaceutical contracting, pharmacy distributor relationships, or overall GPO/hospital strategy are the most appropriate committees on which directors of pharmacy and management should serve so that they understand the contracts and meet the GPO team and leadership.

- Volunteer to be involved in the committee that oversees the portfolio bid process and is involved in product selection. This allows the member to have input into the product criteria (both financial and nonfinancial) as well as input into final product selection.

- Designate an individual in the organization to be responsible for GPO contracts, pharmacy procurement, and supply chain operations. Many large health systems have developed a corporate pharmacy position to oversee supply chain responsibilities for the entire system and to work with each local pharmacy director to develop supply chain efficiency, standardization, and resiliency strategies. This individual should also be involved as a member of a GPO committee focused on contracting and should have an excellent understanding of the GPO contracts—both pharmaceutical and pharmacy distributor agreements. The individual should also be proficient in running a variety of reports that depict departmental or health system pharmaceutical spend by therapeutic and generic class, by on- and off-contract purchases, and in comparing GPO to pharmacy distributor pricing to ensure the correct payments and identify savings opportunities across the organization. If the organization is a disproportionate share hospital, this individual should also understand the regulations affecting 340B pricing and product procurement and inventory control.

- Many manufacturers require GPO declaration forms to be signed before they recognize an organization has joined a specific GPO and allow that organization access to the contract price. Ask the GPO if they have posted manufacturer declaration forms online and if they assist the member in signing these forms. This requirement would also hold true for the letters of commitment that some manufacturers require to participate in specific performance-based contracts. Sign these documents and send copies to both the manufacturer and the GPO, but also keep a copy. If the pricing is incorrect, this copy will serve as documentation to ask for credit/rebills from the pharmacy distributor and the affected manufacturer.

- Understand all performance contracts available through the GPO. If rebate agreements are included, some GPOs can have 70 or more performance-based agreements. Analyze each one within specific therapeutic classes to determine which contract offers the best pricing based on usage of competing products within that therapeutic class. Many organizations do not monitor which tier they qualify for within a specific performance agreement or how close they are to the next tier, which offers better pricing. Understanding the LOC and how the performance agreement tiers are measured will allow the pharmacy director to engage their physicians and clinical staff in discussions regarding appropriate usage, which affects the overall cost.

- Monitor pricing through the pharmacy distributor to ensure that GPO-contracted products are not being substituted but also that the correct price is being invoiced. If a GPO-contracted item cannot be obtained through the distributor, contact the GPO to allow the GPO staff to determine why the product is not available and to seek a remedy.

- Communicate with the GPO if a supplier offers a price below the GPO-contracted price. Suppliers who are not awarded the GPO contract may try to work around the contract award by offering select hospitals a lower price for a generic or branded product, which may not be sustainable or in adequate supply to meet market demand.

- Recognize specialty programs or services the GPO offers and assess their applicability to their respective health system. For example, private label programs or auto substitution programs offer additional savings beyond the contracted acute care price. GPO technology can assist in product selection, product standardization, and education and are valuable to pharmacy staff in gaining efficiencies and controlling overall costs through appropriate usage. Consulting services may be offered to GPO members on a limited basis in-kind versus fee-for-service, and the hospital pharmacy director should consider when to take advantage of the expertise the GPO can offer. Benchmarking tools are also a valuable product many GPOs offer to understand where opportunities to improve may exist.

- Take advantage of GPO educational programs to assist members in keeping up-to-date on regulatory, clinical, operational, and other issues affecting pharmacy practice. Some may be local, web-based, or held in conjunction with national meetings.

- Be aware of communication tools the GPO offers to provide timely information, education, and best practices. Assign staff in the department the responsibility of monitoring the information disseminated by the GPO, which includes communications on contract updates via email newsletters, clinical abstracts and reviews, patent expiration information, Joint Commission information, product safety information, reimbursement and revenue cycle management information, GPO declaration forms and LOCs, performance-agreement contract abstracts, and electronic toolkits that assist in improving medication use across related products. All are examples of information provided by GPOs.

When organizations are considering changing from one GPO to another, questions frequently arise in the discussion and analysis. Listed below are examples of questions to consider if this situation occurs:

- Will the GPO assist the organization in portfolio conversion?

- Does the GPO offer web-based diagnostic tools for the organization to employ in identification of cost strategies?

- Does the GPO have field-based staff to assist the organization in contract usage and optimization opportunities, and are these staff pharmacists?

- Does the GPO offer consultative services?

- Does the GPO offer local and national networking opportunities?

- How does the GPO manage contracted product pricing and how is this information communicated to the membership?

- Does the GPO offer budget forecast analyses to assist with pharmaceutical cost projections that affect the hospital pharmacy budget?

- What programs are in place to assist the member with procurement of products in short supply?

- What technologies and data capabilities does the GPO offer for supply chain resiliency, value analysis, performance improvement, and cost reduction strategies?

The supply chain environment continues to be very dynamic with the development of large integrated delivery networks (IDNs), or large heath systems, that wish to independently contract selected products, the continuing discussion about legislative changes to address the high cost of pharmaceuticals, and the increasing impact of the payer community on providers. It is not within the scope of this chapter to go into detail on all of the above issues; however, several should be discussed.

Many hospitals have integrated into large IDNs, usually anchored by one or two large hospitals (many times a teaching hospital) and several smaller community or rural hospitals, clinics, and other alternate sites of care. Some of these organizations have created positions such as a corporate director of pharmacy or a supply chain executive, whose focus is to drive costs out of the system. One of the methods employed to do so is to develop individual contracts specific only to that organization. This activity does not benefit the entire GPO membership unless the pricing terms offered to the IDN are offered to others within the GPO who meet the same qualifications. Some GPOs now assist their large IDNs in developing contracts that allow other GPO members to qualify if contract criteria (market share requirements, purchase volume requirements, etc.) can be met. In other words, a new pricing tier is created for these large organizations. This activity also benefits manufacturers by demonstrating contract compliance and enhanced volume in return for a contractual relationship with the GPO. Manufacturers typically do not want hundreds of individual contracts with separate organizations; in fact, many manufacturers have very small contracts departments because through GPOs a single contract can be in effect for hundreds of hospitals. The contracting functionality of the GPO has brought efficiency to the supply chain by reducing the administrative burden on both the manufacturer and the individual hospital.

As a result of the Medicare Modernization Act of 2003, hospitals and physician office practices/clinics have been affected by the implementation of the Average Sales Price (ASP) reimbursement formula for Medicare Part B drugs (since 2005 in the Physician setting and 2006 in the Hospital Outpatient setting). The movement away from a percentage of AWP (Average Wholesale Price) model to the ASP+% model has decreased Medicare payments for drugs, but placed an increasing financial strain on healthcare organizations. This change has also affected the extent to which some suppliers are willing to offer discounts to healthcare organizations given the negative impact on lowering the ASP (ie, reimbursement).

GPOs must now consider reimbursement status of separately payable drugs in addition to cost and quality elements. GPOs need to continue to work with CMS, private payers, and other organizations to understand the impact of governmental pricing and reimbursement for drugs, develop new and innovative ways to contract for these drugs, and to assist their membership with reimbursement and revenue cycle management.

Pharmacy distributors have their own generic products under contract that in the past have been sold primarily in the retail markets. Recently pharmacy distributors have attempted to expand their generic presence into the hospital markets, where GPO contracts have traditionally provided this support. This increase in competition in the generic marketplace has created an awareness of the various options hospital members have for contracting certain segments of their pharmaceutical portfolio. However, hospital pharmacy directors should ensure that they thoroughly understand the costs associated with this activity and should analyze the financial impact to their budget, including loss of patronage fees, if they use non-GPO contracts. Monitoring product pricing over time is strongly encouraged because in the generic marketplace the pricing of products and selection of products on-contract can be volatile.

CONCLUSION

GPOs have been in existence for decades, with publications on GPOs first appearing in the mid-1970s in the *American Journal of Health-System Pharmacy*. The concept of aggregated purchasing volume to obtain lower pricing has existed in many manufacturing markets outside of pharmaceuticals. Yet pharmaceuticals are somewhat unique in that they are affected by sole-source manufacturers who may lack competition in the marketplace within a therapeutic class, generic manufacturers who exist in a highly competitive market, and the impact of governmental pricing on overall manufacturer pricing and contracting strategies. GPOs continue to innovate and provide exponentially more services outside of contracting in today's healthcare environment. Consulting, technology and data, resiliency strategies, advocacy, and educational activities are just a few services GPOs are expected to provide to their membership today as demands on health systems and hospitals continue to increase.

REFERENCES

1. Mirchandani P. Healthcare supply chains: COVID-19 challenges and pressing actions. *Ann Intern Med*. 2020;173(4):300–301. PubMed

2. Heathcare Supply Chain Association. About HSCA: What is a GPO? **https://www. supplychainassociation.org/about-us/what-is-gpo/**. Accessed January 25, 2022.

3. Healthcare Supply Chain Association. HSCA member organizations. **https://www. supplychainassociation.org/about-us/member-organizations/**. Accessed January 25, 2022.

4. Opoku-Agyeman W, Weech-Maldonado R, Upadhyay S, et al. Environmental and organizational factors associated with hospital use of GPO services. *Hosp Top*. 2020;98(3): 89–102. 10.1080/00185868.2020.1787804. PubMed

5. 42 CFR § 952.1001(j).

6. Dobson A, Heath S, Reuter K, et al. A 2014 update of cost savings and marketplace analysis of the healthcare group purchasing industry. *Dobson DaVanzo & Associates*. **https://www. supplychainassociation.org/wp-content/uploads/2018/05/hsca_cost_savings_group_ purchase.pdf**. Accessed February 15, 2022.

7. O'Brien D, Leibowitz J, Anello R. Group purchasing organizations: How GPOs reduce healthcare costs and why changing their funding mechanism would raise costs. A legal and economic analysis. **https://www.supplychainassociation.org/wp-content/ uploads/2018/05/Leibowitz_GPO_Report.pdf**. Accessed February 15, 2022.

8. Medicare Prescription Drug, Improvement, and Modernization Act of 2003, Public Law 108–173, Section 1002. **http://www.cms.hhs.gov/MMAUpdate/downloads/PL108– 173summary.pdf**. Accessed June 5, 2018.

9. CuraScript SD. Understanding class of trade. **https://www.curascriptsd.com/Newsroom/ understanding-class-of-trade#:~:text=A%20customer's%20class%20of%20 trade,that%20product%20without%20certain%20authorization**. Accessed February 15, 2022.

10. U.S Food & Drug Administration. FDA Drug Shortages. **https://www.accessdata.fda.gov/scripts/drugshortages/**. Accessed February 15, 2022.

11. American Society of Health-System Pharmacists. Drug shortages statistics. **https://www.ashp.org/drug-shortages/shortage-resources/drug-shortages-statistics**. Accessed February 15, 2022.

12. Vizient. Drug shortages and labor costs: Measuring the hidden costs of drug shortages on U.S. hospitals. June 2019. **https://newsroom.vizientinc.com/doc_library/file/Drug_Shortages_Labor_Cost_Report_Vizient.pdf**. Accessed February 15, 2022.

13. U.S. Food & Drug Administration. List of off-patent, off-exclusivity drugs without an approved generic. **https://www.fda.gov/drugs/abbreviated-new-drug-application-anda/list-patent-exclusivity-drugs-without-approved-generic**. Accessed February 15, 2022.

14. U.S. Food & Drug Administration. Competitive generic therapies. **https://www.fda.gov/regulatory-information/search-fda-guidance-documents/competitive-generic-therapies**. Accessed February 15, 2022.

15. U.S. Food & Drug Administration. Coronavirus Aid, Relief, and Economic Security Act (CARES Act) drug shortage mitigation efforts. **https://www.fda.gov/drugs/drug-shortages/coronavirus-aid-relief-and-economic-security-act-cares-act-drug-shortage-mitigation-efforts**. Accessed February 15, 2022.

16. U.S. Food & Drug Administration. Executive Order 13944 list of essential medicines, medical countermeasures, and critical inputs. **https://www.fda.gov/about-fda/reports/executive-order-13944-list-essential-medicines-medical-countermeasures-and-critical-inputs**. Accessed February 15, 2022.

17. Vizient. Essential medications for high-quality patient care. 2022. **https://www.vizientinc.com/-/media/documents/sitecorepublishingdocuments/public/essential_meds.pdf**. Accessed February 15, 2022.

18. INSCRIPT. Drug shortages: pervasive challenges, proven solutions. Premier, Inc. February 2022. **https://offers.premierinc.com/rs/381-NBB-525/images/PremierRx_INSCRIPTDrugShortages.pdf**. Accessed February 22, 2022.

19. Vizient. Supply chain programs: novaplus enhanced supply program. **https://www.vizientinc.com/our-solutions/supply-chain-solutions/supply-chain-programs/novaplus-enhanced-supply-program**. Accessed February 15, 2022.

20. U.S. Food & Drug Administration. Biosimilars. **https://www.fda.gov/drugs/therapeutic-biologics-applications-bla/biosimilars**. Accessed February 15, 2022.

21. Hagen T. FDA approves Yusimry, the seventh adalimumab biosimilar. December 20, 2021. **https://www.centerforbiosimilars.com/view/fda-approves-yusimry-the-seventh-adalimumab-biosimilar**. Accessed February 15, 2021.

22. Vizient. Resources for payer-initiated policies. **https://www.vizientinc.com/our-solutions/pharmacy-solutions/payer-policy**. Accessed February 15, 2022.

PHARMACY REVENUE CYCLE

Maxie Friemel and Agatha Nolen

Revenue cycle may be defined in many ways and exist in every form of business including healthcare, and more specifically pharmacy. The HFMA defines revenue cycle as all functions, clinical and administrative, that contribute to the capture, management, and collection of patient service revenue. Changes in payment models, government regulations, and increasing costs, among other factors, have highlighted the need to focus on the revenue cycle. Additionally, pharmacy leaders are being asked to oversee the pharmacy aspects of the revenue cycle or be responsible for the revenue in their budgets. This is a major shift in focus from pharmacy being viewed as a cost center to a revenue center.[1]

Disruption has occurred within both the pharmacy and existing revenue cycle teams. Clinical areas require knowledge of accurate billing and revenue capture while revenue cycle requires a deeper understanding of clinical and operational functions. Furthermore, patients as consumers are playing a more active role in their care and are at risk for managing their own health. Consumers seek convenient access, affordable care, and a good experience. Payment models have transformed to a more value based approach, and advanced telehealth and other technologies bring information to the consumer's fingertips. The cost of drugs has consistently outpaced inflation and healthcare, including pharmacy, has increased in complexity. What was once a silo environment has been transformed into a pharmacy revenue cycle service line that bridges the clinical, operational processes, technology, and financial functions with the patient in the center.

In this chapter we will define the pharmacy revenue cycle in four major phases pre-access, clinical care, midcycle, and post access. While these phases are not unique to pharmacy, specific elements within each division require a collaborative team in order to optimize the pharmacy revenue cycle. As show in **Figure 8-1**, these elements are part of a continuous cycle without defined starting or stopping points. In some cases, the cycle is bidirectional with some teams interacting multiple times to process one patient encounter. The teams must recognize that they are part of an interconnected process that requires a high level of communication, collaboration, and respect for the individual skill sets of each team.

DOI 10.37573/9781585287130.008

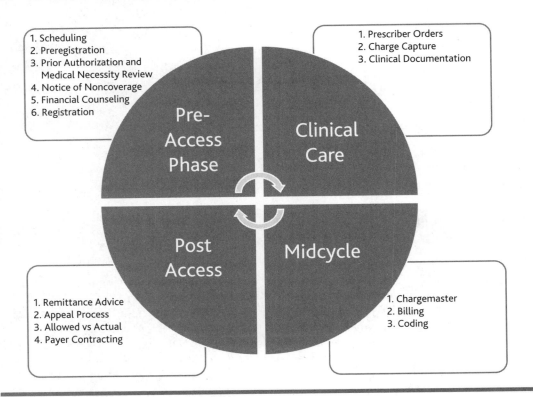

1. Scheduling
2. Preregistration
3. Prior Authorization and
   Medical Necessity Review
4. Notice of Noncoverage
5. Financial Counseling
6. Registration

1. Prescriber Orders
2. Charge Capture
3. Clinical Documentation

1. Remittance Advice
2. Appeal Process
3. Allowed vs Actual
4. Payer Contracting

1. Chargemaster
2. Billing
3. Coding

FIGURE 8-1. Pharmacy revenue cycle phases

PRE-ACCESS

Pre-access, or front-end operations, encompasses many high patient/consumer touches or interactions. The timing, clarity, and consistency of the information provided to patients during this phase can have major impacts on the success of timely and accurate payment. This phase also sets the stage for first impressions and patient experience for the remainder of their healthcare journey. The CMS Healthcare Consumer Assessment of Healthcare Providers and Systems (HCAHPS) is a standardized assessment that measures the patient's perception of their healthcare experience.[2] Questions such as "Would you recommend this hospital to your friends and family?" are geared toward the entire healthcare processes which include many of the interactions patients have within the pre-access phases.

Scheduling

Point of entry into the healthcare system and pre-access phase may occur at different stages, but we will begin with scheduling. A schedule is used for resource planning, optimizing patient throughput, ordering ancillary services such as supplies, devices, or drugs, and ensuring staff are available. Scheduling may be initiated by the patient (ie, unscheduled) or as a result of a physician order (ie, scheduled) for follow up or treatments. There are several methods in which a patient is scheduled and generally referred to as the patient type:

- Scheduled inpatient—as a part of CMS condition of payment, a physician must certify (generally by way of writing) an order that a patient meets the criterion of a hospital inpatient stay.[3;4] Healthcare plans may require a prior authorization or additional approval prior to an elective admission.

- Scheduled outpatients—services delivered as a scheduled outpatient do not meet the criteria for an inpatient stay such as diagnostic tests, physical therapy, and infusions. The majority of these services will require a prior authorization from health plans prior to performing.

- Scheduled recurring series—are services that are a part of an ongoing treatment plan with one order and the same diagnosis. A bill is generated only every 30 days rather than for each date of service and a service must be defined as a recurring service.

- Unscheduled inpatient—patient is admitted through the urgent care, emergency department, or a direct admit. While this still requires a physician to certify medical necessity requiring an inpatient admission, notification to the health plan occurs within 24 hours. Legislation implemented in 2022, "No Surprises Act," provides stipulations around billing when patients who are admitted under, or receive services from, an out of network provider.[5;6]

- Unscheduled emergency—all patients who arrive at the emergency department require an emergency type registration. The patient must be stabilized prior to any financial or coverage information being obtained.

- Unscheduled observation—is used for patient services for further evaluation of the need for inpatient admission, to resolve lower acuity medical problems, for treatments that last less than 24 hours, or other outpatient complications. It is important to note that observation may not be used for medically stable patients in need of further outpatient testing or procedures, patients waiting for nursing home placement, or any other convenience to the patient or family.

- Other patient schedule types include clinics, home health, durable medical equipment (DME), skilled nursing facility, or other ancillary services.

As shown in **Figure 8-2**, events conducted during the pre-access phase can be viewed as a series of gears turning one another and multiple teams simultaneously becoming involved in the patient's

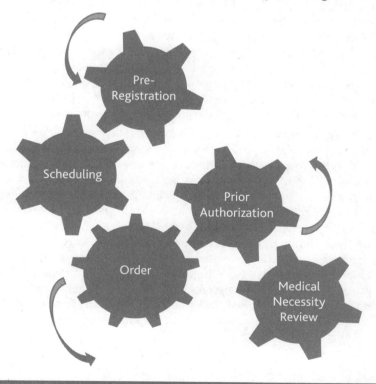

FIGURE 8-2. Pre-access simultaneous processes

care. Patients are identified utilizing demographic information and a medical record number (MRN) is generated to internally identify the patient. A Master Patient Index Number (MPI) is also created which is used throughout a health system for tracking episodes of care. The physician order requests services to be scheduled or the schedule becomes a requested service for a physician order. Then multiple healthcare team members become involved in the care of the patient.

Preregistration

Preregistrations enhance timely and accurate billing and minimizes patient flow interruptions upon arrival. Many revenue cycle teams may have targets to maintain a high rate of patients who are preregistered. Registrars collect thorough demographic information, including guarantor and insurance information. They evaluate the MPI to ensure there are no duplications of patient profiles and that the MRN is tied to the accurate patient. Inaccurate MPI or duplication may have downstream impacts such as wrong medical history, inaccurate billing, use of incorrect medical record, and breach of confidentiality. Early validation of insurance information is a key step during preregistration. Referrals to a financial counselor may occur for those individuals who are self-funded or may require additional financial assistance based on the identified out of pocket requirements. Verification of insurance information is also crucial to begin the prior authorization phase.

Prior Authorization and Medical Necessity Review

Prior authorization is an increasingly complex event especially in terms of the pharmacy revenue cycle. Each commercial payer has various requirements to complete a prior authorization. It is important that the preauthorization process be started as soon as the physician prescribes a medication so that care is not interrupted. The preauthorization process is similar for drug administration as for any outpatient services such as surgeries or radiologic procedures. Separate payer portals are used to conduct the prior authorization. The prior authorization number must be recorded and billed on the claim. Failure to do so, may result in denials. However, the completion of a prior authorization does not guarantee payment for the service. A review of medical necessity is prudent to conduct along with the prior authorization. Each payer publishes a set of clinical policies that explains the service or drug administration and approved diagnosis or treatment. These policies may also detail specific criteria the patients must meet when provided the drug; for example, specific lab values, failure of alternative therapies, etc. When clinical policies are not available from a payer, utilizing published guidelines such as the National Comprehensive Cancer Network (NCCN), other CMS-approved compendia, or other medical literature may help justify the service provided.[7]

In 2020, Medicare implemented preauthorization requirements for five distinct services, including drug product botulinum toxin injections for certain indications. Requirements should be followed exactly for qualifying the patient for coverage as well as billing requirements for claim coding to ensure payment. This is a new process for Medicare that is administered through the Medicare Administrative Contractors, or MACs. It is important to note that these preauthorizations for Medicare are limited and are published each year in the Federal Register with the Final Rule for the Outpatient Prospective Payment System. Starting February 1st, 2021, MACs began calculating the affirmation rate of initial prior authorizations requests submitted. Hospital outpatient providers who met the affirmation rate threshold of 90% or greater received a written Notice of Exemption by March 1st, 2021. Those hospital outpatient departments were exempt from submitting prior authorization requests for dates of service beginning May 1st, 2021. As new preauthorization requirements are added each year, a similar process occurs to determine if certain hospitals have an affirmation threshold of 90% or greater which will then exempt them from submitting prior authorization requests.[8;9]

If a drug is not specified in rulemaking for preauthorization, providers treating Medicare out-patients should review all applicable National Coverage Determinations (NCDs), Local Coverage Determinations (LCDs), and Local Coverage Articles (LCAs) to determine if the provider's MAC has specific instructions for coverage and billing. In some cases when a drug is used for an indication that is not covered either in the FDA-approved package labeling or in these publications, neither the drug, nor the administration of the drug, will be reimbursed. If an LCA outlines coverage for specific diagnosis codes, it is helpful to obtain the indication from the prescriber when the order is written.[10]

If there is a difference between the covered indications and the patient's condition, the physician can be queried prior to the start of therapy to determine if a more specific indication and corresponding diagnosis code is more applicable. If the patient's indication is considered off-label for cancer treatment, CMS-approved compendia should be consulted to determine if the off-label indication is listed in the compendia. As of 2021 the following compendia are recognized by CMS as authoritative sources for use in the determination of a "medically accepted indication" of drugs and biologicals used off-label in an anticancer chemotherapeutic regimen. The drug or biological must receive a favorable rating in one or more of the following compendia and not receive a designation that the drug or biological is not medically accepted (or words to that effect):

- American Hospital Formulary Service-Drug Information (AHFS-DI)

- NCCN Drugs and Biologics Compendium

- Thomson Micromedex DrugDex

- Clinical Pharmacology

- Lexi-Drugs

The MAC may also accept peer-reviewed literature to determine medical necessity if the treatment is included in a postpayment audit review. The following publications are identified in the Medicare Benefit Manual (100-02) and include regular editions of the publications but do not include supplement editions privately funded by parties with a vested interest in the recommendations of the authors:

- American Journal of Medicine

- Annals of Internal Medicine

- Annals of Oncology

- Annals of Surgical Oncology

- Biology of Blood and Marrow Transplantation

- Blood

- Bone Marrow Transplantation

- British Journal of Cancer

- British Journal of Hematology

- British Medical Journal

- Cancer

- Clinical Cancer Research

- Drugs

- European Journal of Cancer (formerly the European Journal of Cancer and Clinical Oncology)

- Gynecologic Oncology

- International Journal of Radiation, Oncology, Biology, and Physics

- The Journal of the American Medical Association

- Journal of Clinical Oncology; Journal of the National Cancer Institute

- Journal of the National Comprehensive Cancer Network (NCCN)

- Journal of Urology

- Lancet

- Lancet Oncology

- Leukemia

- The New England Journal of Medicine

- Radiation Oncology

While prior authorizations are intended to occur prior to the clinical care or treatment of the patient, fluid communication occurs throughout all revenue cycle phases (pre-access to clinical care to midcycle to post access). Many of the outpatient services are routine or continuously occurring on a monthly basis. A patient's insurance may change at any point or a physician may update the orders, which may require a new authorization. Frequent and timely communication to the front-end staff should occur to update prior authorizations, validate medical necessity, and update other information that is billed on the final claim. Insurance changes on January 1st are fairly common which requires all information to be updated. Additionally, prior authorization may only be valid for a select number of treatment cycles. Updating information and staying on top of any clinical changes for the patient is prudent to continue to have an active and valid prior authorization on file.

Notice of Noncoverage

It is an expectation by CMS that a provider or organization screen services in advance to ensure they are medically reasonable and necessary. When the provided service to a Medicare beneficiary does not meet medical necessity, the provider is required to issue a notice of noncoverage. Forms vary based on the patient status. The official title is An Advance Beneficiary Notice of Noncoverage. (ABN) is to be issued to Medicare outpatients.[11] An ABN should be issued when services are considered experimental or investigational, not indicated for the respective diagnosis or treatment, or service exceeds the allowed amount for corresponding diagnosis. Among other reasons, ABNs are also required for custodial care, prior to caring for patients who are considered terminally ill, or prior to providing preventative services that have exceeded the frequency limits. Providers are required to use the most recent CMS-R-131 form and must follow the specified requirements to ensure the patient is able to read and understand the notice. The ABN must be issued far enough in advance to allow time to consider alternative options, must be signed, and filed for a minimum of five years. ABNs are not to be used for service furnished under a Medicare Advantage (Part C) or the Medicare Prescription Drug Benefit (Part D) and are not required for self-administered drugs as this is a statutory exclusion and an ABN is not required.

A hospital provides a Hospital-Issued Notices of Noncoverage (HINN) to Medicare beneficiaries for inpatient admissions. This may occur prior to admission, at admission, or any time during admission if services provided are deemed not medically necessary, service is not provided in the most appropriate setting, or custodial service. Other beneficiary notices may be necessary based on services, patient status, and the setting in which the beneficiary receives the service.

Financial Counseling

Financial counseling or discussions with the patient regarding out of pocket obligations should be consistent, clear, and transparent. The discussion of financial obligations with patients is sensitive, complex, and should be approached with sincerity and compassion. Timing in which these discussions occur is also important to understand. When a patient is seen in an emergency room, a patient must be first screened and medically stable. Emergency Medical Treatment and Labor Act (EMTALA) was enacted in 1986 to ensure public access to emergency care regardless of the ability to pay.[12] Outside of the emergency department financial conversations should occur in a manner in which they do not interrupt the patient flow or impede clinical care. It is recommended that educational sessions and financial discussions be held early or during preregistration prior to any financial obligations occurring which include educating the patient on the varying costs that they may incur, and providing financial assistance, if appropriate. Patients identified as self-insured may require assistance to enroll in Medicaid or other charity plans. This also presents an opportune time to evaluate financial need in conjunction with the prior authorization and medical necessity review to determine if there is a drug manufacturer-sponsored program to help offset the cost of the drug therapy. Pharmacy can play a key role in helping to source, track, and manage a manufacturer-sponsored drug program. Manufacturer-supplied stock should be kept separate unless used as a replacement product, and validation should occur to ensure the sponsored drug is used on the patient that qualified for the product. Additionally, there are further implications downstream in billing properly for a sponsored drug. The patient and sponsored drug should be flagged in the medical record to notify the appropriate coders and billers which will be discussed later in the chapter.

Registration

Lastly, although it may not occur at the end, is the additional layer of registration. Emphasis is placed on thorough and accurate registrations as approximately 40% of the final claim is generated from information gained during registration. Inaccuracies lead to delayed billing, nonpayment, and a significant amount of rework involving multiple teams. Registrars comb through the information and reverify the accuracy of demographics, insurance information, and prior authorization or confirm that authorizations are in place. Registration also collects patient signatures on a variety of authorization forms. Consent to treat is signed prior to each treatment with the exception of emergency care. This form explains the planned treatment, the purpose, risk and benefits of the treatment, and must be voluntarily signed. Other forms may include a condition of admission for a hospital to provide care, release of information, financial agreement, assignment of benefits or the agreement to bill the insurance company, and privacy notices which informs how the provider will safeguard protected health information. An Important Message from Medicare (IM) may also be delivered to inform a Medicare or Medicare Advantage beneficiary of their rights to dispute a hospital's decisions and the appeal process. This form must be issued within two days after an admission, but no earlier than seven days prior to the admission. The Medicare Outpatient Observation Notice (MOON) notifies patients that they are an outpatient receiving observation services and will not be billed as an inpatient admission.[13]

While pharmacy may not be directly involved in all aspects of the pre-access phase of the revenue cycle, having a complete understanding of the roles is important. Pharmacy teams bring a unique skillset to the table and are able to insert themselves in pivotal roles. As previously mentioned, prior authorization and understanding a payer's medical policies as it relates to the drug therapy has increased in complexity and staff historically involved in managing these may not have the skillset required to interpret and verify medical necessity. Thus a pharmacy team member(s) embedded directly on these teams can improve the backend denials. Additionally, site of care restrictions have placed an additional layer of complexity which requires patients to receive care at a lower cost location such as a free standing infusion center, in the home, or other nonhospital based location. Navigating this landscape for a patient is confusing and difficult to explain. Pharmacy has alternative tools that leverage in-home specialty or retail pharmacies. Accessing the patient's pharmacy benefits can have the advantage of sourcing the drug from an alternative location while maintaining the consistency of care for the patient in their original location. This maneuver requires knowledge and understanding of the pharmacy benefits and may also require an additional prior authorization under different payer portals. Furthermore, sourcing manufacturer-sponsored programs may be expanded to pharmacy outpatient/retail co-pay cards in addition to the free or replacement drugs provided under medical services. A coordinated approach among prior authorization teams, financial counselors and pharmacy provides the needed foundation for the clinicians that ultimately provide care to the patient.

CLINICAL CARE

Once the preauthorization and/or coverage determination has been met, it is vital that the patient is correctly registered and that insurance verification is completed prior to the visit and clinical care begins. Standard templates/reminders can be embedded in Provider Order Entry systems to remind caregivers of the insurer's coverage criteria and specific documentation requirements. Clinical documentation requirements may also include process flow documentation such as a stop time on an intravenous infusion that translates into a different billing code on the claim. All documentation elements should be automated as much as possible to relieve the caregiver of paper documentation.

Prescriber Order

One often overlooked element in outpatient care is the determination of the length of time a physician order is valid when no definitive end date is specified. Often in maintenance or other long term treatments, such as with Crohn's disease, a patient may receive infusions every six weeks continuously. Most payers recognize state laws and rules governing "prescriptions" or "orders" with a continuous drug order as valid for a period of one year. However, this may vary from state to state and by controlled substance schedule. It is important that a valid prescriber order be available for each registration date so if medical records are requested the original order is included in the medical records transmitted to the payer when requested. For a request for payment to be valid, the following information should be included each time a patient is registered to receive drug therapy:

- Valid prescriber order with dating timeframes based upon state rules and regulations including signature of the prescriber.

- Prescriber order that contains the name of the drug, dose, route, and duration.

    o   If the dose is prescribed "per body weight" or "per body surface area," the appropriate clinical information used to determine the dose must be included, such as the weight in kilograms or pounds, or for body surface area the weight in kilograms and height in centimeters.

- Documentation that the ordered drug was administered to the patient with the date and time of administration and signature/initials of the person administering the drug. In the case of infusions, the start and stop time of the infusion should be clearly documented.

- Documentation if a portion of a dose must be wasted including the amount wasted.

Charge Capture

After a patient receives care and it has been documented, billing and coding on the claim should be a by-product of the clinical care and provide a 100% match of the clinical documentation. However, it is important that all caregivers are aware of which services (including drugs) have "automated charging" and which services require manual charging by the clinician caregiver. For example, most drugs are billed either when the product is dispensed (or removed from a unit-based cabinet) or when the drug is administered by the caregiver. Failure to set clinical systems appropriately from a charging perspective can result in omitted charges or duplicate charges. One example is when a unit-based cabinet is replaced with a newer model and the charging settings are changed to the hospital default (ie, charge on administration) rather than the unit-specific setting (ie, charge on dispense). Another example may be a unit where charges are not automatically captured and manual charges must be entered into the IT system. This often occurs with specialty units such as wound care clinics that may use specialized software to document clinical care that is not interfaced to provide automated charges.

Charges may also be generated but are unable to be processed through to the final claim. For example, it is not unusual that in emergencies, a "Jane Doe" account may be created in Admissions when a trauma case is coming into the Emergency Department. Although actual patient demographics and insurance information may be corrected on the account later during the admission, drug charges are often generated by a unit-based cabinet and are still listed under "Jane Doe's" account. Typically these charges require manual intervention to match the drugs with the correct patient account either through a "merge account" process or by manually replicating the charges on the new account.

The key to correct drug charging is selecting the correct patient account in the clinical system or unit-based cabinet. Often outpatients are registered with multiple accounts for multiple days within a timeframe such as for laboratory requests, radiologic tests, or may be "preregistered" for a visit. When medication orders are entered on "preregistration accounts" in advance, the caregivers may chart documentation on these preregistration accounts, unaware that the account will subsequently be cancelled and a new account created. Charges generated on the preregistration account may be assumed to be "charging errors" and written off when the account is cancelled resulting in no patient charges.

Pharmacy leaders should thoroughly understand registration processes, clinician patient selection in IT systems, and identify gaps where charges may be lost or inadvertently written off as errors. A quality assurance process to match drug purchases versus drug charges should periodically examine the end-to-end process to ensure that all drugs administered to a patient are correctly billed.

Clinical Documentation and Coding

In addition to selecting the correct patient for order input, pharmacy employees are key to good drug billing practices. Care should be taken to select drug profiles that match exactly what is dispensed to ensure accurate charging. For example, if a drug is available in a 100 mg and 500 mg vial and a patient order is received for 700 mg, the pharmacy employee should select 1×500 mg and 2×100 mg to match what is being dispensed. It would not be appropriate to enter 2×500 mg vials and bill for 300 mg of waste, when there was not waste. When waste does occur, caregivers should be instructed to document the amount of waste and time in the patient's medical record. Some payers may instruct that an automated calculation is acceptable if hospital policies describe the process and it is uniformly followed by the caregivers. Hospital IT systems should be set up to recognize this "wasted" portion and ensure that appropriate modifiers are attached to the HCPCS code on the bill as per payer instructions.

Another important discipline in the charging process is the group of HIM coders. Although most drug charging can be automated through the Chargemaster, some services require specialized coders to review the medical record and place appropriate codes on the claim to represent the services provided. This may include the drug administration services on outpatients, procedure codes, and diagnosis codes. The final coding is critical to payment on the claim as the MS-DRG is determined by the combination of codes on the claim for inpatients, and the revenue codes and HCPCS codes for outpatients. For example, Medicare provides additional "new technology add-on payments (NTAP)" for new services including drugs for a two to three year period. However, since HCPCS codes are not typically detailed on an inpatient claim, Medicare relies on a ICD-10-PCS code to communicate that the drug was administered. Therefore, the coders must be notified when an NTAP drug is used on inpatients so that they can verify the administration and add the appropriate code. Failure to do so results in no additional NTAP payment. The "notification" process can be automated in most IT systems so that a specific drug profile or HCPCS code generates a message in the coders' queue to review the record. Since NTAP payments change each year, a review should be done annually to ensure that all edits are updated appropriately.

Coders also add diagnosis codes to the claim codes which may be considered for payment or may prevent services from being reimbursed. One common example is when a patient is seen in the Emergency Department for an injury and administered a Tdap vaccine or Rabies IG and Rabies vaccine. Based upon brief documentation in the record for return visits for the rabies vaccine series, a coder may code the claim as a "prophylactic vaccination," instead of a therapeutic encounter. In this case, payer software may read the diagnosis code of "prophylactic vaccination" and deny payment if they only pay for therapeutic services. At this point, there is typically a third-party claims processor that manages the step of claims review and preparation. The third-party processor compiles all information and provides a "flat file" in a standard format that is required for all healthcare claims.

MIDCYCLE

Chargemaster (CDM)

The Chargemaster, or CDM, is a critical element to ensure that all HCPCS/CPT codes are correctly attached to the drug products in the clinical system and that a conversion to the appropriate number of billed units is automated. Clinical systems differ in the amount of billing information that is stored, but it is imperative that the linkage between the clinical and billing system is well understood and correctly maintained. For example, temporary HCPCS codes for drugs may be replaced by a more permanent HCPCS code. Billing a deleted HCPCS code will result in no payment or a rejected claim which requires manual correction and decreases cash flow.

Another element of the CDM maintenance includes the use of modifiers that may be hardcoded in the CDM system. In particular, providers who have purchased drugs under 340B pricing will want to ensure that modifiers indicating 340B purchases have been appropriately applied and appear on the submitted claim. Based upon where the "conversion factor/multiplier" is stored (eg, clinical pharmacy IT system, billing IT system, claims production system), the team responsible for maintenance needs to have a thorough understanding of both how drugs are dispensed and administered as well as the structure of the HCPCS coding system. Data integrity in billing systems is critical to appropriate reimbursement.

The most common error occurs when the "conversion factor" or "multiplier" is set incorrectly. For example, a drug may be dispensed in a 100 mg vial, but the HCPCS codes units are "per 1 mg." In this case, the "conversion factor" or "multiplier" must be set to "100." Billing "1 vial" will result in a significant underpayment.

Billing

There are two different claim types submitted to insurers: an 837I, UB-04, or CMS-1450 is a hospital claim format, whereas an 837P or CMS-1500 claim is submitted by physician offices. Different billing and payment rules apply to the two claim types, and it is important to know whether an area is registered with CMS as a hospital outpatient department or a physician office as the same service may be reimbursed differently depending upon the registration. Ambulatory Surgery Centers also have different payment rules but are included in the Outpatient Prospective Payment System (OPPS) Final Rule each year. The claim is then submitted electronically to the payer for review and payment. While that may sound straightforward, in reality, this portion is complex.

Health systems will employ large teams or outsource the billing functions. EMRs or 3rd party software systems contain billing edits that scrub the claim for accuracy. Billing teams are responsible for reviewing each edit and correcting the claim. Generally, the claim is scrubbed in accordance with the National Correct Coding Initiative (NCCI) Edits or customizes edits. Once the team has made the necessary corrections, the claim is generated and passed through to a 3rd party switch that evaluates the alignment of the claim specifications to the payer requirements. For example, insurance A requires an NDC for revenue code 0636. If the claim is populated without the appropriate NDC in the respective field, the claim will be rejected and the billing team will have the opportunity to correct the claims and resubmit to the payer.

Another activity that may not be obvious is that of the relationship between the primary and the secondary payer. By this, we mean that a patient has coverage from two different insurers. This may be a Medicare Fee-for-service patient who also has a "medigap" policy or a Medicare patient who has Medicaid as their secondary insurance. Patients also may have commercial payer coverage through an employer but then have an additional policy for services that are not covered under their employer-based healthcare coverage. Sometimes, a primary payer and a secondary payer may have different requirements that may cause a claim to be prepared "twice." For example, a Medicare Advantage plan may provide coverage for patients who have Medicare primary and Medicaid secondary. These are referred to as "dual eligible" patients. In this case, the State Medicaid plan requires National Drug Code (NDC) numbers on outpatient claims, even though they are not required by Medicare. The process is complex as once Medicare has paid their portion of the claim, the claim is then electronically forwarded to the appropriate State Medicaid plan to determine if the patient has coverage for remaining charges, including copays and deductibles. Since this information is transferred between payers electronically, it is important to meet the secondary payer's requirements when submitting the claim to the primary payer. In this example, NDC numbers will need to be submitted to the primary payer, Medicare, even though it is not their requirement.

It is prudent for billing teams to optimize edits to improve the clean claim rate or the generation of a claim that does not require the payer to investigate (ie, rejection or denial) prior to payment. However, continually evaluating edits for relevance is just as important. Too many edits or edits that are no longer relevant may lead to delays in billing and impair cash flow. Maintaining bidirectional communication between billing teams, other mid-cycle teams, and front end operations will improve the clean claim submissions and reduce the manual interventions made by the billing teams.

POST ACCESS

Remittance Advice

Billing a claim is a continuous process, and many times has a bidirectional flow throughout the phases of the pharmacy revenue cycle. After a claim has been received by the payer, the payer will utilize an EDI 835 transaction set called an electronic remittance advice (ERA) to return the payment or nonpayment information to the provider. There are three types of codes that are used to return information back to the providers, including group codes, claim adjustment reason codes (CARC), and remittance advice remark code (RARC).

The highest level of codes are called group codes which assign financial responsibility to the unpaid portion of the claim. Among these codes include a contractual obligation, or CO, which assigns responsibility back to the provider; patient responsibility, or PR, which assigns the financial obligation to the patient; and other adjustments, or OR, used when no other group code applies. A group code must always be used in conjunction with a CARC. The CARC describes why a claim or service line was paid differently than it was billed. The RARC provides an additional level of explanation already conveyed in the CARC. The RARC are the only codes that may not have an associated group or claim adjustment code associated to them, and in which case they will be reported with an "alert" that provides additional information.[14]

The transfer of electronic files to display the payment information has increased the efficiency and manual process of the standard paper remit. Many electronic health records, or CMS, provides software that allows providers to easily read the 835. A good first step in pharmacy revenue cycle monitoring is to assign a team or program technology to monitor timeliness of payments made by plans and posted to the correct account. Accounts must be reconciled when payment is more or less than expected. As we mentioned previously, there may be situations where no payment has been received because the wrong insurer has been billed. These scenarios require close collaboration among teams that are responsible for different portions of the revenue cycle process. Additionally, it is important to follow the payment through to the secondary payer to ensure actual payment is in line with the expected reimbursement.

Denial Management

When there is a misalignment in the actual versus expected, digging down into the 835 reason codes may help with the denial management. Processing and accurately interpreting the data are not as straightforward as it may seem based on the assigned RARC and CARC codes. Some payers may not report the RARC or CARC code at the line level, but rather at the claim level, making denial information very difficult to decipher which services are causing the denial. Conversely, an error in a billed drug may lead to a claim denial making it difficult for teams unfamiliar with drug billing to determine how to resolve the denial or assign to the right team for follow up. Technical denials may need to be routed to Registration for incomplete insurance information or demographic errors. A pharmacy billing specialist may need to review the billed drug lines to determine if HCPCS, NDC, modifiers, etc. are accurate and reflect the payer specifications.

Another possibility is that the charge was correct, but the coding team had omitted a diagnosis code that indicated why the patient received the drug. In this case, the claim can be corrected and resubmitted under "timely filing." For Medicare, timely filing is one year from the date the service was received by the beneficiary. Other payers may have shorter timeframes; some Medicaid programs require rebilling to be within 90 days so it is important that rejections be worked as soon as they are received. In some cases, the provider determines that the charge was a legitimate charge and feels that the charge should be paid based upon the information that was originally submitted. In this case, the provider can file an "appeal" and provide additional documentation to support the charge. Often this requires submitting the entire medical record electronically for review by the payer. Health systems often have entire departments that work "denials and appeals" to ensure that they are receiving the reimbursement that they are due based upon contracted terms.

Medical necessity denials are among the most frequent denial types for all denials as well as drug related denials. Prior authorization denials are also a common denial when high cost drugs are involved. Involving pre-access teams and reviewing root cause of both denials types can lead to a significant reduction in denials. Frequency limit denials are another frequent denial type that may involve drugs; however, follow up and denial teams may overlook the importance of involving pharmacy in overturning and preventing these denials types. When drugs are involved, frequency limits (generally this is referring to a medically unlikely edit (MUE)) have been exceeded. MUEs are used by CMS as well as Medicaid and commercial payers to reduce the improper payment rate of claims. MUEs are a quantity limit assigned to a HCPCS in which under most circumstances would be the maximum number of billed units on a given date of service. Specifically for drugs, an MUE is assigned an MUE adjudication indicator of three, representing the MUE limit is based upon clinical benchmarks. Many patients, due to weight, failure of alternative therapies, drug tolerance, or other reasons, may require a dose of a medication that is above the average benchmark. Thus, for a drug frequency limit, denial may appear to be a technical denial to a follow-up and in turn a team may need clinical justification to overturn. In some cases, drugs receive FDA-approval for a change in dose frequency (eg, twice the dose every six weeks instead of a single dose every three weeks) which then always exceeds the MUE. Providers can request a reconsideration to have the MUE quantity increased to reflect the new dosage regimen.

Appeal Process

After the internal review of the denial, there are several steps that are taken. First, a review is conducted to determine if there is a technical issue with the claim. The claim should be corrected and resubmitted for reprocessing. This may include missing authorization numbers, drug billing errors, incorrect demographic information, or many others. After the claim has been reviewed for accuracy and it is determined that an appeal will be necessary, an organization may begin the appeal process. Medicare has 5 levels to appeal a claim. The first process is a request for reconsideration or a redetermination request. A request for reconsideration must be submitted within 120 days from the date of the remittance advice. The receipt date is presumed to be five days after the notice date unless there is significant evidence the notice was not received. A redetermination request must be submitted in writing along with the CMS-20027 form. The request must also contain the beneficiary name, Medicare number, specific services, dates of services in which the redetermination is being requested, name of the party or representative party, and an explanation of why the appellant disagrees with the determination. It is also important to include any supporting documentation such as the medical records, supporting literature, or other information that supports the argument.

MAC generally issues a decision within 60 days from the date of the receipt of the redetermination request. The second level of appeal is a reconsideration by a Qualified Independent Contractor (QIC). A provider has 180 days from the receipt of the redetermination to submit a reconsideration to the QIC. The QIC generally issues a response within 60 days of receipt of redetermination. Similar to the first level of an appeal, a provider should fill out the form CMS-20033 and include the beneficiary's name, Medicare number, specific services, dates of service, and name of the party or representative party. Also, to be included in the request is the MAC who made the redetermination, any missing information based on the redetermination, and all supporting documentation including the medical record and supporting literature to support the argument.

The third level of the appeal process for Medicare is to request a hearing before the Administrative Law Judge (ALJ) or an attorney adjudicator within the Office of Medicare Hearings and Appeals (OMHA). The request for a hearing must be filed with the OMHA within 60 days of the reconsideration decision. All supporting documentation must be provided with the appeal along with the form OMHA-100. Unlike level 1 or 2, the request for the ALJ requires a minimum dollar threshold in controversy. This amount includes the amount charges for the service less any payment already made by Medicare and any deductible or coinsurance. Note the threshold controversy amount changes from year to year.

A provider may request a review by the Medicare Appeals Council if dissatisfied with the decision of the ALJ. A request must be submitted to the Council which is a component of the Health and Human Services, Department of Appeals Board within 60 days of the OMHA's decision. A similar process to the first level of appeals should be followed with the exception of no controversy fee at this level. The last level or fifth level of appeal is to request a judicial review in Federal District Court. The request to the federal court must be received within 60 days of the Council's decision. A minimum threshold of amount in controversy must be met prior to engaging the federal court.

Allowed vs. Actual

While a denial may be one reason for nonpayment, it is important to validate full and accurate payment. Many of the electronic health systems have the ability to load contracted rates to determine the allowed amount from the payer. This information may be known prior to billing, but an important step is to ensure that it is compared with the actual amount received. To start, errors may occur when payer contracts are loaded into the health record. Drugs add a layer of complexity as they may have contracts that are percent of charge based on revenue codes, fee schedule based, or adjusted payment rates based on if the drug was purchased under the 340B pricing program. Therefore, a health system with multiple locations may have different formulas to accurately calculate the expected or allowed drug revenue. Secondly, a payer may not process the claims accurately for full payment according to the contract. Payers have the same challenge to upload the drug payment into their systems which present similar challenges. Furthermore, when net revenue is received, health systems may not be able to allocate it based on the line level of service. Thus, it is prudent to collaborate with pharmacy and payer contracting teams to ensure the entire claims are paid accurately, including the drugs. A periodic review is recommended to ensure that payment at least covers the cost of expensive drugs or that reimbursement for certain drugs is flagged for potential renegotiation.

Payer Contracting

Payer contract negotiation activity can be considered the start of the process as most patients prefer to receive care at "in-network" providers. After care has been provided and payment received, the contract must be evaluated to ensure that the payment continues to be reasonable compared with the costs that have been incurred by the provider to perform the services. When payment and costs get out of alignment, an adjustment is requested at the next contract renewal date. Pharmacy can play a vital role in these negotiations by providing the contract negotiation group with updated drug cost information, particularly when any high volume drugs quickly escalate in costs due to manufacturer increases, drug contract expirations, or new drugs are introduced into the marketplace. For example, some payers have negotiated a flat rate for Emergency Department visits regardless of the drugs administered. This may historically be appropriate for the vast majority of patients, but the cost of certain drugs may significantly exceed the average payment. One common example is rabies immune globulin and rabies vaccine where the cost of the drug often exceeds the average emergency department visit payment. In these cases, the pharmacy plays a vital role in communicating with the managed care contract negotiating group that a "carve-out" or other mechanism for separate reimbursement should be considered when the contract is ready for renewal.

ROLE OF AUTOMATION

Automation has played a critical role in advancing health systems. Pharmacy automation has typically been geared toward enhancing safety and efficiency of operations. This has included electronic medical records (EMR) that allow for remote, electronic entry of medication orders and barcode scanning during preparation of medications which allows for the capture of the actual product and amount used in the preparation of a medication. Additionally, barcode administration scanning improved the safety and accuracy of the medications being administered to the patient when combined with electronic patient verification. While these advances may have been geared toward improved patient safety and operational efficiency, they have played a critical role in automating the pharmacy revenue cycle aspects as well. EMRs have the capability to automate actual NDC capture and documentation, convert the amount administered into billing information, and attach other regulatory modifiers prior to billing the claim. Previously this would have been information that was manually inputted onto claims by billers or coders. In addition, billing systems can be customized per payer requirements so that cash flow is not disrupted when incorrect claims are rejected by a payer. Integrated systems may trigger alerts at the time of scheduling. For example, when preauthorization requirements for drug infusions have not been met at the time of registration, providers may be alerted so that the requirements can be met prior to administration, or alternative therapy considered that may be covered by the payer without preauthorization. Integrated IT systems with clinical pharmacy and billing components require specialized teams with both pharmacy and billing knowledge in order for the utility of these IT systems to be maximized.

Technology advancement continues to grow with health systems and most functions of the revenue cycle can be automated as well. A 2021 survey by AKASA revealed a 12% increase from the previous year in health systems implementing automated revenue cycle solutions.[15] Couple the urgency to streamline revenue cycle operations with increased artificial intelligence (AI), machine learning (ML), and natural language processing and understanding (NLP and NLU) enables further aspects of the revenue cycle to become automated. Real time eligibility checks and prior authorizations have benefited from this technology, reducing the turnaround time and denials. Furthermore, access to reliable data are a priority for many leaders. The ability to process data from multiple vendors in a standard format can create the ability to make more informed decisions.[16]

As automation continues to advance the power of NLP and NLU may have substantial impact on the pharmacy revenue cycle functions. Pharmacy leaders should monitor upcoming trends and provide input into the implementation and management automation of the entire revenue cycle that pertains to drug ordering, dispensing, administration, monitoring, and billing. Data combining purchasing, revenue, denials of medication billing, and diagnoses may become a critical element for pharmacy leaders to have a comprehensive view of their operations and budgets and help guide decisions alongside other financial decisions within the organization.

INTEGRATING TEAMS

We've stepped through the activities involved in the revenue cycle, now let's discuss the people involved with these processes. Having full integration and collaborative culture between pharmacy, revenue cycle, and finance teams is the key to success (see **Figure 8-3**). This integration occurs even prior to a patient entering the pre-access phase and an order is written. Providers and pharmacists

FIGURE 8-3. Interdisciplinary teams

should understand the revenue impact to each decision made during the P&T and Medical Executive Committees. Information technology system builds are complex and decisions made for front-end processes may have unintended consequences for back-end billing. More likely, the back-end billing process may not understand changes that impact billing which may lead to billing errors. Pharmacy teams are skilled and positioned to support a holistic approach and manage not only the medication use system, but the pharmacy revenue cycle as well, to bring to light operational processes and understand revenue cycle impact.

Pharmacy teams, not to exclude pharmacy technician involvement, are the drug experts, which is a vital component. Drug names, HCPCS, and billing unit conversions are complicated and may be incorrectly interpreted by the traditional revenue cycle teams. Locations which drive different reimbursement and cost increase the difficulty for the traditional finance or payer analyst to conduct reviews that include drugs. Operationalizing payer bulletins and alerts and government regulations are increasingly impacting the front-end operations rather than solely back-end billing functions. Pharmacists can provide a vital role in appeals, particularly as witnesses in Administrative Law Judge (ALJ) hearings to ensure that good pharmacy practices are recognized, and pharmacy services and drugs are appropriately reimbursed. Disruption is occurring in both traditional revenue cycle teams and clinical operations, and pharmacy can be a conduit to the multidisciplinary team in understanding both worlds.

HIGH PERFORMING REVENUE CYCLE TEAM

The future is bright for pharmacy revenue cycle and pharmacy teams to have a new avenue to develop students, residents, technicians, and current staff into pharmacy revenue cycle roles. Pharmacy leaders should consider developing a high performing revenue cycle team to enable them to keep up with the dynamic and ever changing healthcare and reimbursement landscape. Top five actions to be taken by pharmacy leaders to develop a high performing revenue cycle team are:

1.   Develop collaborative relationships with key revenue cycle, financial, and compliance leaders within the organization.

2.   Educate pharmacy team members on key revenue cycle processes to be able to identify opportunities to both improve patient care and realize appropriate reimbursement.

3.   Educate leaders outside of pharmacy on the complexity that medications pose in all phases of the revenue cycle.

4.   Integrate pharmacy into revenue cycle teams owning the elements pertaining to pharmacy within pre-access, clinical care, midcycle and post access phases. Start with quick wins and then move to long-term strategic roles that provide year-over-year value.

5.   Gain access to key data elements in IT systems and develop a dashboard to measure the performance of the pharmacy revenue cycle, looking for opportunities for continuous improvement.

CONCLUSION

Healthcare complexity is increasing and the revenue cycle and pharmacy are no exceptions. Functions are dynamic and processes are intermingled and play on each other. Technology advances may have improved efficiency in some areas that are complex and require diligent maintenance to stay relevant. Health systems that lack focus and a strategy to support the pharmacy revenue cycle process may experience revenue leakage or are at risk for regulatory infractions. Pharmacy teams play an integral role in the pre-access, clinical care, midcycle, and post access phases of the revenue cycle. Having a keen knowledge regarding drugs and a thorough understanding of operational processes places them in a position to help guide and lead the pharmacy revenue cycle teams. However, the pharmacy revenue cycle team should be supported with an organizational culture that is receptive to traditional roles being expanded.

REFERENCES

1. Choi, S., Murray, C., Leimkuhler, B., Fera, B. 3 key enablers to implementing a successful clinical revenue cycle operating model. HFMA. **https://www.hfma.org/topics/hfm/2019/may/3-key-enablers-to-implementing-a-successful-clinical-revenue-cyc.html**. Last updated May 01, 2019. Accessed January 10, 2022.

2. Centers for Medicare & Medicaid Services. HCAHPS: Patients' perspectives of care survey. **https://www.cms.gov/Medicare/Quality-Initiatives-Patient-Assessment-Instruments/HospitalQualityInits/HospitalHCAHPS**. Last updated December 01, 2021. Accessed January 10, 2022.

3. Centers for Medicare & Medicaid Services. Hospital inpatient admission order and certification. **www.cms.gov/Medicare/Medicare-Fee-for-Service-Payment/AcuteInpatientPPS/Downloads/IP-Certification-and-Order-09-05-13.pdf**. Published September 5, 2013. Accessed January 10, 2022.

4. Centers for Medicare & Medicaid Services. Medicare benefit policy manual. Chapter 1, section 10.2. **www.cms.gov/Regulations-and-Guidance/Guidance/Manuals/Downloads/bp102c01.pdf**. Updated August 6, 2021. Accessed January 10, 2022.

5. Centers for Medicare & Medicaid Services. Overview of rules & fact sheets. **www.cms.gov/nosurprises/Policies-and-Resources/Overview-of-rules-fact-sheets**. Last update August 29, 2022. Accessed January 10, 2022.

6. U.S. Department of Health & Human Services. HHS announces rule to protect consumers from surprise medical bills. **www.hhs.gov/about/news/2021/07/01/hhs-announces-rule-to-protect-consumers-from-surprise-medical-bills.html**. Updated July 1, 2021. Accessed January 10, 2022.

7. Centers for Medicare & Medicaid Services. Compendia 1861 (t)(2) - anti-cancer. **https://www.cms.gov/Medicare/Coverage/CoverageGenInfo/compendia**. Updated December 1, 2021. Accessed January 10, 2022.

8. Department of Health & Human Services. Medicare program: changes to hospital outpatient prospective payment and ambulatory surgical center payment systems and quality reporting programs; revisions of organ procurement organizations conditions of coverage; prior authorization process and requirements. *Federal Register Rules and Regulations.* 2019;84(218):61142-61492. **www.govinfo.gov/content/pkg/FR-2019-11-12/pdf/2019-24138.pdf**. Accessed January 10, 2022.

9. Centers for Medicare & Medicaid Services. Prior authorization and pre-claim review initiatives. **www.cms.gov/research-statistics-data-systems/medicare-fee-service-compliance-programs/prior-authorization-and-pre-claim-review-initiatives/prior-authorization-certain-hospital-outpatient-department-opd-services**. Last updated April 15, 2022. Accessed October 14, 2022.

10. Centers for Medicare & Medicaid Services. Medicare coverage determination process. **www.cms.gov/Medicare/Coverage/DeterminationProcess**. Last updated March 3, 2022. Accessed January 10, 2022.

11. Centers for Medicare & Medicaid Services. Medicare claims processing manual. Chapter 30 – Financial liability protections. **www.cms.gov/Medicare/Medicare-General-Information/ BNI/Downloads/ABN-CMS-Manual-Instructions.pdf**. Last updated February 21, 2014. Accessed January 10, 2022.

12. Centers for Medicare & Medicaid Services. Emergency Medical Treatment & Labor Act (EMTALA). **www.cms.gov/Regulations-and-Guidance/Legislation/EMTALA**. Last updated August 25, 2022. Accessed October 14, 2022.

13. Centers for Medicare & Medicaid Services. Notices and forms. **https://www.cms.gov/ Medicare/Appeals-and-Grievances/MMCAG/Notices-and-Forms**. Last updated December 10, 2021. Accessed January 10, 2022.

14. Centers for Medicare & Medicaid Services. Medicare claims processing manual. Chapter 22 – Remittance advice. **www.cms.gov/Regulations-and-Guidance/Guidance/Manuals/ Downloads/clm104c22pdf.pdf**. Last updated May 12, 2022. Accessed October 14, 2022.

15. AKASA. Automation in healthcare revenue cycle operations jumps from 66% to 78% in less than a year. *Cision*. **https://www.prnewswire.com/news-releases/automation-in-healthcare-revenue-cycle-operations-jumps-from-66-to-78-in-less-than-a-year-301358140.html**. Published August 19, 2021. Accessed January 10, 2022.

16. Becker's Healthcare and Transunion Healthcare. How AI can transform the revenue cycle. **https://assets.asccommunications.com/whitepapers/transunion-wp-november-2021.pdf**. Published November 2021. Accessed January 10, 2022.

MANAGED CARE PHARMACY

Philip Brummond, Susan M. Wescott,
and Brian Davis

Managed care is unlike many other sectors in that consumerism is not the common theme. In many cases, patients rely on expert advice from their healthcare team to choose products and services. Prices for these products are rarely up front and can be difficult for providers and patients to understand. To better understand healthcare and managed care, we must first examine the parties involved in the managed care process.

As of 2020, there are over 297 million insured Americans in the U.S.[1] These 297+ million members are managed by an insurance company also referred to as a managed care companies. Some of the largest managed care companies include United Healthcare (UHC), CVS/Health (Aetna), Blue Cross Blue Shield, and Cigna.

As we evaluate the complexity of the managed care space, we must first understand how these millions of Americans get into a managed care plan and what managed care is. The Oxford dictionary describes managed care as a system of healthcare in which patients agree to visit only certain providers and hospitals, and in which the cost of treatment is monitored by a managed care company.[2] In short, managed care is a type of agreement/contract in which a patient will see certain providers, go to certain pharmacies, and take certain medications in exchange for better/lower prices for those services. The selection of a managed care company may come from an employer selecting a particular company to offer healthcare benefits to their employees. However, if the individual does not work for an employer that has selected a managed care company, or is unemployed, a managed care company may be selected with or without the assistance of government entities.

Managed care companies generally have several services that they offer. Those services are commonly medical and pharmacy benefits and may also include dental and vision benefits. Throughout this chapter, we will focus on the pharmacy benefit that is offered by a managed care organization.

Pharmacy benefits are generally a core component of managed care plans. These benefits provide coverage of medications and include services generally found at a pharmacy. Specifically, managed care companies that provide pharmacy benefits are called Pharmacy Benefit Managers (PBM). Below is the general description and function of a PBM.

DOI 10.37573/9781585287130.009

PBM Service Offerings Cover Clinical and Administrative Functions

- Represent health insurers, self-insured employers, union health plans, and government purchasers in the selection, purchase, and distribution of pharmaceuticals
- PBMs contract with clients interested in optimizing the clinical and economic performance of their pharmacy benefit
- "PBMs are primarily responsible for developing and maintaining the contracting with pharmacies, negotiating discounts and rebates with drug manufacturers, and processing and paying prescription drug claims."

(Davis, 2021)

FIGURE 9-1. PBM service offerings

A relatively small number of PBMs dominate the market, with the top three companies managing about 80% of the total number of insured lives. Listed below are the relative sizes of U.S. PBMs belonging to, or affiliated with, various managed care companies, based on the number of lives that they support.

TABLE 9-1. Relative Sizes of U.S. PBMs

PBM	% of Market Share
CVS Caremark	34
Express Scripts	24
OptumRx (UnitedHealth)	21
Humana Pharmacy Solutions	8
Prime Therapeutics	6
Medimpact Healthcare Systems	5
All other PBMs	3

(Review, 2022)

With a better understanding of managed care and PBMs, let's now look at how these services are paid for. When you think about paying for healthcare it is important to understand how money flows from the many different parties involved. Of all the parties involved in paying for healthcare, patients end up paying twice. Patients pay once with the premium they pay to have a managed care plan and a second time when getting a service (eg, a prescription). The other parties involved with this process are:

1. Employer—Hires a managed care company and pays a premium to insure employees.

2. Managed Care Organization—Typically an insurance company that charges a premium and underwrites insurance benefits for the employer. Also pays a provider/hospital for services.

3. Pharmacy Benefit Manager (PBM)—Pharmacy managed care company that contracts with a managed care company to deliver pharmacy benefits. Contracts with a managed care organization or with an employer directly and pays a pharmacy for dispensing drugs.

4. Providers—Healthcare workers or entities that deliver services to patients per with a managed care organization.

5. Pharmacy—An entity that fills prescriptions written by providers for patients. Patients pay a contracted fee at the pharmacy or provider when getting services.

Later in this chapter an exploration of the financial flow will be reviewed in depth. For additional information at this time please refer to the section titled "The Pharmaceutical Value Chain."

FUNCTION OF MANAGED CARE

Now that you have a basic understanding of managed care, let's dig deeper into the function and role of managed care. We will focus more on the PBM side as we work through this section. In the first section we mentioned the overview of a PBM and their general services, but now we need to understand how PBMs came about and what services they offer. PBMs started as card processors in the 1960s and started to process electronic claims in the 1970s. Over time, PBMs have added more services. As defined by Truveris, a PBM has two functions:

PBMs have two main objectives: to curate pharmacy prescription benefits plan options; and to help patients achieve better health outcomes through greater access to appropriate medications.[3]

The benefit plans mentioned are put together with a number of different strategies that have been developed. Below is a list of the common strategies that PBMs use to develop plan options:

1. Formularies—A list of covered or preferred drugs, including the coverage tier for each drug.

2. Step Therapy—A utilization management tool that requires the use of one or more preferred products before another product may be approved for coverage.

3. Prior Authorization—A list of drugs that must be approved prior to being covered.

4. Pharmacy Networks—A list of pharmacies that are authorized to dispense medications for a member of the health plan.

5. Mail Order Pharmacy—A central fill pharmacy that is allowed to dispense drugs and send to a patient via home delivery.

PBMs should use these utilization management programs to guide patients and providers to the medications that provide the best possible outcome at the lowest net cost.

The goal of achieving better health outcomes is what managed care companies aim for. There are a number of different services and products on the market that can be used for patients. Managed care organizations focus on an intense evaluation process to compare and contrast all of the different options to choose the best product or service for the patient. Although the intent of managed care organizations is noble in driving toward better outcomes, the managed care market generally does not have standards and processes in place to ensure fair consistent reviews of products. This can lead to different recommendations and benefit plans being offered on the market. This leads to confusion for patients and providers when trying to select the correct products and services and can have a negative effect on outcomes with an unintended increase in cost.

Driving better outcomes has been an increased focus on managed care companies over the past several years. This has led to organizations engaging in a number of integrations that expand offerings. These integrations have been focused on all aspects of the managed care space and include pharmacies, providers, data, and product offerings. The next section will conduct a closer look at these integrations and how they are impacting managed care.

VERTICAL INTEGRATION IN THE HEALTHCARE SUPPLY CHAIN

What Is Vertical Integration and Why Is It Important?

Vertical integration is a concept that stretches across many industries, including healthcare and pharmacy services. There are two common types of business integration strategies: horizontal and vertical integration.

Horizontal integration occurs when a company buys one or more of its competitors operating in the same space. The result of a horizontal integration strategy is consolidation of the market, with fewer total competing entities. The acquisition allows the purchasing entity to grow and own a bigger piece of the "pie." In the healthcare example, horizontal integration occurs when a hospital or health system buys another hospital, clinic, or health system.

Vertical integration seeks to strengthen a company by buying or establishing businesses upstream or downstream in the supply chain. By gaining control over supplies and services that were previously only available through vendor or client relationships, vertical integration creates resiliency and the ability to manage adjacent supplies or customers in a way that favors the company. Profit is increased because margin is no longer paid to other parties. The company has direct access to consumers and end users of its products and services.

There are significant financial liabilities for hospital or health systems wishing to integrate vertically. The cost of building out capabilities must be weighed against the benefits to the health-system. Benefits include greater efficiencies and reduced costs or increased revenue in the long term.

There are two types of vertical integration, backward and forward:

- **Backward integration** occurs when an entity buys a supplier that provides inputs such as raw materials or manufactured goods which are needed for the products and services it ultimately sells in the marketplace. A good example of backward integration in healthcare might be a health system buying into a partnership with a laboratory or pharmaceutical supplier. This relationship would allow the health system to guarantee supplies of laboratory reagents and medications when other hospitals are unable to purchase sufficient quantities. It could also allow the hospital to customize these products to better meet their unique needs or to support an area of specialization that is not common in the industry.

- **Forward integration** looks up the value chain toward the consumer of goods or services in the supply chain. In healthcare, the consumer is typically the patient. Patients can either physically come to the clinic, pharmacy, laboratory, or hospital for care, or may be reached further afield with products and services offered remotely. Examples of more global reach include telehealth, digital tools, devices, apps, or websites providing health information, remote care, or virtual visits. A health system pharmacy department might engage in forward integration by opening a retail pharmacy to support an expanding area of the primary care practice or decide to offer prescription fulfillment through the mail.

What triggers a health system, pharmacy chain, or insurance company to vertically integrate? Sometimes market events can draw attention to vulnerabilities in the supply chain and inspire leadership to explore opportunities to have a greater degree of vertical integration. The COVID-19 pandemic created global supply shortages which led many hospitals, chain pharmacies, and integrated delivery networks (IDNs) to exert more control over the supply chain for core essentials like drugs and personal protective equipment (PPE). Often, expanding needs or frustration with existing vendors can lead a business to further develop a specific capacity, such as information technology, if the existing market is unable to sufficiently meet their needs. Finally, vertical integration offers an opportunity to grow the business in new and innovative ways to meet the evolving needs of the market.

Whenever a healthcare company considers whether they should acquire or purchase services they are doing a "buy vs. build" analysis. It is important to clearly understand the objectives of the business, both in the short-term and the long-term. It is often cheaper and more efficient to contract with another business, particularly when the expertise needed is foreign to the core competencies of the business. For many health systems, information technology changes so quickly that it makes more sense to hire an expert, such as an IT consulting firm, to perform a system integration or to set up a new electronic health record. Because this activity only occurs every 10 to 25 years, there may be no significant benefit to build the capability in-house, and outsourcing services makes the most sense. However, if the skills needed are an extension of existing capabilities and align with the strategic goals of the health system, establishing a new adjacent business may make more sense. Larger integrated delivery networks often own their own video companies, portrait studios, interior decorators, food services companies, and waste management services. The bigger a health system gets, the more sense it makes to own services that are used frequently in order to gain efficiencies, reduce costs, meet unique needs, or improve levels of service and quality.

Vertical Integration In the Pharmacy Ecosystem

Healthcare systems are in the business of providing care. One way that care providers such as physicians and pharmacists can vertically integrate is to partner with or establish insurance services. Creating insurance products allows the healthcare entity to directly market their services to the end user, the consumer. By controlling health plans, healthcare providers can ensure that their services are preferred or included in the network, thus capturing a higher volume of patients at their facilities. Other advantages include the ability to align population health programs and data to optimize value-based care. When healthcare providers accept the inherent risk that insurance involvement brings, they are more highly motivated to deliver a return on that investment.

If we further focus on the pharmacy value chain, partnering with health plans to provide pharmacy benefits offers pharmacists a number of opportunities to vertically integrate. Many hospitals and health systems own and operate retail, specialty, and mail order pharmacies, or provide pharmacy services like medication therapy management (MTM) to patients for a fee. Pharmacists sell the value that these services represent through contractual agreements with insurance companies, or less commonly, direct to consumers. Increasingly, ultra high-cost medications require the involvement of insurance in order to sustain the financial model. Few patients could ever afford to pay for CAR T-cell therapy without the assistance that health insurance provides. Thus, partnering with an insurance company to provide PBM services can be a logical next step for health system pharmacists. Pharmacy participation in providing PBM services often starts as a way to gain efficiency and savings for the employer's self-funded health plan. It can also create revenue opportunities by marketing PBM services to surrounding businesses to bring more patients to the hospital and the pharmacy.

The Pharmaceutical Value Chain

If we follow the life cycle of a drug from market entry to administration to the patient, we can gain a basic understanding of the pharmaceutical value chain. **Pharmaceutical manufacturers** research and develop new drugs in their own basic science laboratories or through partnerships with academic centers or "think tanks." The barriers to entry are high in the pharmaceutical industry because only a small number of all drug candidates eventually move to Phase I trials in humans. The cost to research and develop new drug therapies is staggering. Drug companies seek approval from the FDA and other governmental agencies around the world in order to manufacture and market drugs to prescribers and patients. Approved drugs are then distributed by pharmaceutical companies through **national drug wholesalers**, who offer smaller quantities for sale to pharmacies, often overnight. **Pharmacies** dispense medication and information to patients, and patients use their relationship with an **insurance company** to help pay for a prescription. **Technology interfaces** controlled by tech companies like Surescripts, CenterX, CoverMyMeds, and Arrive Health connect prescribers to insurance companies and pharmacies to integrate the data needed to inform the prescription and prior authorization transaction. In microseconds data flows between the prescriber's medical record, the PBM, and the pharmacy to confirm the patient's insurance eligibility, formulary coverage, refill history, and prescription cost at point-of-sale. Algorithms leverage data from all sources to provide alerts and warnings to caregivers in real time to support decision-making and improve efficacy and safety. Finally, the **consumer** walks out of the pharmacy—or opens their mailbox—and takes their medication.

One of the best illustrations of the complex flow of pharmaceutical goods, services, and the funds to pay for it all, is this diagram created by Adam Fein of Drug Channels Institute:

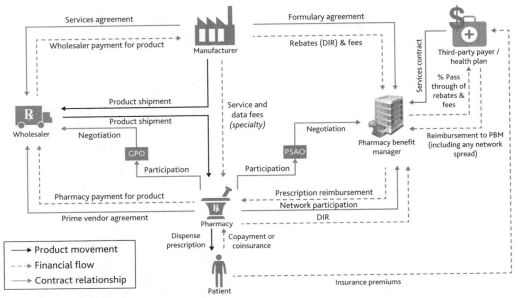

GPO = Group Purchasing Organization; PSAO = Pharmacy Services Administrative Organization; DIR = Direct and Indirect Remuneration
Source: The 2021 Economic Report on U.S. Pharmacies and Pharmacy Benefit Managers, Drug Channels Institute, March 2021, Chart illustrates flows for patient-Administered, Outpatient Drugs. Please note that this chart is illustrative. It is not intended to be a complete representation of every type of product movement, financial flow, or contractual relationship in the marketplace. Full report available at https://drugh.nl/pharmacy

DRUG CHANNELS
INSTITUTE

FIGURE 9-2. The U.S. pharmacy distribution and reimbursement system for patient-administered, outpatient brand-name drugs

DIFFERENT TYPES OF MANAGED CARE PROGRAMS FOR THE PHARMACY BENEFIT

Health Plan Financial Models

PBMs are a type of third-party administrator. PBM services are focused on administering coverage for outpatient prescription drugs, typically filled through a pharmacy. PBMs develop and maintain formularies, adjudicate prescription drug claims, negotiate rebates and discounts with pharmaceutical manufacturers, and provide utilization management and other clinical services.

The plans that PBMs manage include several "buckets," or groupings of plan types, each with similarities and differences with respect to the financial model:

Self-funded health plans are those where the plan sponsor takes financial risk. This type of plan is most commonly an employer-sponsored health plan, provided to employees of the company. The plan sponsor sets premiums and may choose to subsidize these premiums as part of the benefit package it offers to attract and retain talented employees. The health plan is part of a suite of benefits, which may also include compensation, retirement programs, dental and vision coverage, and paid time off. Many employers also offer wellness benefits, particularly in healthcare, where the employer's mission is focused on the prevention and treatment of disease. Examples of wellness benefits might include access to a gym membership or mental health support programs. Self-funded health plans seek to manage the cost of medical and pharmacy care as an expense, and do not typically set these plans up as a for-profit business. However, the PBMs that serve self-funded health plans are usually for-profit entities.

Advantages of self-funding the pharmacy benefit include:

- *Lower cost*—because there is no profit component and no built-in cushion to protect against risk, the total cost of the pharmacy benefit is often lower in a self-funded model. Administration costs can also be lower.

- *Customization*—self-funded plans can set the formulary, choose discounts in their own pharmacies in lieu of rebates, and choose to include or exclude coverage for certain drugs (eg, weight loss medications).

- *Cash flow*—the plan sponsor and the member pay for claims as they occur instead of pre-paying through a set premium.

- *Pharmacy network*—self-funded health system plans can choose network options that better meet the needs of their members and their geographic region, by excluding one or more national pharmacy chains in return for lower rates or by choosing to favor their own pharmacies with lower co-pay.

- *Regulatory exemptions*—self-funded plans are generally regulated under federal law (ERISA) and not state law, which simplifies the operational impact of compliance. In addition, there may be savings for self-funded plans related to health insurance premium taxes.

Fully insured health plans are those where the consumer is either an individual seeking coverage for themselves and/or their family, or a corporation, health plan, union, or government entity negotiating coverage for a group. In a fully insured model, the PBM takes on the financial risk. Underwriters calculate the expected cost of coverage on a per member basis and estimate future costs, factoring in knowledge of new drugs entering the market in the coming year and other risk factors. The insurer or health plan markets the plan with a set monthly premium, which includes and excludes certain services. This premium contains a profit margin for the seller. Because the model involves a degree of upside and downside risk, profits can fluctuate significantly when unknown events occur.

Advantages of a fully insured model for the pharmacy benefit include:

- *Predictability*—Plan sponsors that choose a fully insured model face fewer cost variances month-to-month and can budget with greater accuracy. The cost of the pharmacy benefit is fixed each month and more evenly distributed from a cash flow perspective.

- *Limited liability*—the insurer assumes all risk and the plan sponsor does not have to worry about catastrophic high-dollar claims that could impact their bottom line or even put them out of business.

- *Standard offering*—the PBM manages all aspects of pharmacy benefit administration. The plan sponsor does not have to provide the expertise needed to customize or manage the pharmacy benefit and can default to standardized plan offerings from the vendor.

Stop loss insurance is a "reinsurance" product that can be purchased to protect the plan sponsor from catastrophic or unpredictable costs. This type of insurance is often purchased by self-funded health plans, particularly where the employer does not have the financial resources to withstand certain levels of volatility but prefers a self-funded model for their health plan. A smaller health system with 2,000 members can more than double the spend on pharmacy benefits overnight if a member is diagnosed with hemophilia or cystic fibrosis.

Stop loss plans can either be specific or aggregate:

- **Specific** stop loss protects the employer against a high claim for any individual on the plan, usually above a certain dollar limit (eg, $50,000).

- **Aggregate** stop loss provides a maximum, or ceiling, on the total plan spend for the year. If total benefits costs exceed to the limit, the stop loss pays the employer the difference.

Pharmacy Benefits for Commercial and Government Health Plans

PBMs often specialize their service offering to serve the commercial or government markets. So how are commercial and government plans different?

Commercial health plans are offered by public or private organizations that are not considered government entities. Two common types of commercial health plans include preferred provider organizations (PPO) and health maintenance organizations (HMOs). For the pharmacy benefit, these distinctions are less important because they refer to limitations related to the medical network, and do not directly impact the pharmacy network.

Brokers or insurance agents can sell commercial plans to small or large businesses, groups, or to the general public, including self-employed individuals who don't access health insurance through their employer. The Affordable Care Act established a form of commercial insurance sold to individuals through an "exchange," or online marketplace. The marketplace is run by states or by the federal government. The health plans on the exchange are offered by private companies, but also have significant government oversight and protections, which are designed to protect consumers.

Most hospitals, clinics, and health systems that sponsor health plans for their own employees are considered commercial health plans. The majority of employer-sponsored health system health plans are also self-insured. Some health systems also market commercial health plans to local businesses or at a state or national level. The goal of sponsoring a commercial health plan can include generating a profit while driving care to the health system providers or the in-house pharmacy. Large health systems with both a self-insured employee plan and a commercial health plan can benefit from a larger number of total members, which can provide economies of scale and bring down the net cost of the employee health plan.

Government insurance plans typically include outpatient prescription benefits. There are a number of different types of government insurance plans, including Medicaid, Medicare Part D, the Federal Employees Health Benefits Program, state government employee plans, and Tricare. The two biggest types of government health plans are described in more detail below.

Medicaid is a federal-state partnership with shared authority and financing. It is a government sponsored program that serves low-income individuals, with more than 70 million beneficiaries participating in the program. Although state participation is not mandatory, all 50 states do participate, albeit with different levels of spending. The Affordable Care Act offered states the option to expand Medicaid eligibility to 133% of the federal poverty level in return for federal funding, and a majority of states agreed to participate. Pharmacy benefits paid through Medicaid require broad coverage of drugs and do not allow states to limit the scope of drugs covered in order to contain costs. Many common types of utilization management are allowed under Medicaid, such as preferred drug lists, prior authorization, drug utilization review, and cost-sharing provisions. Regulations limit participants from accessing co-pay assistance programs for prescriptions covered under the program. There are some differences in the level of restrictions on drug pricing for fee-for-service and managed care organizations for Medicaid plans. Some states require mandatory drug pricing transparency, with no "spread pricing" allowed. Because regulations vary from state to state, management of Medicaid plans can be very complex from a PBM perspective.

Medicare Part D is a voluntary prescription drug plan option for Medicare participants. Part D plans are sold by private health plans approved by the federal government and are available as standalone prescription drug plan (PDP) to supplement Medicare, or as a Medicare Advantage prescription drug plan (MA-PD) which covers all Medicare benefits, including drugs. Enrollees with low income are eligible for assistance through the Low-Income Subsidy (LIS) program. These plans have the option to offer a defined benefit with financial limits and cost-sharing set by phase, or an equivalent. Payment phases for the defined benefit include a deductible, initial coverage phase, a coverage gap, and catastrophic coverage. Premiums vary considerably. Costs are shared, based on a complicated formula which varies for each phase, by the health plan, the member, the pharmaceutical manufacturer, and the Medicare program. Similarly to Medicaid drug programs, regulations limit participants from accessing co-pay assistance programs for prescriptions covered under the program. Prior to 2023, the federal government could not interfere in drug pricing negotiations between the plan sponsor and pharmaceutical manufacturers. The Inflation Reduction Act of 2022 allows the federal government to negotiate prices for a limited number of high-cost medications, starting in 2026. The Act also requires drug manufacturers to provide rebates to CMS for brand-name drugs costing $100 or more, that incur price increases exceeding the rate of inflation. Medicare Part D plans have been very profitable for plan sponsors but are also quite complex to administer from a regulatory and compliance perspective for the PBM.

The Managed Care Horizon Both Near and Far

As outlined throughout this chapter, there are many complexities in navigating the managed care environments especially as it relates to pharmacy. The unprecedented mega mergers have impacted the market, and large insurance companies have been acquiring pharmacy assets in an attempt to drive value for their clients and shareholders. This has created a challenge for health systems but also presents new future opportunities and partnerships. Health systems are uniquely positioned, especially those that have sophisticated ambulatory pharmacy operations, to navigate the changing landscape from fee for service to value-based care. As population health management and risk-based contracting becomes more prevalent, healthcare providers will need to pivot quickly while having systems in place to manage ambulatory pharmacy medication use, as this will be an essential part of managing a population. Having a mature and sophisticated pharmacy service offering will allow health systems to manage medication therapy needs, especially for populations at high risk. Offering services such as a comprehensive ambulatory pharmacy clinical services, specialty pharmacy, home infusion, and retail/home delivery along with support for medication benefit design and management, will be critical for success.

Healthcare institutions are some of the largest employers in their markets. Utilizing comprehensive pharmacy management strategies within their employee health plan population provides the perfect opportunity to develop the framework that will allow health systems to pivot and offer these services to other employers within their market. This service offering will allow pharmacy services and the medical management of complex patients to serve as a health system critical asset where pharmacy can be used as a front door for patients into the health system. The cost of medications continues to be at the forefront of employer and consumer concerns, and offering unique solutions to reduce operational costs and manage appropriate medication utilization will position health systems to strengthen relationships with the employers in their markets. The management and service offerings to patients receiving specialty medications will need to be targeted to reduce overall healthcare costs. Health systems developing and offering services and solutions to address this critical need will allow for enhanced partnerships to form with large vertically integrated payers. Healthcare costs are rising at an unsustainable rate, and action is needed to drive down these costs while also meeting the service needs of patients.

The future of managed care, specifically as it relates to pharmacy, will need to focus on reducing healthcare costs, improving clinical outcomes, and making sure patients and consumers are satisfied in order to stay relevant in the marketplace. Consumer experience and satisfaction with managed care services continues to be a pain point for many patients and employers. Organizations that develop new and innovative business models will position themselves to outpace their peers in the industry. There has and will continue to be significant investment put into solving some of these challenges in the healthcare market segment. The most difficult task ahead will be coordinating all these solutions and innovative offerings to get the outcomes needed to drive down cost and improve outcomes. Health systems have the ability to be at the center of patient coordination but will need to be nimble in order to meet current and future consumer demands. This is an area where pharmacy leadership can play a large role, especially if positioned correctly at the strategic level of the organization.

The PBM business model has changed dramatically over the years and transparency will become more and more important in both the near and long term. As consumers and employers alike demand transparency, the current pharmacy business model will also need to evolve. Pharmacy leaders will need to take action, especially as it relates to pricing models and charge structures. Utilizing pricing tools embedded in the medical record and providing patients with up front and accurate pricing will be important aspects of moving toward price transparency for medications. Challenging the status quo will require new and innovative approaches to balancing growth and revenues. It is important to start with a controlled population such as your health system's health plan, focusing on high-risk patient populations such as diabetes, coronary artery disease, and poly pharmacy. Below are some key considerations for pharmacy leaders that will allow health systems to innovate and drive value to stakeholders in this paradigm shift toward true transparency in the managed care market:

1. Develop a strategic plan and pharmacy value proposition related to payers

2. Establish a business case proving your value proposition with both internal and external stakeholders

3. Partner with your Human Resources Benefits leader to review business case and seek their support on driving lowest net cost for medication therapy within your covered health plan

4. Design services to expand medication use management and outcomes from current pharmacy service offerings for your organization's health plan

5. Gain buy-in and support from executive leaders to expand the pharmacy service offerings to employers within your market

As the managed care market continues to evolve, pharmacy leaders must take action. Spending time understanding the market dynamics and learning from internal and external industry experts can position yourself and your health system to innovate. Keeping patients and customers top of mind will be an important part of achieving the outcomes needed to achieve results.

REFERENCES

1. Department, Statista Research. U.S. Americans with health insurance 1990-2020. Published 2021. Accessed April 2022.

2. Oxford English Dictionary. managed, adj. In: *OED Online*. **www.oed.com/view/Entry/113216**. Accessed April 2022.

3. Truveris Team. What is a Pharmacy Benefit Manager (PBM) and how does a PBM impact the pharmacy benefits ecosystem? Truveris. **https://truveris.com/what-is-a-pharmacy-benefit-manager-pbm-and-how-does-a-pbm-impact-the-pharmacy-benefits-ecosystem/#:~:text=PBMs%20are%20hired%20by%20corporate,%2C%20pharmacies%2C%20and%20drug%20companies**. Published February 17, 2021. Accessed April 2022.

LEADERSHIP: THE PHARMACIST ENTREPRENEUR OR INTRAPRENEUR

Calvin H. Knowlton and Orsula V. Knowlton

This chapter is not intended to be a recipe for entrepreneurship or intrapreneurship. Our goal is to provide you with an array of insights that we have gleaned from our entrepreneurial experiences, both past and present. We will provide you with topical tidbits and point you to references and treatises that go into depth on these topics. It will be your choice to dig deeper or, if not, to hopefully enjoy our 30,000 foot typology.

Arguably, the first pharmacist entrepreneur (EP) was John Morgan, whose hospital pharmacy practice (1755-56) and medical achievements helped lead to the development of professional pharmacy in North America. First as a pharmacist and later as a physician, he advocated for prescription writing and championed independent practice of the two professions. The first pharmacist intrapreneur (IP) was, again arguably, Jonathan Roberts, as he started the first hospital pharmacy (1752) within the first hospital in colonial America located in Philadelphia, Pennsylvania.[1]

So, what is the difference between an entrepreneur and an intrapreneur? The etymology of entrepreneur derives from "entra" (between) and "prendre" (to take or to fold). Think of undertaking an endeavor typically as a "start-up" initiative—to take hold between the current situations. The etymology of intrapreneur derives from "intra" (within) and "prendre," to undertake within, or to fold into an established organization.

Another perspective is that an entrepreneur is a person who organizes and manages a business with considerable initiative and takes some risk in the process. An intrapreneur is a person with a similar creative urge, drive, and compassion, who implements ideas or initiatives in their place of employment.[2]

Typically, an entrepreneur starts a practice or business ex nihilo, whereas an intrapreneur starts a practice or business within an ongoing entity, such as a hospital, clinic, etc. Either way, the common denominator is an art rooted in the belief that uses creativity, passion, and inspired vision to generate value in the world. Both entrepreneurs and intrapreneurs (EP/IP) exhibit a mindset that encompasses passion, creativity, resourcefulness, courage, and resilience. This mindset is not narrowly confined to starting a business or practice, as it can apply to pursuing such interest in government, philanthropic, faith-based, and other sectors as well.[3]

DOI 10.37573/9781585287130.010

Amina Aububakar, PharmD, CEO, Avant Pharmacy and Wellness, Charlotte, North Carolina, is an example of an entrepreneur. Originally from Kenya, she held fashion shows with friends to fund her travel and move to the United States. She started her practice 13 years ago. The practice includes a retail pharmacy and two provider-based practices. Amina was driven by her vision of wanting to make the practice of pharmacy better and her belief that pharmacists could do more. She considers herself a "hypervisionist"—she envisions and dreams about how things could work and then makes it happen. After meeting with local physician providers in her community, she realized that the things she wanted to do in her practice were things that the providers did not want to do. She realized how similar providers and pharmacists are and that they can complement each other. Many providers are incentivized to support the positive outcomes of patients and are even taking downside risk. Amina's proposal to provide complex therapy consultation and wellness programming to referring physicians met a need that resulted from value-based care models in Accountable Care Organization practices in her community.

CONSIDERING EP/IP AS A CAREER CHOICE

The only way to be truly satisfied is to do what you believe is great work. And the only way to do great work is to love what you do. If you haven't found it yet, keep looking. Don't settle [time is your enemy]. As with all matters of the heart, you'll know it when you find it.

—Steve Jobs

There are many apologetics that apply to EP/IP practitioners. Here are few:

1.   External happiness

     Approbation and recognition are always welcomed and nice to receive, but those gestures are often superficial and only conferred when success seems to be at hand. EP/IP practitioners know that peaks and troughs are the norm. Someone has remarked—I don't know the key to success, but the key to failure is trying to please everyone...

2.   Internal joy

     Differing from external happiness is internal joy. This is more than perceived autonomy or control. Partly, internal joy is living a life that is true to yourself, and not the life that others expect of you.[4] Much of it revolves around the notion of intentional and considered purpose and meaning, which foretell your own priorities of life. Priority is a fundamental tailwind for EP/IP practitioners. The word priority came into our language in the 1400s. It was singular. It meant the very first or prior thing. It stayed singular for the next 500 years, when in the 1900s we pluralized it and started talking about priorities.[5]

3.   Harmony vs. Balance

     Part of this plural bifurcation of priority was due to change in our work-life routine. Balance is derived from the Latin "bis," meaning twice, and "lanx," meaning dish or plate. In thinking about a pharmacist's balance, balance means that we spend an equal amount of time in each area of life. Harmony comes from the Greek "harmonia," meaning agreement of feeling, concord. An EP/IP practitioner tries to integrate values and vision by setting aside time for those things that really matter. Harmony focuses on integration, fitting together, and joining. Perhaps the notion of harmony for EP/IP practitioners relates to appropriate partitioning of doing well (eg, financially) and of doing good (for others, especially family and the community).

4.   Stress Control

     Discord, disharmonization, and multiple priorities can induce entrepreneurial stress. However, while there are many causes for EP/IP stress, Greiner argues four preventable measures to mitigate stress[6]:

a. Time management—EPs/IPs must be cognizant of how they partition their time, such as working on the highest-priority task first, to-do lists, and/or time-tracking software to assist you in staying on task.

b. Procrastination—is a self-handicapping behavior that prevents you from meeting deadlines and needing extensions. Procrastination is one of the most common workplace stressors.

c. Delegating—is foremost for EPs/IPs to embrace. While perhaps not top of mind for EPs/IPs, effective delegating not only reduces leaders' stress and burnout, but it also enhances team capacity. I recall the informative story in the Old Testament (Numbers 11:16-17 NIV):

   The Lord said to Moses: "Bring me seventy of Israel's elders who are known to you as leaders and officials among the people. Have them come to the tent of meeting, that they may stand there with you. I will come down and speak with you there, and I will take some of the power of the Spirit that is on you and put it on them. They will share the burden of the people with you so that you will not have to carry it alone."

d. Avoid overcommitment—not doing so can lead to paralysis. The most effective antidote is to be firm and set boundaries. Stay within your stated mission and vision guardrails, and as tempting as it might be for you to do it "just this time" and get distracted…it can be a slippery slope. You will note many references to staying on course in this chapter.

5. Mentorship

   Recall the adage, "if you see a turtle on a fence post, the one thing you know is that it didn't get there by itself." The first thing that EPs/IPs need to ponder is that although your idea to fill an unmet need is your idea, that does not mean that you know it all: how to idealize, finance, productize, market, close deals, etc. If you know someone with more experience than you, that might be your best start. If not, we strongly recommend that you contact a CEO Leadership and Networking organization like Vistage, a national, confidential peer advisory group of CEOs, business owners, and key executives. There are Vistage groups, comprised of 12 to 16 high-caliber executives and one trained and experienced leader, in every state. Each group meets once monthly, normally alternating among the members' corporate offices.

Ron Jordan, Dean, School of Pharmacy, Chapman University, considers himself both an entrepreneur and an intrapreneur. He was always looking for opportunities to improve things early in life. At one of his first jobs, he helped a long-term care pharmacy implement the first version of the QS1 computer system, helping the owner capture all the claims for invoicing. At a health plan in Rhode Island in the '90s, he would receive shoe boxes of receipts for medication. He started working with the lobbyist in the company to legislate a medication assistance program drug benefit. They started small with chronic medications and slowly added categories. They wrote the law and coverage based on AHFS guidelines and began processing claims using NCPDP standards. As the founding Dean of Chapman University, the same principles of entrepreneurship apply. Dean Jordan notes, "All pharmacy students are entrepreneurs at heart. They become pharmacists because they are committed to helping people and see opportunity to do this with the additional desire of autonomy, management, etc."

UNDERSTANDING WHICH BUSINESS TO START

We mentioned intentional and considered purpose, but let's delve in a little deeper. Scanning the environment each day can provide you with one problem or one issue that needs to be solved.

It may be one anachronistic process that needs to be reinvigorated or reconsidered. But it should be something that you are really interested in attacking.

In our most recent company, we are attacking the "pandemic" of preventable Adverse Drug Events, which have been listed as the third to fifth cause of premature death over the past decade. Why has this not been abated? Because the "tool" that pharmacists use is a one-to-one drug inter-actions report that is 50 years old. This "tool" only reveals that "it has appeared in the literature that if these two medications are taken simultaneously, then X may happen." It fails to provide sufficient medication decision support to enable the pharmacist to effectuate an intervention that targets a material outcome.

A preponderance of people, as they age, consult many medical disciplines and take more that two medications. Furthermore, to use this old one drug to one drug "tool" with a medication regi-men of ten or more drugs, one still would not understand the best path forward, while also experi-encing "alert fatigue."

So, we developed a multidrug, simultaneous digital analysis system, embodying the major drug disposition sciences pharmacists learn in pharmacy school—pharmacokinetics, pharmacogenomics, pharmacodynamics, and an array of medicinal chemistry. Pharmacists using this system materially reduce falls, ER visits, hospitalizations, rehospitalizations, and even premature death.[7] The study showed a huge odds ratio reduction in the independent variable of premature death covered by a span of seven years, with 427,000 patients.[8]

Whatever business you pursue (EP or IP), a focused framework is foremost. While a plethora of writers and lecturers have stated this percept, we would like to quote a poignant statement from Stephen Covey:

The main thing is to keep the main thing the main thing.[9]

Covey has also been said to remark (paraphrased):

You must decide what your highest priorities are and have the courage—pleasantly, smilingly, unapologetically—to say "no" to other things. And the way you do that is by having a bigger "yes" burning inside. The enemy of the best is often the good.

These decisions to stay focused on your mission and vision are not easy. Temptation to stray from the best to append the good is rampant. Remember that the Latin root of decision is "cis," to cut or to kill.

The practice you initiate will be the practice you find interesting, rewarding altruistically and financially, and focuses on a problem that you believe needs to be solved or reimagined.

David Medvedev (CEO, AspenRx) started two businesses ex nihilo, AspenRx, and VUCA Health. His entrepreneurial spirit started when he worked at Eckerd Drug, where he was able to be creative and innovative. This lit a spark for David that eventually put a fire in him to be a fearless entrepre-neur. He started VUCA Health as a result of a confluence of experiences, including working for a hospital survey company, that he grew and found that the lowest score of the patient journey was medication communication. His vision was to move away from long documents to short video clips about medications that explained medication information to patients. He spoke with his profes-sional contacts at large drug chain stores to see if they had ever heard of a company doing this and they had not. He launched VUCA Health and built a library of thousands of videos that eventually integrated with pharmacy management systems.

EP/IP ATTRIBUTES: A FOCUS ON RELATIONSHIPS[10]

It is said that W. Edward Deming, who led the quality revolution around the world, believed that the fundamental job on a leader is prediction. EPs/IPs must know "where the puck is heading" when they decide their path forward.

How is the EP/IP going to be so prescient? Arguably the key attribute, which should be honed, is that of relationships. The EP/IP head of the innovation forms a team and takes seriously that there is no "I" in the word "team." Michael Platt, Wharton's Director of Neuroscience Initiative, posits, "When people have a strong connection with each other, or are cooperating well together during a task, their brains go in synchrony: patterns of neuronal activity become aligned. And when their brains go into synchrony, other physiological processes, like their heart rates, go in synchrony…"

Tips for you, when addressing issues with your team:

a. Use storytelling to get a group to embrace an idea, which will prime people's brains to be more receptive to that idea.

b. Modulate your volume, focus on the present, and directly address the team to increase the perception, confidence, and trust in your ideas.

c. If it's a difficult message, prime the team to think about something bigger than themselves—the vision, the progress to date, the outcome benefits scored—to overcome their human default resistance.

d. Use feedback as two-way street. Bidirectional communication, transparency, and specificity are watchwords.

Jannet Carmichael, PharmD, BCPS, FCCP, FAPhA, started her career in academia at the University of Iowa and spent 35 years in the VA health system as a Regional Pharmacy Executive. She considers herself a clinical pharmacy pioneer and intrapreneur. She was initially intrigued with the notion of pharmacists being involved in the drug therapy decision making process. Dr. Carmichael was the first PharmD the VA hired; fast forward, and she's built an incredible staff of clinical pharmacy specialists, in line with what the VA desired, while also filling the void of primary care. As an intrapreneur, she started the first clinical data warehouse at the VA.

Initially Jann could not afford to hire additional clinical pharmacists, so she started a residency program. She surrounds herself with people who have different talents. She can always figure out where the North Star is to know where she is going. She realized very quickly that she needed to surround herself with people who had different skillsets that also complemented hers.

Did Jann ever have to pivot? "It was never a straight line from A to Z. Things take so much longer than you think they will. The path is more like a big, crooked maze, with the end in mind. We always think it should be faster, easier, and less bumpy. When thinking of her younger self, her advice to pharmacists today is to "rely more on relationship currency over performance questions." Jann always thought that the more data she had, the more likely prescribers would take her recommendations. However, once she got to know the prescribers and built credibility with them, they would take recommendations without hesitation. Having more data would not have helped—it was the relationship that drove clinical outcomes.

METHODOLOGY FOR TEAM DECISION MAKING

The bottom line in team decision making is to use the scientific method you learned in school. If your hypothesis is disproven, pivot. Professor Amar Bhide showed in his *Origin and Evolution of New Business* that 93% of all companies that ultimately become successful had to abandon their original strategy—because the original plan proved not to be viable.[11] So they pivoted to another approach—not changing their mission or vision, but their strategy—the "how" to get to their mission/vision purpose:

Idea>Hypothesis>Testing>Results>Positive=continue

>Negative=pivot

To put a construct around it, here is a five sequential step process your team's brains' goes through:

Sense the options

Weigh the evidence

Consider the value of the options

Make a choice and act

Evaluate the outcome (then either stay the course, or pivot)

With a team approach, you as the leader must be aware of positional power versus charismatic power. The first is legitimized by your role and your title as the leader. The second is based upon your personal qualities and behaviors as the leader. The first is distancing for your team, while the latter is inspirational and collaborative. Typically, in functional teams, draconian edits may be tolerated but not embraced, whereas the inspirational approach is embraced more readily and more appreciatively.

Brad Stulberg, in his book *The Practice of Groundedness*, mentions a precept—the people with whom you surround yourself shape you. He shares the story, which you may have heard before, that while the tall redwoods in Felton, California, tower two hundred feet in the air, the roots that support them are only six to twelve feet deep. Instead of growing downward, they grow outward, extending hundreds of feet laterally, wrapping themselves around the roots of their neighbors. This expansive network of closely intertwined roots supports the trees' ability to withstand rough weather.[12]

Is it not the same for us?

FIRST THINGS FIRST: UNDERSTANDING THE VALUE OF INTENTIONAL CULTURE

Culture in any company will be created. The EP/IP can either just let it form itself or you can take important steps to formulate the culture. If you do nothing, culture will take its own path.

We believe that the culture of our company is the most important dimension to influence team behavior. The culture of the team has a distinct impact over everyone's performance. Culture is not a few signs on the wall: Attitude, Teamwork, etc. These are nouns. Culture has to do with what we believe is important, which shapes and informs how we act or behave (ie, culture is an accumulation of appropriate verbs).

One company that we acquired a few years ago had many suitors. Our valuation came in under some of the others, yet that company's leadership selected us. Why? They informed us after the process was completed that they very much liked our culture. Cultural embodiment can trump financial performance.

What is culture? Culture is not about what we do; it simply is about how we behave and how we act in doing it. It's how we work together and how we treat clients and suppliers. In our company, we have 32 Fundamentals, which are explained as behaviors.[13] Each Monday a team member who has written a one-page communication about the Fundamental of the Week, opines personally on what that Fundamental means to them. Their "story" is posted on our T-net (our internal message board) for all to then read and write comments. Then, every internal meeting we hold during the week starts with one or two minutes of open reflection on the Fundamental of the Week. In circulating emails throughout the week team members will often write something and then parenthetically refer to one of the Fundamentals that aligns with the email message (eg, #24, which discusses how to Assume Positive Intent). We have a Chief Cultural Officer and Deputy Culture Officers at each of our locations.

Lastly, there are three important examples of how driving the culture in your practice is rewarding[14]:

1. Creating a focused culture yields a competitive advantage. It is wrapped up in how your people behave.

2. Creating a focused culture attracts and retains talent. People want to feel connected to their work along with a sense of shared purpose.

3. Creating a focused culture impacts productivity. The environment wherein people work has enormous influence over what we do and how we do it.

Do you know the root of the word company? It is "com" meaning "with," plus "panis" meaning "bread." It implies persons associated with one another in some "way"—maybe breaking bread together. Maybe golfing and betting. Or golfing and never betting. Maybe sharing off-color jokes or finding that to be offensive. That "way we comport" is the culture.

One lesson we are learning now, post COVID-19, is that culture with a hybrid workforce is more difficult to perfect than when everyone is together in one workplace. We have implemented different tactics[15] and will have retrospective insight at some point. For instance, we request each department to have a "purpose" day every week, every two weeks, or every month, when all department team members get together. The purpose is twofold—to discuss a few business topics, but equally important, to socialize and have fellowship interactions. The venue could be the office, a bowling alley, an ice skating rink, or some other fun activity spot.

ATTRACTING PEOPLE TO YOUR BUS

Jim Collins, in Good to Great, states:

> Those who build great companies understand that the ultimate throttle on growth for any great company is not the markets, or technology, or strategy, or products. It is one thing above all others: the ability to get and keep enough of the right people.

The most powerful information we can provide you is not regarding attracting people with the "right stuff" in terms of a wonderful résumé or CV. It's not what is on paper that is most important. Neither is it a successful track record, per se. The idea that some people have innate talents that just need to be identified has proved to be an unreliable predictor of success.[16] Harvard Business School professor Clay Christensen argues that the interview focusing on the person's experience is foremost.

This is especially true in a start-up practice. Therein, process capabilities to be probed would include, simply, has the person ever started and built anything before? Does the person you are considering know how to adjust a strategy when the first one didn't work? Has the person dealt with such pressure before? It's tempting to judge success by a résumé, but experience in learning to navigate the complex social and financial existential propositions of life, especially considering unexpected impinging externalities (eg, like new regulations or payment structures), is paramount in your recruitment and selection process.

We would strongly suggest that you read chapter eight of Christensens' book, The Schools of Experience.

Another pertinent treatise is Bradford Smart's Topgrading. In it he quotes Charles Darwin: "'It's not the strongest of the species that survives, nor the most intelligent, it is the one that is most adaptable to change.'" Smart also provides several interviewing techniques that are somewhat unique but insightfully effective. These focus on experiences but also on culture, which is refreshing and practical.[17]

We were also intrigued by Verne Harnish's notion of organizing your Employer Handbook around the cultural core values or fundamentals[18] (or cultural behaviors). Harnish's book, *Scaling Up*, is a powerful treatise on how to help your company or practice grow, in addition to being "radically practical."

Getting the right team on the bus was critical according to Dennis Helling (PharmD, ScD-Hon), retired Executive Director of Pharmacy for Kaiser Permanente in Denver, Colorado. In 1992, the Board Certification for Pharmacotherapy Specialists (BCPS) was just starting. Dennis was the first in the country to require certification for clinical pharmacy practice at Kaiser, which at that time employed 150 board certified pharmacists with only a couple that did not pass the test. "Having a clear vision, expectations, holding people accountable, following-up when people are not performing and using the 'good to great' principals to understand that on occasion, there will be someone who is not the right person for the bus, is how to assure success."

FUNDING YOUR SOLUTION

Revenue is Vanity, Profit is Sanity, and Cash Flow is King.

—Verne Harnish

Once you have figured out the "what" you want to do, you will need access to capital in order to fund your business or idea. If you are starting a business, and are like most people, you don't personally have the funds to support your business until breakeven, so you will likely need to raise funds from others. If you are an intrapreneur, you will have to secure a company sponsor in order to gain funding to support your idea. In either case, it is important to understand the mindset of investors or sponsors and to not overcapitalize.

Investors and sponsors want to have a clear understanding of the risk and reward at any stage of their involvement. Some questions they will want answered are: How risky is the venture? What specifically is the use of proceeds? What is the probability of success? What factors can contribute to the likelihood of success? What are material milestones of success? When will you need more capital? What is the potential upside for me or our business?

As an entrepreneur it also will be critical that you understand the use of cash for your business. Raising capital often takes longer than expected so be sure you have a reliable cash flow model and start the fundraising process well in advance of when you anticipate needing the funds.

Investors will be betting on two things: you and your idea. So contributing the appropriate amount of your own capital or "sweat equity" in order to demonstrate your commitment is going to be important. If you aren't willing to put your own capital or time into your idea, then it will be difficult to convince others to do so.

In many cases the first place to look for seed funding is friends and family. These are typically called Angel investors and this round of funding is to get your business started. The nice thing about Angels is that they will retain a lot of interest in what you are doing, and expect to be updated quarterly, but (unlike the next round investors) they do not have a seat on the Board of Directors. Often companies do one Angel investor round, and if the practice is taking off, can offer an additional, optional round for Angels to invest at a higher strike price (eg, if the first round was, for instance, $0.50/share and the value later grows to $1.50/share), the first-round Angels are often interested in taking a larger position by investing addition funds. After the Angels are the more formal rounds of funding routinely referred to as Series A, Series B, etc., and involve institutional investors like Venture Capital or Private Equity. These investors are really not your best friends, even though they put on a great façade; their sole purpose is to have their investments grow by many multiples and then sell. Their horizon is usually much shorter than yours or Angel investors.

In the early stages of your business, valuation (ie, how much is the business worth) is subjective, and generally comes down to what is a post-Angel investor is willing to pay for an equity position and what type of dilution you as the founder are willing to accept. An investor wants to get as much equity as possible for as little capital as possible to maximize their return so you, as founder, will need to be prudent with your negotiations to protect your percent ownership. In other words, you want to limit dilution while at the same time ensuring you have capital to grow your business and take advantage of the market opportunity.

Therefore, companies usually have multiple stages of fundraising, allowing you to raise enough money to bridge to the next round of fundraising, hopefully at a higher valuation. These negotiations can be complex and so it can be helpful to engage a third party to manage the fundraising process to ensure the optimal outcome. When the company attains a positive cash flow stability, these investors become pleased.

As your company grows, access to different types of capital will become available, like debt and even noninstitutional investors (eg, public investors). Using debt can be a great way to limit dilution and get access to growth capital. Founders should not ignore the benefits of using debt at the right time versus raising more equity. While there are scheduled repayments under the debt arrangement that you will need to be prepared to meet, they often come with fewer demands related to governance.

In any scenario, it will be just as important for you to perform due diligence of your potential investor or debt partner (ie, check references to ensure that what they pitched to you aligns with how they behave with other companies in which they have invested). Be aware that the potential investor will also perform due diligence on you. It is prudent for you to try to explore and understand how they handle tough situations when the business hits a speed bump and if they have a good network you can leverage to grow your business.

When I started my first practice, Amherst Pharmacy in Mt. Holly, New Jersey, it followed an unexpected trajectory. I had just finished my one-year postpharmacy degree internship at a hospital in Mt Holly. It was a fantastic internship. The first half of the day I made rounds with the Chief of Internal Medicine, then lunch, then the second half of the day I was in the pharmacy. Often, at lunchtime, a couple of the pharmacists would walk about 1/2 mile to a local pharmacy and have lunch in the back room of the pharmacy with the pharmacist-owner. Often, I joined them. After the internship I went back to Temple Pharmacy School where I had enrolled in a PhD pharmacology/teratology graduate program. About a year into the program, I received a phone call from the pharmacist who owned Amherst Pharmacy—the same pharmacy where we would walk for lunch.

He mentioned that he had a terminal cancer diagnosis and wanted to know if I would like to buy his pharmacy. I was ecstatic but told him I did not have the resources (he was asking for $75,000). He responded if you come up with $1,000, I'll take a note for the remainder. I was shocked. I left my mice and rats in the teratology lab and took over his pharmacy. We worked hard and long and paid back the owner's wife in 24 months. We then transitioned the practice from a "typical" pharmacy to a professional apothecary.

Fast forward 20 years and I had a one-year Community Pharmacy Residency program, and five of the residents did the same thing—they leveraged purchased pharmacies while honoring the legacy of the previous owner (eg, keeping his/her name on the pharmacy).

Dr. Abubakar also had a very conservative approach to starting her pharmacy practice. When she wanted to start the business, she had no money. She received a line of credit of $150K with no payment for one year from her wholesaler and she funded the labor, rent, and licenses. Her friends also helped while she worked elsewhere for two days per week. She was able to accumulate the $150K in six months to satisfy the note.

If you are an intrapreneur, your company may have a process or mechanism to vet breakthrough ideas. In fact, there may be a "think tank" where these ideas get funding and are allocated resources to explore viability and impact. Most often these ideas need to align with the overall company strategy to get the "green light," so it is important to be able to articulate how your idea(s) support the strategy and create significant benefit to your organization. Whether your company has a formal process or not, you will need to get an executive sponsor in order to help you secure funding for your idea.

In any scenario, it will be essential for you to be able to clearly articulate what are the interim milestones that will showcase success in order to continue receiving funding to support your solution in the future.

Where there is a will, you can figure out how to make it happen!

MARKETING AND SALES

Fortune favors the well-prepared.

—Dr. Louis Pasteur

In his recent book, *Momentum*, Marc Emmer asserts that a deficit found in some entrepreneurial companies is a lack of synergy between marketing and sales. He professes that step one is for the CEO to assure that marketing and sales have common goals and work collaboratively to ensure conversions and sales productivity. He further notes that your unique value proposition and branding are key; companies must identify at least three unique points of difference. All marketing and sales activities should reinforce these differences and prove their value.[19]

Like accounting, public relations, advertising, finance, marketing, and sales are specialty areas. When an EP/IP starts many of these tasks fall to you; you'll be wearing many hats! In each of these specialties, do not hesitate to hire or lean on friends who have such expertise. Or create an Advisory Board with people pedigreed in these domains and pay them an annual stipend with stock.

Some ideas on how to approach a new idea in a market is to consider a SWOT Analysis—evaluating the strengths, weaknesses, opportunities, and threats that your new business has compared with what already exists. The idea is to identify the weaknesses and threats and to consider how to make them strengths and opportunities.

Second, consider hiring marketing students or MBA graduate students to use your business idea as a project to understand the competitive landscape. How many organizations already offer your idea? How can your idea outperform what exists in the market from a feature, benefit, or price perspective? What other questions would you want answered in this process?

In addition, consider investing in a professional market analysis of willingness to pay. The product may only exist as a prototype, but it is important to understand if there is indeed a market for the business idea *and* that people are willing to pay for the products and services.

This is the start of the business plan that your investors will want to review, including your Angel investors, prior to putting money into the company. Understanding market size and willingness to pay are paramount to taking the risk of starting a new business.

If your idea is unique, you will need to figure what "area" it fits into or what "area" is ripe for you to induce a demand. If that is the case, consider starting by servicing one type of client to demonstrate your idea or novel product. If it works and the client is highly satisfied, you are onto something. If you are constantly managing complaints, quality issues, and/or lukewarm client reception, it may be time to reconsider the business model or how you are presenting it! Our mantra is First Comes Outcome, Then Comes Income. In other words, start your pitch with what's in it for your audience, then provide content, followed by repeating what's in it for our audience. In certain books, Cal always read the last chapter first (you can't do that in pharmacology book!), so he knew where the author was heading. It is the same when you are presenting a new concept or construct or process. The language of results (outcomes) trumps the language of efforts (process).

A great book on marketing to consider reading is Martin Sheridan's *They Ask, You Answer*.[20]

Kevin P. Boesen, PharmD, Chief Sales Officer, Tabula Rasa HealthCare, had been founder of SinfoniaRx. As an intrapreneur, Boesen's SinfoniaRx was a spin-off of a call center based MTM program he started while faculty of the University of Arizona. Dr. Boesen started in retail pharmacy. He had many customers but didn't feel like he had the opportunity to connect with them because he was so busy. He left for pharma and worked in drug information answering calls from patients about neuroscience products. When he spoke to patients telephonically he really enjoyed it. From there, he went into sales, pharma sales, medical device sales, and then to University of Arizona School of Pharmacy to help with rotation sites. He found problem solving to be a key driver for his motivation to start SinfoniaRx. Kevin feels that some of his success was based on how naïve he was. Had he known how hard it was going to be, he may have not done it. Kevin's advice is to be brave. "People think they need to be smart enough, need more education or mentorship. Be brave and trust yourself. No one is going to eat you. At the end of the day, you are still a pharmacist and can still make a living. Be brave and tackle the opportunity you have uncovered!"

SPECIAL ADVICE FOR YOU

Of the many books and other reference materials you may want to consult, these seven percolate to the top for us, in order of importance:

1. Harvard Business School Professor Clayton Christensen's *How Will You Measure Your Life?* This is a short book that highlights harmony in your work life and your non-work life. The late Dr. Christensen was an amazing writer and public speaker. He was the spark behind Disruptive Innovation.

2. MIT Professor and Harvard Scholar John Donovan's *The Entrepreneur-Intrapreneur*. His focus is more on Intrapreneurs and it's an easy read.

3. The University of Maryland School of Pharmacy division that is focused on Pharmapreneurship. Check their website, then the tab "Research & Discovery" for more information.

4. Entrepreneur David Friedman's *Culture by Design: Eight Simple Steps to Drive Better Individual and Organizational Performance*. It's almost "all you wanted to know about culture." About 300 companies have adopted his model (including us), and the demand is strong.

5. Greg McKeown's *Essentialism*. This is a wonderful treatise about when to say yes and when to say no in your non-work life and in your practice. It helps you refine what is purposeful and meaningful.

6. Human Performance Coach Brad Stulberg's *The Practice of Groundedness: A Transformational Path to Success that Feeds—not Crushes—Your Soul*. The author urges us not to separate the mind from the heart. Like a New Years' resolution, which 90% of people "fall-off" by year end, his observation is when we do fall-off the EP/IP explorational path that we want to go down, get back on. It's as simple and hard as that.[21] This is a thought-provoking book and somewhat of a natural sequel to *Essentialism*.

7. Martin Sheridan's marketing treatise *They Ask You Answer*. This is not top of mind in the beginning for an EP or IP, but down the road it provides a helpful perspective.

As you develop your EP/IP preparation, or if you have already launched it, the one adage that we hope you assimilate is to understand what your outcome will be. Visualize and define what outcome you want to harvest with your disruptive innovation. Keep your eyes focused on that desired outcome. Know your Big Hairy Audacious Goal. And, as mentioned, don't be surprised if you have to pivot your strategy one or more times while keeping your vision and mission intact.

We will finish this EP/IP overview with a quote from the stellar intrapreneurs, Dennis Helling and Samuel Johnson, both from Kaiser Permanente:

Few clinical pharmacy programs were ever "gifted" to any pharmacy department. In reality, each program was evaluated on its merits and costs. Ultimately, business cases were developed and justified before authorization was given…[and a business case included these relational] requirements: exceptional interpersonal communications, symbiotic partnerships at every level of management and leadership, and a bedrock foundation of mutual trust, accountability, and perseverance.[22]

REFERENCES

1. From Great Moments in Pharmacy collection, Robert Thom's painting, The First Hospital Pharmacy in Colonial America, C.1952. Courtesy of the American Pharmacist Association Foundation, on display at the APhA Headquarters Building, Washington DC.

2. Baskar P. *The Intrepreneur*. United States: Biztech Bridgers; 2021:18.

3. Pinkett R, Robinson J, Patterson P. *Black Faces in White Places*. New York, NY: Amacom; 2011:156-159.

4. Ware B. The Top Five Regrets of the Dying. *Huffington Post*, January 21, 2012. **www.huffingtonpost.com/bronnie-ware/top-5-regrets-of-the-dying_b_1220965.html**.

5. McKeown G. *Essentialism*. New York, NY: Crown Business; 2014:16.

6. Greiner, N. *Stress-less Leadership*: *How to Lead in Business and in Life.* Irving, CA: Entrepreneur Press; 2019:203-209.

7. American Journal of Managed Care. Innovative enhanced medication therapy management model: MedWise risk score, medication safety review, and health care outcomes. *The American Journal of Managed Care Supplement*. Vol. 27, No. 16, Sup; Sept 2021.

8. Ratigan AR, Michaud V, Turgeon J, et. al. Longitudinal association of a medication risk score with mortality among ambulatory patients acquired through electronic health record data. *J Patient Saf.* 2021;17(4):249-255.

9. Covey SR. *7 Habits of Highly Effective People*. New York, NY: Simon & Schuster; 2020:202.

10. Platt ML. *The Leader's Brain*: *Enhance Your Leadership, Build Stronger Teams, Make Better Decisions, and Inspire Greater Innovation with Neuroscience.* Philadelphia, PA: Wharton School Press; 2020:12-15.

11. Adopted from Christensen CM, Allworth J, Dillon, K. *How Will You Measure Your Life*? New York, NY: Harper Business; 2012:87.

12. Stulberg, B. *The Practice of Groundedness: A Transformative Path To Success That Feeds—not Crushes—Your Soul*. New York, NY: Penguin Random House; 2021:139.

13. TabulaRasa Healthcare. How we work. Updated 2022. **https://www.tabularasahealthcare.com/how-we-work/#fundamentals**.

14. Friedman DJ. *Culture by Design: 8 steps to drive better individual and organizations performance*. Moorestown, NJ: High Performing Culture; 2018.

15. Hancock B, Weddle B, Schaninger B, and Rahilly L. *Culture in a Hybrid Workplace*. McKinsey Global Publishing. June 2021.

16. Christensen CM, Allworth J, Dillon K. *How Will You Measure Your Life?* New York, NY: Harper Business; 2012:141.

17. Smart BD. *Topgrading*. London, England: Portfolio Penguin; 2012.

18. Harnish V. *Scaling Up: How a Few Companies Make It…and Why the Rest Don't.* New York, NY: Forbes Books; 2014.

19. Emmer M. *Momentum: How Companies Decide What to do Next*. Valencia, CA: Optimize Inc.; 2017.

20. Sheridan M. *They Ask Your Answer*. Hoboken, NJ: John Wiley & Sons; 2019.

21. Stulberg B. *The Practice of Groundedness: A Transformational Path to Success that Feeds—Not Crushes—Your Soul.* New York, NY: Portfolio Penguin Random House; 2021.

22. Helling KD, Johnson SG. Executive Leadership: Critical to Developing Clinical Pharmacy Programs and Services. *Am J Health Syst Pharm*, Vol 72 Dec 1, 2015: 2060.

The authors acknowledge Brian W. Adams for his review of and refinements to this chapter.

APPENDIX: Business Cases

DOI 10.37573/9781585287130

ANTIMICROBIAL STEWARDSHIP SYSTEM EXPANSION

CASE 1

Eric Friestrom, David Hager, and Lucas Schulz

EXECUTIVE SUMMARY

Proposal

To add 1.0 full-time equivalent (FTE) Pharmacist Coordinator and 1.0 FTE Infectious Disease Pharmacist to improve antimicrobial use, lower drug spend, and decrease healthcare-acquired infections (HAIs) across the University Hospital System inclusive of our clinics and community hospital.

Core Positional Duties

1. Conduct prospective and retrospective audits and provider feedback for antimicrobial orders (eg, de-escalation, drug-bug mismatches, dose optimization, parenteral to oral conversion) within the University Hospital System

2. Develop and maintain clinical tools for inpatient and clinic-based patients (clinical practice guidelines, formulary restrictions, order sets, delegation protocols) to improve safety and quality of antimicrobial use

3. Collaborate with infection control on drug-related initiatives related to healthcare-acquired infections

4. Lead initiatives focused on meeting organizational population health goals related to the use of antimicrobials

5. Lead efforts related to drug budget forecasting and targets related to antimicrobial use

6. Coordinate the development of clinician-focused antimicrobial education and competencies

7. Participate on rounds with Infectious Diseases consult services to reduce variation and maximize value

8. Integrate care with the System Community Hospital by providing centralized antimicrobial stewardship services

9. Support the medical director of system antimicrobial stewardship

DOI 10.37573/9781585287130.011

Key Benefits to Health System

1. Safety and Quality
    a. Reduce antimicrobial use variation with the development and implementation of standardized, evidence-based guidelines, policies, protocols, workflows, and prospective auditing.
    b. Maximize medication use systems to improve HAIs (eg, ensuring pre-op order sets are optimized to use best antimicrobials to prevent surgical site infections; reduce inappropriate antimicrobial use that may increase patient risk for the development of *Clostridioides difficile)*
    c. Minimize the development of antimicrobial resistance from inappropriate antimicrobial utilization
2. Value Management
    a. Ensure that antimicrobial therapy will achieve the best outcomes by optimizing antimicrobial selection and dosing (eg, pharmacokinetics and pharmacodynamics)
    b. Reduce drug costs by preventing the use of unnecessary antimicrobials recommended by Infectious Diseases Consult Services (1% of patients account for 50% of inpatient antimicrobial spend)
3. Compliance and External Reporting
    a. Achieve compliance with ever evolving Centers for Medicare & Medicaid Services conditions of participation related to antimicrobial stewardship
    b. Achieve compliance with Joint Commission requirements for ambulatory antimicrobial stewardship
    c. Achieve and/or maintain status of Infectious Diseases Society of America Center of Excellence
4. Alignment with Strategic Plan
    a. Achieve integration and consistency in approach to antimicrobial use
    b. Achieve reduced total cost of care in alignment with population health goals

Financial Implications

The position will be staffed as two FTE with a total annual operating expense (salary plus fringe) of approximately $300,000. Annual savings from the additional 2.0 FTE are estimated at $750,000 average annual savings ($3,760,000 over the next five years).

Conclusion

The addition of 2.0 FTE antimicrobial stewardship pharmacist resources will optimize safe, efficient, evidence-based, and cost-effective antimicrobial use. Furthermore, the program has a hard dollar return on investment ratio 2.5:1, and soft dollar benefits related to reduced antimicrobial resistance and improved regulatory compliance and external reporting.

BUSINESS/SERVICE DESCRIPTION

Antimicrobial stewardship programs, or ASPs, promote appropriate antimicrobial use, improve patient outcomes, reduce microbial resistance, decrease the spread of infections caused by multidrug-resistant organisms, and ensure fiscally responsible antimicrobial therapy is provided to all patients. Multiple regulatory bodies, including the Centers for Medicare Services (CMS) and the Joint Commission, mandate ASPs because of their documented impact on patient outcomes. Under-resourced or fragmented ASPs are less likely to be effective in meeting their goals.

Systemness is a key strategic priority for the University Hospital System. Patients, providers, and staff move across sites to receive and provide care. Antimicrobial use uniquely requires a system approach—as differences in formularies, drug policies, and restricted drug approvals creates inefficiencies and service gaps. In addition, any inappropriate use that increases the development of resistant organisms at any of the sites increase the cost of care at all sites. Inconsistent approaches also increase costs as leveraging purchasing power for medications is not possible. Providers routinely comment that these types of differences create confusion in their practice.

In its current state, the University Hospital and regional System Community Hospital's ASPs work independently, focused on respective hospital priorities. The University Hospital antimicrobial stewardship team (2.4 FTE) oversees the system's flagship adult hospital, children's hospital, rehabilitation hospital, and the orthopedic hospital (~800 beds). They focus on preventing inappropriate antimicrobial use by performing daily prospective audit and feedback, standardizing treatment through clinical practice guidelines, and delegation protocols at the flagship hospital with a focus on the inpatient setting. The Infectious Disease clinical pharmacist monitors antimicrobial utilization and identifies areas of opportunity based on this information. Initial work has been done in establishing an ambulatory stewardship program to meet Joint Commission regulatory requirements; however, a robust program is not yet in place due to resource constraints. At the System Community Hospital, ASP services are completed by frontline staff and minimally resourced infectious disease pharmacist staff. Much of the program is carried out one-on-one between providers and pharmacists and does not address antimicrobial stewardship holistically. This nonintegrated approach results in fragmented stewardship practice, variable practice standards, minimal data sharing, and high variability in antimicrobial utilization. Variability in antimicrobial utilization, driven by differences in clinical practice, leads to increased costs, reduced efficiency, provider dissatisfaction, and poorer outcomes. In addition to these negative outcomes, the lack of a system approach to antimicrobial use means there are no opportunities or resources to create synergy between hospitals.

There is an opportunity to invest in antimicrobial stewardship at a system level drive standardization. Through a moderate increase in resources, variable antimicrobial utilization and non-standard clinical practice can be standardized, improving patient outcomes. This ties to the system's five-year strategic plan's goal of system integration. While standardization is resource intensive, the initial informal partnership has demonstrated an ability to systematize the ASP and reduce variation. A favorable soft and hard dollar return on investment exists as a result of standardization through program expansion.

ENVIRONMENTAL/NEEDS ASSESSMENT

Despite the System Community Hospital having a long-standing antimicrobial stewardship program, significant opportunities remain. The System Community Hospital has had some successes, resulting in hard dollar savings, (eg, reporting low antibiotic resistance rates and documenting pharmacist interventions). Unfortunately, as a result of inconsistent personnel availability, medication use is suboptimal. Although physicians have established relationships with clinical pharmacists, the lack of required expertise and in consistent presence is limiting physician uptake of evidence based medication recommendations. For example, inpatient ordering of two high-cost antimicrobials, ceftaroline and daptomycin, increased abruptly in July 2021 when the past-year's pharmacy resident, who had an infectious disease focus, left upon completing their training. (**Figure 1**, **Figure 2**). Together, increased use resulted in excessive antibiotic monthly spend of $15,000 ($180,000 per year).

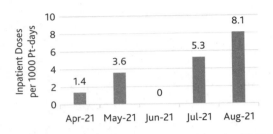

CASE 1, FIGURE 1. Ceftaroline inpatient doses per 1000 pt-days (Cost per Dose ~$215)

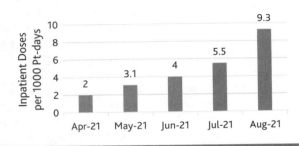

CASE 1, FIGURE 2. Daptomycin inpatient doses per 1000 pt-days (Cost per Dose ~$300)

Despite past success, the increasing demands for ASP support and the absence of dedicated ASP pharmacist support created a resource gap. Currently, stewardship efforts at the System Community Hospital rely on the Clinical Pharmacy Manager, nonspecialized or infectious disease (ID) trained decentral clinical pharmacists, and, inconsistently, pharmacy residents. This fluctuating level of service also creates challenges for providers who desire a consistent approach, often undermining ongoing stewardship efforts. In addition, tracking and monitoring of antimicrobial utilization at the System Community Hospital is limited and not visible to providers or pharmacists.

The Joint Commission medication management standard MM.09.01.01 addresses antimicrobial stewardship. Compliance with this standard requires a single pharmacist leader responsible for improving antimicrobial use who systematically evaluates ongoing treatment needs and tracks antimicrobial prescribing. Prospective audit and feedback performed daily by an ID-trained pharmacist best accomplishes this requirement. Based on a recent publication, the minimum FTE support recommended for a hospital of 100 to 300 beds is 1.0 ID-trained pharmacist FTE.[1]

The Joint Commission began surveying ambulatory clinics on the presence of an ambulatory antimicrobial stewardship program on January 1st, 2020 (MM.09.01.03). Five elements of performance, similar to the inpatient elements, are necessary for full compliance. Currently, the community hospital is at risk for Joint Commission noncompliance because they lack an ambulatory stewardship program with all five elements of performance.

OPERATING PLAN(s)

There are two areas of opportunity within this expansion: the System Community Hospital service expansion and the University Hospital System ASP leadership support. One of the requested FTE (Infectious Disease Pharmacist) will primarily support the System Community Hospital routine antimicrobial stewardship review while the other FTE (Pharmacist, Coordinator) will work to develop strategic initiatives across the system with a focus on reducing HAIs, standardize clinical guidance with input from stakeholders, and track and report system antimicrobial use.

Specific antimicrobial stewardship opportunities that would be pursued by the additional FTEs are below:

Variable antimicrobial utilization between the University Hospital and the System Community Hospital stems from practice variation. Additional resources allows for implementation of prospective audit and feedback across the system.

Fluoroquinolone utilization at the System Community Hospital has run 750% higher than at our academic site, despite a higher acuity (45 versus six Days of Therapy (DOT) / 1000 Patient Days (PD), respectively, 2021 data). The academic center targeted fluoroquinolone use reduction as a mechanism to curtail *Clostridioides difficile* infections (CDI). Utilization reduction was accomplished through guideline modification, electronic medical record (EMR) clinical decision support, targeted evaluation during daily prospective audit and feedback, and a formal drug restriction program. Other opportunities to reduce broad spectrum use includes vancomycin and β-lactam/β-lactamase inhibitor combinations (ie, piperacillin/tazobactam). The System Community Hospital use is 18% higher than similar patients at the University Hospital (65 versus 55 and 77 versus 65 DOT/1000PD, respectively; **Figure 3** below).

Other targets for standardizing drug utilization at the System Community Hospital include implementation of prolonged infusion β-lactams (piperacillin/tazobactam, cefepime, and meropenem), standardized vancomycin dosing and monitoring, reduced utilization of carbapenems (ertapenem and meropenem). Opportunities may also exist for antifungal stewardship and antiviral stewardship to control costs of posaconazole, micafungin, and oseltamivir.

The requested FTE would coordinate and perform daily prospective audit and feedback on all System Community Hospital patients and similar services at the University Hospital (Gen. Med, Hospitalist, Family Medicine), reducing antibiotic utilization variance. Daily prospective audit and feedback facilitates identification of practice standardization opportunities. Practice standards are determined by clinical practice guidelines, delegation protocols and clinical support tools. **Table 1** (Appendix)

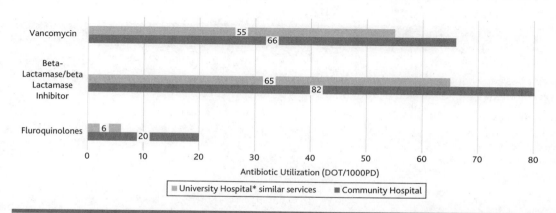

CASE 1, FIGURE 3. Antibiotic utilization variability between the university hospital and the community hospital

outlines the guidelines available at the University Hospital and the System Community Hospital. Only guidelines pertinent to the System Community Hospital patient types are shown for comparison (excludes liver transplant and bone marrow transplant guidelines available at the University Hospital, for example).

The University Hospital pharmacist utilizes the EMR to effectively and efficiently review every patient on antimicrobials every day. Daily prospective audit and feedback by an ID-trained pharmacist ensures the stewardship program has a comprehensive understanding of antimicrobial utilization and emerging treatment trends. This familiarity with prescribing practices allows the ASP to rapidly correct practice deviations or adapt guidelines based on the most current evidence-based medicine. All University Hospital System guidelines are available in the EMR with links to appropriate guidelines built into orders and order sets. The System Community Hospital also utilizes the EMR to build in order sets, policies, and protocols, and additionally utilize paper-based algorithms.

Consistent treatment between hospitals improves provider satisfaction and workforce efficiency. The System Community Hospital and the University Hospital share a physician workforce. Drug formulary and guideline variability lead to confusion and frustration. For example, fluoroquinolone antibiotics are restricted at the University Hospital and unrestricted at the System Community Hospital; all anti *Pseudomonas* β-lactam antibiotics are given as prolonged infusion (three to four hours) at the University Hospital and over 30 minutes at the System Community Hospital. These differences result in variability in fluoroquinolone prescribing rates and in differences in achievement of dosing targets. Unnecessary fluoroquinolone use results in *CDI* and suboptimal dosing may result in prolonged ICU and hospital length of stay.[2;3]

> Nonstandardized patient care results in inconsistent patient outcomes. The requested FTE will implement practice changes aimed at improving patient outcomes at the System Community Hospital and the University Hospital.

Fluoroquinolone reduction at the University Hospital was associated with an 80% decrease in hospital-acquired *Clostridioides difficile* infection (CDI) rates. Other stewardship factors associated with reduced CDI include lower broad spectrum (eg, vancomycin, β-lactam/β-lactamase inhibitor, cefepime) antibiotic utilization. **Table 1** shows opportunities for improving patient outcomes through antimicrobial stewardship. Timely sepsis care at the System Community Hospital is 10% lower than the University Hospital. Timely sepsis care is associated with lower mortality.[4]

System Community Hospital patients experienced 48 hospital onset CDI cases. Implementing guidelines, protocols, clinical decision support tools, and daily prospective audit and feedback could

CASE 1, TABLE 1. Variability in Patient Outcomes Based on Medicare Reported Data September 2021

	University Hospital	System Community Hospital
Hospital-acquired *CDI*	102 reported/138 predicted Infections (73.7%)	48 reported/43 predicted infections (111.6%)
Sepsis Care (Percent of patients receiving appropriate care for severe sepsis and septic shock)	61%	51%
Methicillin-resistant *Staphylococcus aureus* (MRSA) blood infections	No different than national benchmark	No different than national benchmark
Central line-associated blood stream infections	No different than national benchmark	No different than national benchmark
Catheter-associated urinary tract infections	Better than national benchmark	No different than national benchmark
Payment for pneumonia patients	No different than national average payment	No different than national average payment

conservatively reduce fluoroquinolone use by 50%. A moderate reduction of 25% results in twelve fewer cases. This is expected to reduce attributable costs associated with hospital length of stay of 5.2 days for primary CDI and 1.96 days for recurrent CDI and healthcare costs of $24,205 and $10,580 per episode.[5]

CASE 1, TABLE 2. Opportunity for Reduction of CDI Cases at System Community Hospital

	Year 1	Year 2	Year 3	Year 4	Year 5
CDI 25% reduction = 12 cases	$193,640	$199,499	$205,432	$211,595	$217,943

The University Hospital System includes a long-acting lipoglycopeptide in the Skin and Soft Tissue Infection Guideline. The antibiotic provides 10 days of therapy with a single administration. The University Hospital Emergency Department employs this antibiotic tool to avoid unnecessary admissions. In the past year, the ED has administered oritavancin to 10 patients. All patients' symptoms improved without hospital admission or subsequent therapy.

CASE 1, TABLE 3. Opportunity for Reduced ED Admissions for SSTI at System Community Hospital

	Year 1	Year 2	Year 3	Year 4	Year 5
Reduced ED admissions for SSTI (Assumes five cases/year at $8,023 per admission[6])	$40,115	$41,318	$42,558	$43,835	$45,150

Antimicrobial utilization variation driven by clinical practice variability results in other patient outcome differences. Data available from MedPar, a publicly accessible, limited data set available through the Centers for Medicare & Medicare Services, demonstrates opportunities for cost savings and revenue generation when treating patients for: complicated intra-abdominal infections (cIAI), urinary tract infections (cUTI), skin and soft tissue infection (cSSTI), and uncomplicated skin and soft tissue infection (ucSSTI). Assuming that through standardization of practice outcomes at the System Community Hospital can match those of the University Hospital, annual savings and revenue generation would total $215,768 and 138 hospital days would be saved.

CASE 1, TABLE 4. Opportunity for Standardization of Practice Across Sites

2020 Cases		n	LOS	Costs	Medicare Payments	Revenue	Annual Savings	Hospital Days Saved
cIAI	University Hospital	119	3.1	$6,000	$4,864	($1,136)	System Community Hospital = $22,627	System Community Hospital = 20 days
	System Community Hospital	61	3.6	$6,071	$4,529	$1,542		
cUTI	University Hospital	110	3.2	$6,913	$4,464	($2,449)	University Hospital = $160,710	University Hospital = 77 days
	System Community Hospital	17	2.5	$5,432	$4,444	($988)		
cSSTI	University Hospital	27	5.3	$10,991	$8,446	($2,545)	University Hospital = $8,883	System Community Hospital = 11 days
	System Community Hospital	23	5.8	$10,564	$8,348	($2,216)		
ucSSTI	University Hospital	119	3.1	$6,000	$4,864	($1,136)	System Community Hospital = $23,548	System Community Hospital = 30 days
	System Community Hospital	61	3.6	$6,071	$4,529	($1,542)		

	Year 1	Year 2	Year 3	Year 4	Year 5
Improved patient outcomes through standardized work	$215,768	222,241	$228,908	$235,776	$242,849

Therapeutic dose monitoring for vancomycin is a proven and effective way to reduce vancomycin induced nephrotoxicity.[7] Each case of vancomycin induced nephrotoxicity costs $22,000 in additional expenses and prolongs a patient's hospital stay. The System Community Hospital and the University Hospital use internally developed vancomycin dose monitoring calculators. Evaluation and expansion of these tools and pharmacist driven monitoring across both enterprises may decrease the costs associated with vancomycin-induced nephrotoxicity. By aligning with the System Community Hospital's vancomycin therapeutic dose monitoring and utilizing optimized level monitoring with Bayesian dosing algorithms, we expect a decrease in the overall number of drug-induced nephrotoxicity cases. An increase in the infectious disease pharmacist FTE will provide the resources necessary to implement and standardize the vancomycin monitoring program across both systems, strengthening and improving the program at each institution. Based on the System Community Hospital's experience, standardization may result in a vancomycin-induced nephrotoxicity reduction of 1% per year.

CASE 1, TABLE 5. Opportunity for Vancomycin-Induced Acute Kidney Injury Avoidance

	Year 1	Year 2	Year 3	Year 4	Year 5
Vancomycin-induced acute kidney injury avoidance (two patients per year)	$ 44,000	$ 45,320	$ 46,680	$ 48,080	$ 49,522

Increased resources will identify cost-savings opportunities from improved system-wide tracking and reporting of antimicrobial utilization.

The proposed coordinator FTE will work across systems to develop a tracking and reporting structure to measure antimicrobial utilization and identify future targets. Tracking and reporting antimicrobial utilization and resistance patterns identifies opportunities to optimize use of novel, new, and costly antibiotics. Comparing the University Hospital and the System Community Hospital drug budgets identifies some cost-saving targets.

Currently $937,161 (7.28%) of the System Community Hospital total drug spend is on antimicrobial agents. The variation in nonadjusted percentage of total drug budget demonstrates opportunities for standardization of antimicrobial prescribing, guidelines, protocols.

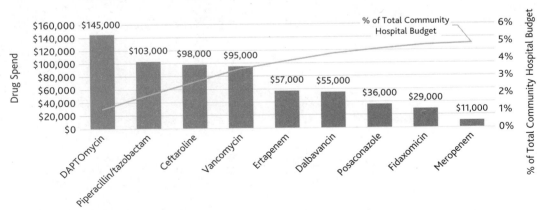

CASE 1, FIGURE 4. System community hospital drug spend

Daptomycin, ceftaroline, piperacillin/tazobactam, vancomycin, ertapenem, fidaxomicin, and posaconazole represent targets for drug cost savings.

CASE 1, TABLE 6. Opportunity for Antimicrobial Drug-Spend Reduction at the System Community Hospital

Antimicrobial	System Community Hospital Drug Spend 2021	Target Reduction	System Community Hospital Cost Avoidance for Year 1
DAPTOmycin	$145,000	30%	$43,500
Piperacillin/tazobactam	$103,000	30%	$30,900
Ceftaroline	$98,000	50%	$49,000
Vancomycin	$95,000	10%	$9,500
Ertapenem	$57,000	50%	$28,500
Dalbavancin	$55,000	10%	$5,500
Posaconazole	$36,000	5%	$1,800
Fidaxomicin	$29,000	90%	$26,100
Meropenem	$11,000	10%	$1,100
Total			$195,900

	Year 1	Year 2	Year 3	Year 4	Year 5
Antimicrobial cost savings at System Community Hospital	$195,000	$200,850	$206,876	$213,082	$219,474

Emerging antimicrobial drugs target highly resistant pathogens. A system-wide approach to monitoring resistance patterns and antimicrobial utilization improves the use of novel drug therapies. Small, but significant, cost savings can be expected for the University Hospital also. This includes improved market share and improved contract prices, as demonstrated with oritavancin contracted rebates.

CASE 1, TABLE 7. Opportunity to Optimize Emerging Antibiotic Cost Savings

	Year 1	Year 2	Year 3	Year 4	Year 5
Antimicrobial cost savings for emerging antibiotics at the University Hospital	$15,000	$15,450	$15,914	$16,391	$16,883
Improved contracting price based on market share (10% cost reduction at the University Hospital and the System Community Hospital)	$12,789	$13,173	$13,568	$13,975	$14,394

FINANCIAL PLAN

Implementation of additional FTE to support ASP opportunities results in a net operating savings of $3.7 million over a five year period (~$750,000 annually). Annual gross financial benefits are estimated to start at $715,000 (year 1) and grow to $785,000 by year 5. Annual operating costs reflective of personnel costs start at $280,000 (year 1) and grow to $312,000 by year 5. This results in an estimated hard dollar return on investment ratio of 2.5:1.

A summary of identified savings and operating expenses is below:

CASE 1, TABLE 8. Summary of Financial Benefits and Costs

	Year 1	Year 2	Year 3	Year 4	Year 5
Reduced Drug Spend					
Drug cost savings based on gaps between the University Hospital and the System Community Hospital care	($195,000)	($200,850)	($206,876)	($213,082)	($219,474)
Improved resistance detection results in reduced use of new drug therapies	($15,000)	($15,450)	($15,914)	($16,391)	($16,883)
Improved Patient Outcomes					
Reduced rate of hospital-acquired infections (12 fewer CDiff cases per year at the System Community Hospital)	($193,640)	($199,499)	($205,432)	($211,595)	($217,943)
Reduced vancomycin-induced AKI and improved care of cIAI, cUTI, cSSTI, ucSSTI through standardized work	($259,768)	($267,561)	($268,921)	($270,321)	($271,763)
Increased Infusion Center Revenue Capture					
Improved contracting price for antimicrobials (10% cost reduction to the University Hospital and the System Community Hospital)	($12,789)	($13,173)	($13,568)	($13,975)	($14,394)
Reduced SSTI admissions from ED due to lipoglycopeptide use (assumes five cases per year treated as outpatient)	($40,115)	($41,318)	($42,558)	($43,835)	($45,150)
Benefits Total (avoided costs)	$716,312	$737,851	$753,269	$769,199	$785,607
Incremental Operating Expenses					
Coordinator Pharmacist 1.0 FTE	$150,000	$154,500	$159,135	$163,909	$168,826
Clinical pharmacist 1.0 FTE	$130,000	$133,250	$136,581	$139,995	$143,495
Net Operating Savings/Benefit	$436,312	$449,451	$456,217	$463,235	$470,464

LEGAL OR REGULATORY CONCERNS

Internal Health System legal counsel must review and approve all data sharing and privacy agreements with the System Community Hospital prior to implementation of services. Expected timeline will depend on organizational legal review prioritization but is estimated to be completed within 60 days of request. No additional internal or external legal considerations are needed for this program.

IMPLEMENTATION PLAN

Implementation of the program will follow eight strategic priority domains including recruitment and onboarding. Each domain has associated Key Performance Indicators (KPIs) to track throughout implementation to monitor success.

1. SP0: Recruitment and onboarding
2. SP1: Prospective audit and feedback
3. SP2: Dose optimization strategies

4.   SP3: Laboratory stewardship

5.   SP4: Track and report antibiotic utilization

6.   SP5: JC accreditation readiness and success

7.   SP6: ID pharmacist visibility

8.   SP7: Fiscal outcomes

Following approval of the FTE, an estimated three month recruitment and three month onboarding period would take place. After onboarding is completed, initial work on strategic priorities 1, 3, 4, 5, and 6 would begin. Core responsibilities would be split across both FTEs with the coordinator focusing on strategy and integration and the infectious disease pharmacist focusing on daily operations and clinical work. Projects milestones will be met following the launch of the proposal as outlined in **Figure 5**.

If the venture experiences unexpected barriers that do not allow the implementation to continue, the following exit strategy would occur:

- After attrition of current clinical pharmacist, the additional clinical pharmacist would be placed at the System Community Hospital and services would return to pre-implementation state

- The Coordinator FTE would be skill-mix changed down to a clinical pharmacist and through attrition would be integrated back into the University Hospital inpatient pharmacist team

- Protocol and antimicrobial standardization across systems would be paused until resource allocation supports system collaboration

- Accreditation requirements are the responsibility of the individual sites regulatory teams to manage. The System Community Hospital would need to identify existing resources that could be allocated to their ASP program to meet new ambulatory requirements.

SUPPORTING MATERIALS

Supporting materials for this business case are in the appendix and include:

- ASP related organizational guidelines analysis (**Appendix 1, Table 1**)

- Gantt chart of implementation timeline (**Appendix 2, Figure 5**)

LESSONS LEARNED

1.   Collectively building the business case with the community hospital is essential to success. It cannot be seen as a way for the academic center to control the community hospital. It is important to include their successes and how they can help improve care at the academic center as well.

2.   Community hospital leadership may be easier to engage as they are often closer to the work and to patients—determining what is in it for them early is a key step.

3.   Physician support is essential. Stewardship and "standardization" can imply a lack of autonomy. Having a history of small wins can aid in the support.

4.   Tracking and reporting of antimicrobial utilization is paramount to a successful stewardship program. Clarity about where data comes from, who data are shared with, and how data are acquired is essential to determine early in the planning and performance stages.

5. While it is difficult to tie new revenue to clinical expansion—be creative about the financial implications of improved care. A lot of time was spent in the literature to identify costs (and revenue) associated with complications of inappropriate medication use to tie financial outcomes to the clinical outcomes.

6. Determining where the resources will "live" in terms of cost-centers is an important discussion for system positions. At the end of the day, who is writing their checks gets to determine their priorities.

7. Where the FTE lives may also have impacts on recruitment. Specialists may perceive differently a position "located" within the academic center versus a position at the community hospital.

8. After approval, system positions require clear accountability structures. There needs to be an identified leader to hold the new ASP team to the promises made within the business case. This will likely then have multiple stakeholders across sites. A regular cadence of meetings is necessary if such structures do not already exist.

9. Many organizations strive for "systemness" and are unclear about what they exactly desire. It will be important for leaders to understand what "systemness" means to their stakeholders.

10. Regulatory compliance, while seemingly compelling, is not always an easy sell. Unless there is a history of findings, senior leaders may not be compelled to act based on undefined "risk." Oftentimes, departments are able to show compliance with low investments.

11. Clinical service expansion is most often justified on improved quality, reduced harm, and/or regulatory requirements—not true hard dollar savings or increased revenue. Positioning these improvements in quality as financial improvements for the organization may be a necessary way to communicate most persuasively to your audience.

REFERENCES

1. Doernberg SB, Abbo LM, Burdette SD, et al. Essential resources and strategies for antibiotic stewardship programs in the acute care setting. *Clin Infect Dis*. 2018;67(8):1168–1174. PubMed

2. Owens RC, Donskey CJ, Gaynes RP, et al. Antimicrobial-associated risk factors for clostridium difficile infection. *Clin Infect Dis*. 2008; Vol. 46, Issue SUPPL. 1.

3. Van TT, Minejima E, Chiu CA, Butler-Wu SM. Don't get wound up: revised fluoroquinolone breakpoints for enterobacteriaceae and pseudomonas aeruginosa. *J Clin Microbiol*. 2019;57(7):e02072–18. PubMed

4. Kumar A, Roberts D, Wood KE, et al. Duration of hypotension before initiation of effective antimicrobial therapy is the critical determinant of survival in human septic shock. *Crit Care Med*. 2006;34(6):1589–1596. PubMed

5. Zhang D, Prabhu VS, Marcella SW. Attributable healthcare resource utilization and costs for patients with primary and recurrent clostridium difficile infection in the United States. *Clin Infect Dis*. 2018;66(9):1326–1332. PubMed

6. LaPensee KT, Fan W, Wang Y. PIN22 Economic burden of hospitalization with antibiotic treatment for absssi in the United States: an analysis of the premier hospital database. *Value Health*. 2012;15(4):A240–A241.

7. Neely MN, Kato L, Youn G, et al. Prospective trial on the use of trough concentration versus area under the curve to determine therapeutic vancomycin dosing. *Antimicrob Agents Chemother*. 2018;62(2):e02042–17. PubMed

APPENDIX 1

TABLE 1. Guidelines and Delegation Protocols Available at the University Hospital and the System Community Hospital

University Hospital System	System Community Hospital
Clinical Practice Guidelines • Diagnosis and management of sepsis • Surgical and Interventional Radiology Antimicrobial Prophylaxis • Skin, Skin Structure, and Soft Tissue Infection Diagnosis and Treatment • Diagnosis and management of infections of the urinary tract • Prevention, Diagnosis, and Treatment of *Clostridioides difficile* infection • Treatment of Community-Acquired Bacterial Pneumonia (CABP) • Use of Procalcitonin Monitoring Related to the Diagnosis and Treatment of Respiratory Tract and Emerging Sepsis • Management of Neutropenic Fever • Infective Endocarditis • Clinical Monitoring of Outpatient Parenteral Antimicrobial Therapy (OPAT) and selected oral antimicrobial agents • Anti-infective Lock Therapy • Medication Route Interchange • Renal Function-based Dose Adjustments • Continuous Renal Replacement Therapy Dose Adjustment • Dosing of medications in patients receiving continuous enteral feedings • Intravenous Vancomycin Use • Pharmacokinetic/Pharmacodynamic Dose Optimization of Antibiotics for the treatment of Gram-negative Infections • Treatment of Patients with Reported Allergies to β-lactam Antibiotics • Influenza and Pneumococcal Vaccination • Treatment and Prevention of Influenza with Antiviral Medications **Delegation/Practice Protocols** • Renal Function-based Dose Adjustment • Pharmacist Medication Route Interchange • Continuous Renal Replacement Therapy (CRRT) • Immunization • Perioperative Antimicrobial Prophylaxis • Vancomycin Dosing and Monitoring • Antimicrobial Dosing Based on PK/PD Principles • *Clostridioides difficile* • *Clostridioides difficile* Testing • Probiotic Ordering to Reduce Primary *Clostridioides difficile* Incidence • Immunization Ordering • Influenza Screening and Treatment • Antibiotic Therapy for Urodynamics Testing • Asymptomatic Bacteriuria Preoperative Screening and Treatment • *Candida* Intertrigo and/or Cutaneous Candidiasis and Peristomal Yeast Infection Medicated Topical Treatment • Lyme Disease Prophylaxis • Management of Streptococcal Cultures of the Throat, Rectum or Vagina • Treatment of Sexually Transmitted Infections (STIs) or Genital Infections	**Clinical Practice Guidelines** • ER antibiotic outpatient prescribing algorithm • AUC vancomycin-based dosing • Clinical monitoring of antimicrobials including lab and drug titration orders • Influenza/pneumococcal vaccination monitoring • Broad spectrum de-escalation algorithm • Antibiotic PK/PD dosing program • Vaccination program for newborn visitors **Delegation Protocols** • IV/PO protocol • Renal and indication dose adjustment • Vancomycin and aminoglycoside dosing protocol

APPENDIX 2

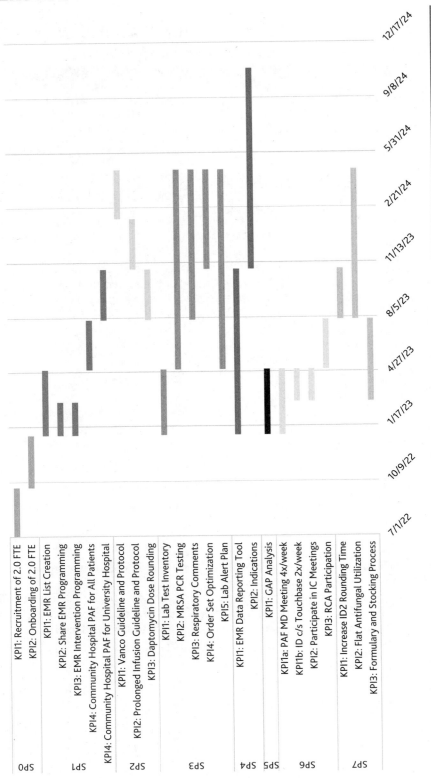

CASE 1, FIGURE 5. University hospital system antimicrobial service expansion implementation plan

RESIDENCY PROGRAM EXPANSION

Halena Leah Marcelin and Michael DeCoske

EXECUTIVE SUMMARY

The need to expand pharmacy residency programs nationwide is urgent. The value of pharmacy residency programs is well described in the literature as is the stated desire to ensure those in direct patient care roles receive this valuable training. However, the number of residency program applicants far exceeds the number of training programs currently available. While starting or growing a residency program may seem daunting, it can be accomplished with a reasonable amount of planning and creativity. A thoughtful approach of demonstrating program value with senior leadership, building solid residency program infrastructure, and ensuring sustainability through direct and indirect financial measures has demonstrated success.

BACKGROUND

Baptist Health South Florida (BHSF) is an internationally renowned health system with various centers of excellence, 11 hospitals, more than 25,000 employees, 4,000 physicians, and more than 100 outpatient centers, urgent care facilities, and physician practices spanning across Miami-Dade, Monroe, Broward, and Palm Beach counties. BHSF is an anchor institution of the South Florida communities we serve. Through our healthcare services, human capital, and community investments we are committed to improving the health and economic well-being of our communities and their residents.

The Clinical Pharmacy Enterprise was established in 2018 with the goal of supporting the vision and mission of BHSF. The BHSF Clinical Pharmacy Enterprise vision is to be the leading provider of world class clinical pharmacy services in the communities we serve. To bring that vision to fruition a clear mission statement was developed. The mission is to transform and advance clinical pharmacy practice through innovation, evidenced-based care, and a commitment to education.

A dynamic pharmacy education program is paramount to developing and retaining clinical and administrative pharmacy experts. For a high-value pharmacy enterprise, it is also a critical way to advance the organization's patient care model.[1] In growing a pharmacy education program, a clear mission statement underscoring the overall commitment to training is paramount. From there a strategic plan can be developed and an annual work plan can be refined with training at the epicenter of growth and expansion.

DOI 10.37573/9781585287130.012

At BHSF, in order to achieve our mission and vision, we set out to strategically grow our pharmacy residency programs. This has proven to be an essential strategy in building a pharmacist career ladder, increasing the expertise of pharmacists across the enterprise, and supporting recruitment efforts. Particularly in areas where national recruitment can be challenging, having a robust internal training program is critical.

Institutions considering starting or growing a pharmacy residency program may be concerned about the financial sustainability of doing so. Additionally, there may be hesitation with having insufficient preceptors or infrastructure to support the program. While those are valid concerns, they can be overcome with planning and some creativity. Some who are committed to growth may postpone getting started until all the fine details are worked out. While good planning is needed, the approach of waiting until all aspects are perfect, until the Is are dotted and Ts are crossed, as it were, does not line up well to support the national need for expansion.

That national need is urgent. In recent years, PGY1 and PGY2 programs have grown, as illustrated in **Table 1**. However, that growth has not kept up with demand. According to ASHP,[2-4] in 2021 there were 2,167 applicants who did not match for a PGY1 program, despite only having 19 unfilled PGY1 positions nationwide. That illustrates the wide chasm between the number of programs and the incredible demand for candidates entering the match. We have put out the call that the standard for our profession must be elevated and now we must match that call with action. Starting or expanding a program may seem like a daunting task to plan and justify; however, much economy of scale is derived from growing a program and often the need for additional resources is not proportional for each additional resident added.[5]

CASE 2, TABLE 1. Pharmacy Residency Statistics—2019-2021[2-4]

Category	2019	2020	2021
PGY1 Positions Matched	3,530	3,671	3,741
PGY2 Positions Matched	1,167	1,252	1,380
Total Matched	5,090	4,768	4,873
Matched Phase 1	4,697	4,425	4,527
Matched Phase 2	393	343	347
Unfilled Positions	37	43	53
Unfilled PGY1	11	5	19
Unfilled PGY2	26	38	34
Unmatched Applicants	1,229	2,596	2,448
Unmatched PGY1	1,138	2,281	2,167
Unmatched PGY2	91	315	281

Additionally, it is well understood that growing residency programs is a critical component in the development of pharmacy practice. According to the ASHP Practice Advancement Initiative 2030, organizations "should require the completion of an ASHP-accredited residency training as a minimum credential for new pharmacist practitioners."[6] In order to make that goal a reality, program expansion is essential.

Over the last five years, BHSF recognized the need to expand the pharmacy residency program to support its strategic plan. BHSF currently offers a wide range of postgraduate residency and fellowship programs across its various institutions. Our goal is to attract, educate, and retain exceptional healthcare talent for the communities we serve. In recent years, we have successfully increased the number of PGY2 offerings across the health system (eg, Infectious Disease, Ambulatory Care, and Corporate Pharmacy Administration and Leadership) and added a nontraditional PGY2 program (**see Table 2**).

CASE 2, TABLE 2. Pharmacy Residency Program Growth—2018-2022

	2018-2019	2019-2020	2020-2021	2021-2022
PGY1 Positions	13	13	13	13
BHM	8	8	8	8
SMH	2	2	2	2
WKBH	2	2	2	2
HH	1	1	1	1
PGY2 Positions	2	4	7	9
Oncology	1	3	4	4
Critical Care	1	1	1	1
Cardiology	0	0	1	1
Ambulatory Care	0	0	1	2
Infectious Disease	0	0	0	1
Total Residency Positions	15	17	20	22

While we have expanded our PGY2 programs, the size of the PGY1 programs have remained the same. Currently, we have an opportunity to expand the PGY1 program at one of our large hospitals. This is particularly time sensitive given the recent implementation of a pharmacy career ladder across BHSF. Our goal is to elevate the pharmacy practice model and ensure that patient care related positions (both inpatient and outpatient) require at least PGY1 residency training. This, coupled with the increase in vacancy rates for pharmacist positions that we have experienced, substantiates the need for more internal programs to support recruitment initiatives.

Historically, we have been able to justify expanding our residency programs by demonstrating program value with senior leadership, building a solid program infrastructure, and ensuring a sustainable program based on direct and indirect financial measures.

PROGRAM VALUE

The value of pharmacy residency training is well understood by those reading this case study. Thus, the key is translating the value proposition to health system senior leadership in terms that are well received. Intertwining the resident's learning experience with goals of the pharmacy department and hospital is paramount to being able to clearly communicate the meaningful and tangible value that starting or growing a residency program can provide. It is helpful for senior leaders to have a firm understanding of the value of pharmacy residency programs. Pharmacy leaders can facilitate this by ensuring that the value of the program is routinely discussed and that the current residents get face time with senior leaders at various points during the residency program.

Expansion of pharmacy residency programs has shown to well support departmental goals. Brophy et al. demonstrated that growing a residency program increased documentation of clinical interventions, prevented adverse drug events, and increased the educational programs provided to hospital staff.[5] Clinical and operational objectives that might be difficult to resource could be piloted or started using resident staffing and then expanded as value is observed.[7] This might even include advanced services such as expansion of pharmacy clinical services to a new clinic or patient population. Also, while traditional staff already have work allocated to them, many organizations rely on pharmacy residents to support unplanned initiatives, such as we have seen with COVID-19 vaccination efforts.

Next, the cost of pharmacist recruitment can be significant between the resources needed to advertise, recruit, and train new pharmacists. Also, prolonged vacancies put a drain on the pharmacy workforce and can often cause a negative impact on patient care. When positions are unfilled for a long period of time, pharmacy leaders are forced to make difficult decisions between prioritizing basic drug distribution services and advanced clinical pharmacy functions. Being able to recruit and retain talent from an organization's own training program is an excellent justification for growing a PGY1 program.

During the development of the strategy to grow our program, we referenced the seven strategies Wheaton Franciscan Healthcare leaders utilized to grow their program.[8] Ultimately, the goals supporting the request to grow the pharmacy residency program in this case centered on increasing the talent pool within the health system to meet the pharmacy's mission and vision while providing additional staffing support to the hospital.

Specific goals referenced are listed below:

- Benefits of growing residency program at Baptist Hospital Miami:
    - Support planned growth of inpatient beds at Baptist Hospital of Miami (residents could provide supplemental centralized and decentralized staffing as well as occupy future positions)
    - Resident contributions planned to support requests for increased FTEs by facilitating pilots or expansion of new pharmacy services
    - Participation in implementing/supporting cost reduction strategies/initiatives
    - Cost-friendly labor pool
    - Clinical initiative participation
    - Support of projects to improve patient care (quality, expansion of services)
    - Added staff in an areas mitigating staff burnout
        - COVID-19 related impact on the labor pool
    - Facilitate positive learning environment for all learners: students, residents, and pharmacy staff

It is important to note while one focus is strategically advancing the profession, relating the value of the residency program in financial terms is essential. We routinely work to document the impact residents have on cost savings initiatives and reimbursement-tied measures through their work on rotations, staffing, or projects. This is even more critical for successful justification of a PGY2 program where CMS reimbursement is not available.

PROGRAM INFRASTRUCTURE

At BHSF, it has been essential to build a solid infrastructure in order to ensure appropriate growth and expansion of our residency programs. This has proven to be a firm foundation on which to build. Taking the steps to educate and partner with pharmacy and nonpharmacy team members who play a role within the pharmacy residency program ensures continued success and growth of the program.

Some key milestones in the development of a solid infrastructure include:

- Implementation of a Director, Pharmacy Education position
- Positioning Pharmacy Education under the broad oversight of our Academic Affairs (Graduate Medical Education) department
- Development of a system-wide Residency Oversight Committee to ensure the uniformity in program design in hospitals across the health system
- Close coordination with system-wide finance leadership and our Reimbursement Consultant/Medicare Cost Report Expert
- Strong partnership with local colleges of pharmacy
- Harmonization between the pharmacy residency programs and the development of strategic plans to provide continual development opportunities for preceptors

The implementation of a Director of Pharmacy Education position has been the single most important addition to the pharmacy leadership team to support residency growth. This position works with Residency Program Directors (RPDs) to ensure the training environment at all sites meets the ASHP standards. Additionally, when new residency programs or positions are added, the Director works as a coach to the RPD and Residency Advisory Committees to help build a solid foundation and ensure adjustments are made as necessary. This position has also been invaluable to support accreditation visits, organize system-wide residency functions, and to serve as a role model for RPDs and residents alike. As shown in **Figure 1**, the Director serves to coordinate functions between all parties related to Pharmacy Education.

CASE 2, FIGURE 1. Pharmacy residency infrastructure

Note: This position also works to coordinate student training with multiple colleges of pharmacy in the area and oversees our growing pharmacy technician training program.

Further, over the past few years, BHSF Pharmacy Leadership has made a concerted effort to partner with the Academic Affairs Department, Finance, and our Reimbursement Consultant/ Medicare Cost Report Expert. Our growth within the Academic Affairs Department has allowed us to utilize resources and support backend functions (eg, logging preceptor hours in the correct cost center). Ongoing discussions with Finance have provided a baseline understanding of the financial value a pharmacy resident can bring through their support of clinical initiatives (quality and cost savings) and operational optimization (eg, staffing). The partnership with our reimbursement Consultant/Medicare Cost Report Expert has allowed us to increase our understanding in CMS reimbursement, strategically organize our program cost centers, and optimize our management of program-related expenses.

Finally, prior to our central coordination, each residency program in our system operated independently. While well intentioned, as our organizational imperative to provide a cohesive system throughout the pharmacy enterprise emerged, it became clear that the only way to grow was to grow as one cohesive program. We chose to be one health system with multiple residency sites, all aligned around our Clinical Pharmacy Enterprise strategy. Over time, key committees were formed to ensure standardization in program design, preceptor development, and residency research, among others. This has not only added value to our residency programs, but also increased the quality of the research, projects, and initiatives the residents participate in, allowing the reach and depth of the effort to be across the health system.

As we work to grow PGY1 residency programs at Baptist Hospital Miami, this infrastructure will ensure that we do it in an organized and sustainable fashion.

FINANCIAL SUSTAINABILITY

Our goal was to add two additional PGY1 pharmacy residents to Baptist Hospital of Miami, growing the program from four PGY1 residents, to six PGY1 residents. Two residents were selected based on an assessment of the capacity of the department to support the growth of the program. Areas considered included capacity and number of current preceptors, office/cubical space for the resident, and overall needs of the department/health system, including ability to retain residents after completion of their PGY1 year.

CASE 2, TABLE 3. Baptist Hospital of Miami Residency Program Costs

Six Resident Stipends (including fringe benefits)	$378,000
RPD/Preceptor Salary	$300,000
Direct and Indirect Expenses	$20,000
Total Expense	**$698,000**

*Values provided are examples and rounded for illustrative purposes

We calculated the resident stipend ($50,000/year) and added 26% for fringe benefits. RPD and preceptor salary expense was used based on averages from time logs multiplied by the average salary. Medicare reimbursement also covers accreditation fees, resident travel, costs for recruitment, dues, subscriptions, books, and other materials. We included all of these related expenses, taking growth due to the two additional residents into consideration, under Direct and Indirect Expenses. This growth included additional preceptors to support the two new residents.

CASE 2, TABLE 4. Baptist Hospital of Miami Residency Program Medicare-related Reimbursement

Medicare Percentage	20%
CMS Pass-through Funding[a]	$139,600
Medicare+ Choice NAHE Funding[b]	$30,000
Total Reimbursement	**$169,600**

*Values provided are examples and rounded for illustrative purposes

[a]CMS=Center for Medicaid and Medicare Services

[b]NAHE=Nursing and Allied Health Education

Medicare Reimbursement supports funding of PGY1 programs through Medicare pass-through reimbursement. An additional payment option our PGY1 programs access is Medicare+ Choice Nursing and Allied Health Education (NAHE) programs. Using both kinds of reimbursement methodologies can maximize and secure funding to expand or create additional pharmacy residency PGY1 programs. We worked with our Reimbursement Consultant/Medicare Cost Report Expert to trend the Medicare Percentage and Medicare+ Choice NAHE Funding to determine the estimated total CMS-related reimbursement.

At the time of this writing, only PGY1 pharmacy residency programs qualify for Medicare reasonable-cost payment. Specialized PGY2 pharmacy residency programs are not eligible for reimbursement because the certification achieved is not recognized as a requirement to work in the specialty area by "industry norm." CMS defines "industry norm" as more than 50% of hospitals in a random, statistically valid sample. In the future, if the industry norm expands to require a PGY2 residency, these programs would also become eligible for Medicare reasonable-cost payment.[9]

Note: PGY1 programs receiving Medicare reimbursement need to be familiar with the requirements of the program and be prepared for CMS audits. Accurate documentation of reported expenses, preceptor relationship with the teaching site, and resident oversight are some highly scrutinized areas during program audits.

CASE 2, TABLE 5. Resident Staffing Value

PGY1 Salary	$50,000
PGY1 Staffing	0.25
Avg. Pharmacist Salary	$120,000
Avg. Pharmacist Salary with Fringe (26%)	$151,200
Value of (1) Resident Staffing	$37,800

*Values provided are examples and rounded for illustrative purposes

Another direct form of support to supplement the expenses of the resident is the value of their staffing component. Our residents work every third weekend, one four hour evening shift weekly, and two major and one minor holidays. The value of each resident staffing component when compared with the average pharmacist salary is $37,800. The total value for all six residents (four current plus two new) staffing is $226,800.

CASE 2, TABLE 6. Baptist Hospital of Miami Residency Program Net Costs

Total Expense (minus RPD/Preceptor salary/fringe)	($398,000)
Total Reimbursement	$169,600
Value of Staffing	$226,800
Total Net Costs	($1,600)

*Values provided are examples and rounded for illustrative purposes

In our example, the resident salary/fringe benefits and expenses related to the program (recruitment, travel, etc.) are supported by the Medicare pass-through payment, Medicare+ Choice NAHE payment, and value of staffing, less $1,600.

Initial funding of the inception or growth of the residency program can be supported by the pharmacy department with subsequent reimbursement through CMS. ASHP Foundation also awards $25,000 grants to assist institutions with offering a new or expanded residency position.[10]

Other considerations:

- Space for additional residents

- Additional preceptor availability that may be needed

- Construction, equipment, or onetime capital expenditures needed to support the start or growth of the residency program

IMPLEMENTATION PLAN

When growing a residency program, it is helpful to be keenly aware of your entities' budget timelines and approval process and initiate justification early to meet start dates for recruitment activities. This can take some significant planning and working backward to ensure everything is in place well in advance. At BHSF, our fiscal year is from October 1st-September 30th. Based on our budget timelines, our goal would be to start initial discussions on residency program expansion 12 to 18 months prior to the resident start date.

CASE 2, TABLE 7. Expansion of a Residency Program

Activity	Time Period
Residency Program Expansion Justification	January-July 2022
Final Budget Approvals	August/September 2022
Recruitment Activities	November 2022-March 2023
Resident Start	June/July 2023
Program Completion and Possible Retention	June 2024+

*Fiscal Year October 1st-September 30th

Measuring success and the ongoing value of the program is unique to the justification on which the program is built and the needs of the department and health system. Our initial justification of the expansion of the program centered on the successful matriculation of the residents into either PGY2 programs (internal and external) or retention within BHSF post program completion. However, continual tracking of the impact that the residents have on supporting cost savings initiatives, improving quality of patient care, and achieving reimbursement measures, and then sharing that value with the stakeholders involved in supporting the program, is key.

- Lessons Learned:

  ○ Starting or expanding a program may seem like a daunting task to plan and justify, however, much economy of scale is derived from growing a program and often the need for additional resources is not proportional for each additional resident added.

  ○ Intertwining the resident's learning experience to goals of the pharmacy department and hospital is paramount to being able to clearly communicate the meaningful and tangible value a residency program can provide.

  ○ At BHSF, it has been essential to build a solid infrastructure in order to ensure appropriate growth and expansion of our residency programs. Taking the steps to educate and partner with pharmacy and nonpharmacy team members who play a role within the pharmacy residency program ensures continued success and growth of the program.

  ○ Optimizing both kinds of reimbursement methodologies, Medicare pass-through reimbursement and Medicare+ Choice Nursing and Allied Health Education programs, can maximize and secure funding to expand or create additional pharmacy residency PGY1 programs.

  ○ Be aware of your entities' budget timelines and approval process and initiate justification early enough to meet start dates for recruitment activities.

  ○ Continual tracking of the impact the residents have on cost savings initiatives and patient care is valuable.

  ○ Storytelling is a valuable method to ensure key stakeholders remain acutely aware of residency program value and the need for expansion. This may be even more valuable in organizations where Graduate Medical Education is not a major part of the organizational culture.

REFERENCES

1. Rough S, Shane R, Armitstead JA, et al. The high-value pharmacy enterprise framework: Advancing pharmacy practice in health systems through a consensus-based, strategic approach. *Am J Health Syst Pharm*. 2021;78(6):498–510. PubMed

2. American Society of Health System Pharmacists. *The Communiqué*. 2021 spring issue. **https://www.ashp.org/-/media/assets/professional-development/residencies/docs/communique-newsletter/communique-2021-spring.pdf**. Accessed December 23, 2021.

3. American Society of Health System Pharmacists. *The Communiqué*. 2020 spring issue. **https://www.ashp.org/-/media/assets/professional-development/residencies/docs/communique-newsletter/ASHP-Communique-Spring-2020-final.pdf**. Accessed December 23, 2021.

4. American Society of Health System Pharmacists. *The Communiqué*. 2019 spring issue. **https://www.ashp.org/-/media/assets/professional-development/residencies/docs/communique-newsletter/ASO-Communique-Spring-2019-02.pdf**. Accessed December 23, 2021.

5. Brophy A, Bente J, Sobolewski K, et al. Impact of expansion of PGY1 pharmacy residency program 2 to 4 residents. *J Pharm Pract*. 2021;34(5):761–765. PubMed

6. American Society of Health System Pharmacists. PAI 2030 Recommendations. **https://www.ashp.org/pharmacy-practice/pai/pai-recommendations**. Accessed December 30, 2021.

7. Host BD, Anderson MJ, Lucas PD. Expansion of a residency program through provision of second-shift decentralized services. *Am J Health Syst Pharm*. 2014;71(24):2149–2152. PubMed

8. Ticcioni A, Erdman D, Scott B, et al. Strategies that facilitated expansion of a postgraduate year 1 pharmacy residency program across a community hospital-based health system. *Am J Health Syst Pharm*. 2017;74(6):375–381. PubMed

9. L'Hommedieu TR. Maximizing funding from the Centers for Medicare & Medicaid Services for pharmacy residency programs. *Am J Health Syst Pharm*. 2012;69(17):1468–1471, 1470–1471. PubMed

10. American Society of Health System Pharmacists Foundation. Pharmacy resident expansion grant. **https://www.ashpfoundation.org/grants-and-awards/pharmacy-residency-expansion-grant**. Accessed December 30, 2021.

MEDICATION ACCESS PROGRAM

Christine Collins and Michelle C. Corrado

EXECUTIVE SUMMARY

A Medication Access Program (MAP) provides a vital link between patients and the medications they need. With the continuing rise of the prices of prescription drugs and the increasing complexity of health insurance and pharmacy benefit management (PBM) prior authorization (PA) processes, there is a heavy administrative burden placed on physician clinics that often results in a delay in care for their patients. Pharmacist-run MAPs have proven to decrease labor costs, reduce turnaround time to PA approval, and increase prescription adherence. In addition, health systems can see an increase in prescription capture for their retail pharmacy programs—which helps to increase the overall quality of care the patient receives at the health system. This also results in an increase in margin the pharmacy can contribute, which is especially true for those health systems that participate in the 340B program.

SERVICE DESCRIPTION

Health systems are in continuous pursuit of opportunities to improve patient care and financial viability. A pharmacy-driven, centralized Medication Access Program (MAP) can help achieve both objectives by improving patient outcomes, reducing unnecessary healthcare costs, improving patient and provider satisfaction, improving patient flow, and increasing revenue through increased prescription capture.

With a pharmacy-driven MAP design, there is a coordinated approach to removing barriers to treatment for the patient. The services provided include obtaining prior authorizations for complex medication therapies, performing benefits investigation, identifying financial assistance programs, and managing refill requests. Often this work is fragmented and decentralized when performed within individual medical clinics by office staff, medical assistants, or nurses, if provided at all. By developing a centralized, streamlined program run by pharmacists and pharmacist extenders, not only is the process more effective and efficient, but providers and medical office resources can also spend more time on direct patient care.

While ensuring access to medications through implementation of a pharmacy-driven MAP can provide value in nearly any setting, it is particularly advantageous for health systems that have their own retail pharmacy locations, including a specialty pharmacy. Health systems that qualify for 340B discounts can derive the most financial value from a MAP, however, financial savings are

DOI 10.37573/9781585287130.013

also achieved through reducing unnecessary healthcare utilization (eg, avoiding emergency room visits, readmissions).

NEEDS ASSESSMENT

Ensuring access to medications is essential for avoiding unnecessary healthcare costs and utilization and has been recognized, along with access to healthcare, as a primary aim within the Agency for Healthcare Research and Quality's National Quality Strategy.[1] Studies have found that nearly 75% of adults do not follow their doctor's orders when it comes to taking medicines (ie, non-adherent: not filling new prescription, taking less than the recommended dose, or stopping the medicine).[2] The result of medication non-adherence includes increased risk of hospitalization, re-hospitalization, increased emergency room visits, and premature death, especially in those with chronic conditions, as well as a significant economic burden, estimated at $100 billion to $300 billion per year in 2011.[1,2,3]

There are several drivers for prescription non-adherence, the main one typically being the cost of the medication. A recent survey identified that over 7% percent of U.S. adults, representing an estimated 18 million persons, reported that they were unable to pay for at least one doctor-prescribed medication for their household during the prior three months. Of those with three or more chronic conditions, 11% could not afford their medicine, and 18% for respondents taking eight or more prescriptions.[4]

In addition to prescription cost, other barriers to medication access exist, including insurance, health literacy, and provider attitudes and beliefs.[1] Examples of these types of barriers include treatment restrictions, denials, prior authorizations, and refill authorizations.

Health system pharmacies are uniquely situated to assist patients in overcoming these barriers, and do so more efficiently and effectively than traditional office-based models.[1,5,6,7,8] Through establishment of a medication access program, the health system's pharmacists and technicians work collaboratively with providers (inpatient and outpatient), clinic/office staff, retail pharmacies (internal and external), payers, manufacturers, and non-profit patient assistance programs to ensure a patient's access to necessary medications.

In addition to improved patient outcomes through access to treatment, other benefits of a pharmacy-led MAP include higher patient and provider satisfaction, decreased provider disruption, increased provider efficiency, safer patient care, and increased retail and specialty pharmacy revenue through higher prescription capture rates at internal and contracted pharmacies.[1,5,6,7,8] Underserved populations, in particular, benefit from MAP services since these individuals are likely to encounter several of the barriers to medication access mentioned.[1,3]

Implementation should follow a phased approach, starting with a single provider practice/clinic then expanding to other practices/clinics as efficiency, productivity, effectiveness, and staffing permit. Practices and clinics should be prioritized based on their percent of patients with highest need for medication access assistance. The potential financial contribution of prescriptions (eg, 340B-eligible, high-cost specialty medications) should also be considered to fund the expanding program.

OPERATING PLAN

The MAP team consists of pharmacists and pharmacy technicians (and students/residents) working in either a physical location or virtually. Whether in-person or remote, all MAP team members must have adequate equipment and workspace to ensure effective and confidential communications with providers, office staff, payers, patients, and other team members. They also must have full access to electronic health records and prescription management software (eg, prior authorization processing, financial assistance applications, etc).

Providers and office staff are educated on the services provided by MAP, methods of communication, expectations for turnaround time, and how to initiate assistance. A point of contact is established in the practice and routine meetings set up to ensure effective communication, share feedback and enhancement opportunities, and to maximize collaboration.

Workflows and protocols are developed to maximize efficiencies and ensure team members are operating at the top of their licensure. Software is utilized for processing (benefits investigation, prior authorization, and financial assistance), documentation, and communications.

MAP services may be initiated by the provider, office/clinic staff, or pharmacy (internal or external). MAP staff are typically alerted to the need for services electronically via the EHR, prior authorization management software, or fax.

Pharmacy technicians obtain required patient, prescription, and clinical information from the electronic health record. They will also reach out to the provider's practice site for missing clinical information and/or clarifications and the patient for missing insurance and financial information.

Pharmacy technicians process prior authorization requests from payers on behalf of the provider. To enhance efficiency and timely communications, provider accounts in the prior authorization processing software are linked to the MAP team so notifications from external pharmacies are received automatically and required data is entered into the software directly by the MAP pharmacy technician. Responses to prior authorization denials are also facilitated by the pharmacy technician. See Workflow A example.

Patient need for financial assistance is dependent on their financial situation as well as their insurance plan, medication prescribed, and medical expense payments year to date (eg, reaching the "donut hole"). Prescription assistance software is utilized to assist with identifying and applying to manufacturer and other available prescription assistance programs. Other prescription and co-pay assistance funds and programs are also utilized when available and applicable, depending on insurance and financial status. Payer restrictions (eg, Medicare) are followed to ensure compliance. See Workflow B, C, D, and E examples.

Depending on state regulations, pharmacy technicians or pharmacists may authorize refill requests on behalf of the providers in accordance with any established health system criteria and protocols. See Workflow F example.

Pharmacists provide guidance and supervision for the pharmacy technicians, perform functions that are out of scope for pharmacy technician licensure, provide medication information to providers and other healthcare professionals, provide medication education as needed to patients, and serve as a resource for escalating clinical questions or concerns.

Pharmacy technicians reach out to patients directly, when possible, to inform them of the status of their prescription and/or financial assistance. During this outreach they will also discuss the option of utilizing the health system's retail or specialty pharmacy and the benefits of doing so.

Communications are documented in the EHR to ensure transparency between providers, office/clinic staff, MAP team, and health system's retail and specialty pharmacies. Software utilized by the health system's retail and specialty pharmacies is integrated with EHR to ensure maximum visibility into prescription fill status and patient adherence for prescriptions filled at these sites.

Key performance indicators (KPIs) are identified, measured, and monitored. These include clinical (eg, A1C, BP), productivity (eg, PAs processed), efficiency/effectiveness (eg, PA turnaround time, financial assistance funds identified), satisfaction (patient and provider), and financial performance (eg, increased revenue capture). Analytical data tools and software (eg, Microsoft's PowerBI) are utilized to share and track KPI measures; trends and dashboards are reviewed for opportunities for improvement.

Medication Access Program Prior Authorization Workflow

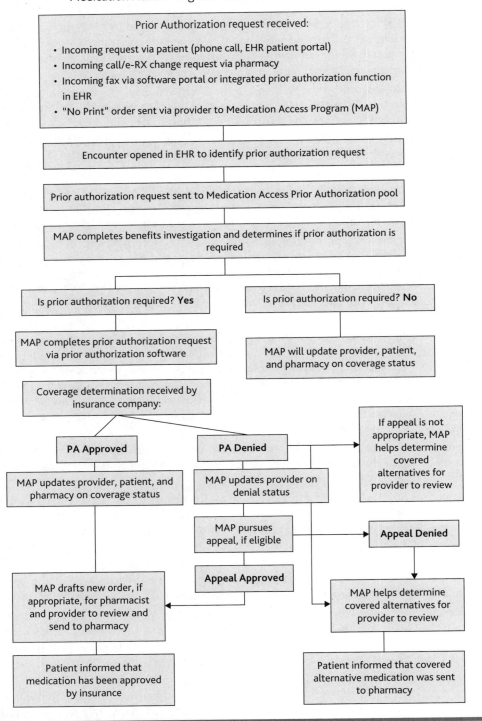

WORKFLOW A. Workflow for the prior authorization process from the point of request through PA resolution, including appeal process where applicable.

Medication Access Program Financial Assistance Workflow

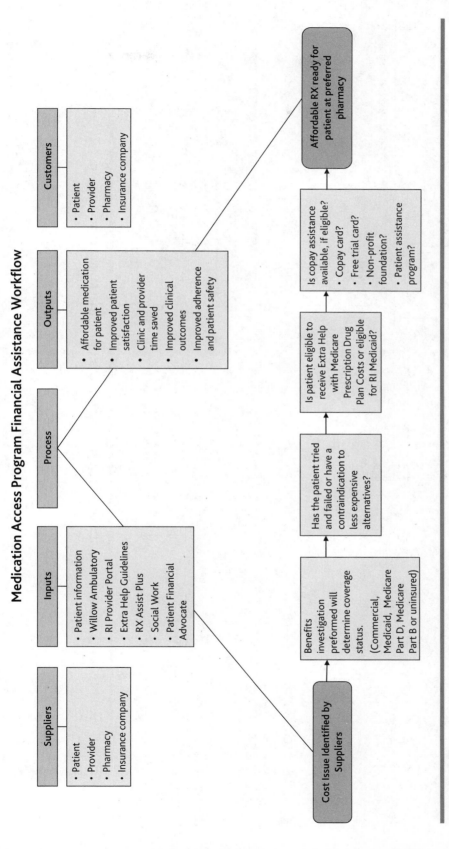

WORKFLOW B. Overview of Financial Assistance support, represented through a SIPOC diagram (SIPOC = Suppliers, Inputs, Process, Outputs, Customers).

Medication Access Program Financial Assistance Workflow – Commercial Coverage

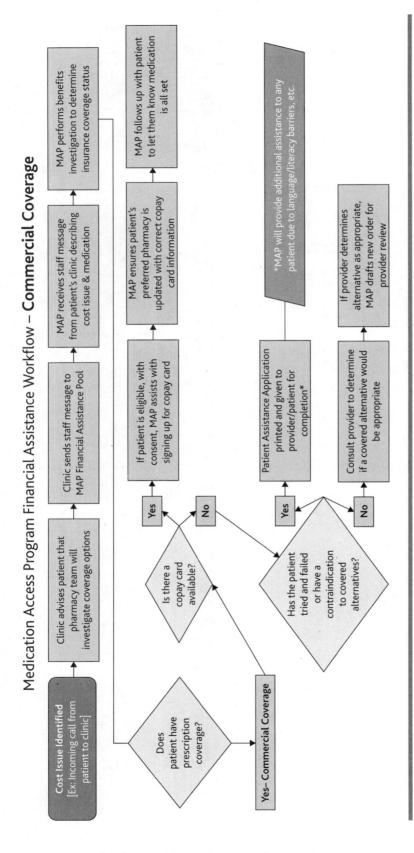

WORKFLOW C. Workflow for the Financial Assistance process for patients with commercial insurance coverage.

Medication Access Program Financial Assistance Workflow – Medicare Part D Coverage

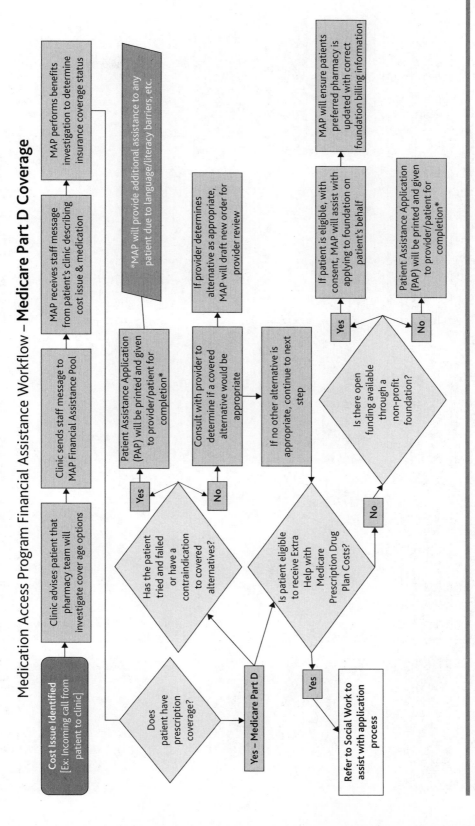

WORKFLOW D. Workflow for the Financial Assistance process for patients with Medicare Part D insurance coverage.

Medication Access Program Financial Assistance Workflow – Uninsured [No prescription coverage]

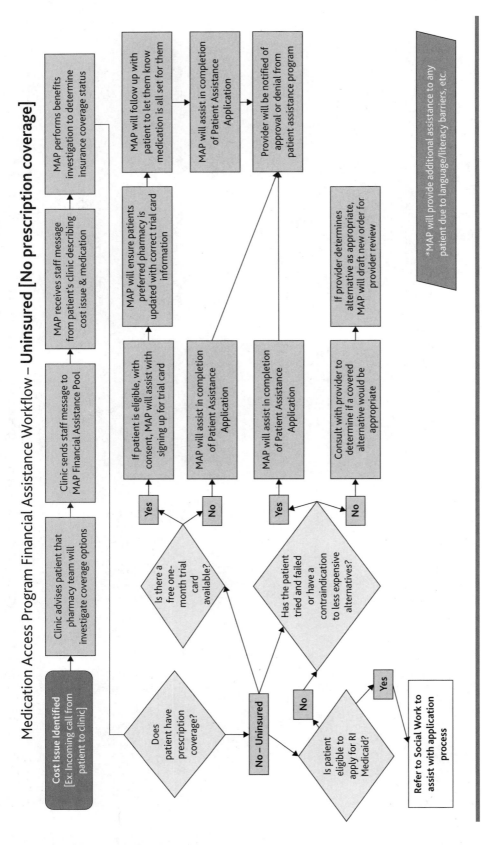

WORKFLOW E. Workflow for the Financial Assistance process for patients without prescription insurance coverage.

Medication Access Program Refill Authorization Workflow

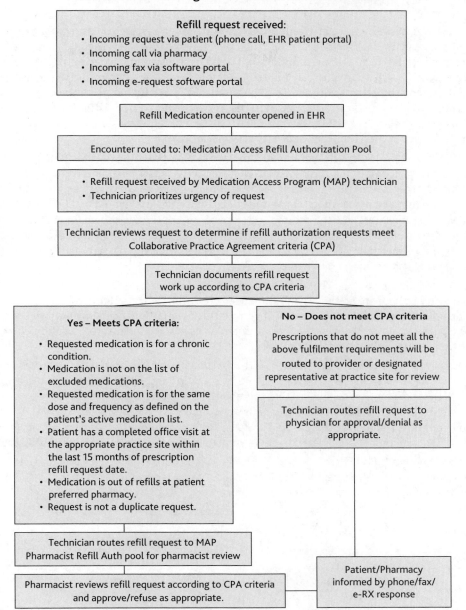

Refill request received:
- Incoming request via patient (phone call, EHR patient portal)
- Incoming call via pharmacy
- Incoming fax via software portal
- Incoming e-request software portal

Refill Medication encounter opened in EHR

Encounter routed to: Medication Access Refill Authorization Pool

- Refill request received by Medication Access Program (MAP) technician
- Technician prioritizes urgency of request

Technician reviews request to determine if refill authorization requests meet Collaborative Practice Agreement criteria (CPA)

Technician documents refill request work up according to CPA criteria

Yes – Meets CPA criteria:

- Requested medication is for a chronic condition.
- Medication is not on the list of excluded medications.
- Requested medication is for the same dose and frequency as defined on the patient's active medication list.
- Patient has a completed office visit at the appropriate practice site within the last 15 months of prescription refill request date.
- Medication is out of refills at patient preferred pharmacy.
- Request is not a duplicate request.

No – Does not meet CPA criteria

Prescriptions that do not meet all the above fulfilment requirements will be routed to provider or designated representative at practice site for review

Technician routes refill request to physician for approval/denial as appropriate.

Technician routes refill request to MAP Pharmacist Refill Auth pool for pharmacist review

Pharmacist reviews refill request according to CPA criteria and approve/refuse as appropriate.

Patient/Pharmacy informed by phone/fax/ e-RX response

WORKFLOW F. Workflow for the protocol-driven Refill Authorization process for providers opting into this program. State regulatory and licensing restrictions may apply.

FINANCIAL PLAN

Medication Access Programs are sometimes funded through research or innovation grant programs. But often, health systems are left to find their own funding source(s). The main source of this funding comes through increased prescription capture at health system owned retail pharmacies. Health systems with 340B programs can typically demonstrate a greater return on investment (ROI) than those health systems without 340B programs. In fact, a higher percentage of 340B hospitals reported providing medication access services as compared to non-340B hospitals.[9] To fund the various activities of the MAP program, a health system usually relies on an increase in prescription capture at their owned retail and specialty pharmacies.

It is important for health systems to know what their potential revenue (and net margin) capture is. This is accomplished through analyzing electronic prescribing data through the EHR. Group purchasing organization (GPO) pricing and 340B pricing can be cross-walked into the data set. An assumption must be made about percentage of prescriptions that would be filled at GPO and those that are 340B eligible. Once the volume and price of prescriptions is known (or estimated), the gross income can be calculated. Then an assumption must be made about level of expenses, so that the net income (or net margin) can be calculated. This can typically be garnered from existing 340B prescription business in the retail pharmacies.

The calculations in **Figure 1** assume that 100% of prescription volume is captured—which of course will not happen. So the organization needs to estimate the volume they think their program will be able to capture. Many factors will go into this assumption including, but not limited to: risk profile of the organization, density of retail pharmacies in surrounding area, location of owned retail pharmacies, and current prescription capture rate.

It is important to note that there is already *some* capture of prescriptions. What you need to demonstrate is what the *incremental* capture of prescriptions will be because of the efforts of the MAP. For that reason, it is suggested that this estimate be conservative (15% to 25%). As can be seen from **Figure 1**, at 25%, the net margin benefit would be $841,875 ($3,367,500×25%). So with a fully flushed out financial model, there would likely be several hundred thousands of dollars (and perhaps a few million dollars) of anticipated benefit—depending on the size of the hospital/health system.

Year-over-year (YOY) growth of the MAP should be budgeted at the same rates as other retail prescription volume. However, as additional clinics are added to the MAP, that should be budgeted using the same methodology illustrated in **Figure 1**.

	A	B	C	D	E	F	G	H	I	J
1										
2	Drug	Rx Volume	AWP Price	GPO price	GPO % of business	340B price	340B % of business	Estimated Reimbursement (AWP - 20%)	Estimated Drug Cost	Estimated Drug Margin
3	ABC	1,000	700	$ 350	25%	$ 50	75%	$560	$125,000	$435,000
4	BCD	2,000	600	$ 300	25%	$ 45	75%	$480	$217,500	$742,500
5	CDE	3,000	500	$ 250	25%	$ 40	75%	$400	$277,500	$922,500
6	DEF	4,000	300	$ 150	25%	$ 35	75%	$240	$255,000	$705,000
7	EFG	5,000	200	$ 100	25%	$ 30	75%	$160	$237,500	$562,500
8	TOTAL	15,000								$3,367,500

CASE 3, FIGURE 1. Sample spreadsheet that can be used to estimate MAP margin impact

Formula for cell I3 is: =((B3×E3)×D3)+((B3×G3)×F3)

Formula for cell J3 is: =(B3×H3)−I3

Revenue			
	Drug Margin	$ 841,875	*assumption: 25% capture rate*
	TOTAL	$ 841,875	
Expenses			
	Salaries & Wages	$ 200,000	*assumption: 1 RPh, 2 technicians*
	Fringe/Benefits	$ 50,000	*25% of salary*
	Office Supplies	$ 2,000	
	Equipment	$ 5,000	
	Building Lease	$ 10,000	
	Printing	$ 1,500	
	TOTAL	$ 268,500	
Income from Operations		$ 573,375	

CASE 3, FIGURE 2. Pro forma

The MAP team typically consists of clinical pharmacists and pharmacy technicians. When standing up a MAP, it is advantageous to have clinicians who have ambulatory experience. Once the program is running, it is easier to provide training and support for pharmacists and technicians who have more of an acute-care background. There should be a designated leader of the MAP, and is typically at least at the level of manager. The leader often reports to the Director of Ambulatory Services, although in some programs it reports to the Director of Specialty Pharmacy. The manager of the MAP should not only have strong clinical skills, but also be able to work independently and cultivate relationships. They also must have a keen eye for customer service and an ability to apply the principles of the lean management system is a bonus. The manager should be innovative, entrepreneurial, and visionary about how to integrate with other aspects of the pharmacy service line as well as a growth mindset in how to quickly build the program to be able to benefit as many patients as possible.

Staff clinical pharmacists and pharmacy technicians often develop tight relationships with the clinics they support. The physicians and nurses in those clinics come to rely on the help of their assigned pharmacist(s) to efficiently and effectively secure the medications their patients need, at a cost they can afford. They must be collaborative, transparent, communicative, and compassionate. They also must be able to work independently and be held accountable to not only caring for the patients referred to them, but also to ensuring the highest level of pharmaceutical care, which includes having as much of their pharmacy care done at the health system level. The literature is replete with examples of higher quality of care, when a patient receives their medications from the healthcare system they receive their care from.

There is no clear-cut formula for staffing ratios for a MAP. One study found that it took about 15 minutes for the pharmacist-run program to process a prior authorization (PA).[6] Most clinics have a general idea of the volume of PAs that their staff is currently processing (or at least how many FTEs they have dedicated to this work). This information can be used to develop a complement of staff for a pilot program. As the MAP matures, a more defined staffing ratio for the health system's program will emerge. This data can then be used to develop additional pro formas, as the program evolves and expands.

It is important that the MAP not begin their work until they are properly staffed. If there are recruitment challenges, then an agreement should be worked out between the MAP and the clinic where there is a hybrid model until the MAP is sufficiently staffed. Ideally, the MAP should have its staff in place at least three months before the go-live date. This gives the team enough time to ensure all policies and procedures are in place, training has been completed, and some test cases have been run.

LEGAL/REGULATORY CONCERNS

State regulations should be reviewed prior to designing the MAP services and process to ensure appropriate scope of practice, need for collaborative practice agreements, pharmacy technician oversight, and site of service limitations. In addition, the health system's compliance policies should be reviewed and/or compliance officer consulted to ensure compliant practices around financial assistance programs, in particular with patients receiving insurance coverage under Medicare, and patient choice for pharmacy selection.

IMPLEMENTATION PLAN

Note: Steps do not necessarily need to be performed sequentially and many steps may be done in parallel. Timeframes provided are for general reference; institutional practices, priorities, and governance should be considered and timeframes adjusted accordingly.

CASE 3, TABLE 1. Implementation Plan

Action Step	Considerations	General Timeframe
1. Identify project lead, program management oversight, and organizational structure	Assess feasibility of incorporating into existing structure, such as retail or specialty pharmacy, versus overhead required for new oversight structure	7 to 8 months prior to go-live
2. Obtain and analyze electronic prescribing data for health system's practices and clinics	Analysis should include prescription volume, percent of medications at high risk for barrier issues (eg, treatment/prevention of chronic diseases, prior authorization required), and percent of patients likely requiring financial assistance (eg, uninsured/underinsured)	7 to 8 months prior to go-live
3. Identify prioritized sites	Decision-making should include variables such as prescription volume, percent of prescriptions and patients access vulnerabilities, 340B eligibility, engagement of physician and administrative leadership, and existing level of pharmacy collaboration	7 to 8 months prior to go-live
4. Develop business plan, receive executive approval	Revenue: increased prescription capture for internal and/or 340B contract pharmacy Cost avoidance: utilize published estimates for outcome improvements and/or narrative Expenses: labor, software, equipment, drugs and supplies, space Capital: renovations, physical buildout, electrical, networking Other: EHR build	7 to 8 months prior to go-live (or earlier depending on health system budget cycle)
5. Obtain support of site physician and administrator leadership	Ensure engaged leaders, strong communication, high enthusiasm for program	6 months prior to go-live

CASE 3, TABLE 1. continued

Action Step	Considerations	General Timeframe
6. Determine location of staff (eg, remote versus onsite or hybrid service); identify space if onsite	Potential for considerable cost savings if staff are remote or partially remote	6 months prior to go-live
7. Select information system (IS) for processing prior authorization, benefits investigation, and financial assistance	Review vendor options, including networking with other health systems for feedback. Work with IS department to determine implementation resources and costs, including interfacing and integration if applicable	6 months prior to go-live (or earlier depending on health system IS project lead time)
8. Develop staffing plan, including number of pharmacists and technicians, hours of operation	Estimate based on anticipated prescription volume, increased prescription capture, program oversight	6 months prior to go-live
9. Identify equipment needs	Depending on remote versus onsite, include computers, telecommunications, office furniture, etc.	6 months prior to go-live
10. Develop workflow for each process (ie, refill requests and prior authorizations)	Work with key stakeholders, (eg, site staff, IS, pharmacy, providers) to map out current process and design future state. Consider auto-directing all prescriptions for specific medications requiring prior authorization to MAP work queue in the EHR.	5 months prior to go-live
11. Build out EHR workflow	Work with key stakeholders to develop EHR aspects of workflow for each process; maximize use of technology for efficiency and to enable effective communication	4 months prior to go-live
12. Build out facilities	Assess onsite staffing and resource needs; plan for growth	4 months prior to go-live
13. Order and setup equipment	Engage IS and facilities teams	4 months prior to go-live
14. Develop collaborative practice agreement; obtain necessary approval (eg, Pharmacy & Therapeutics (P&T) Committee, board of pharmacy, etc)	Delineate services (eg, refill request approvals), exclusions (eg, specific medications, no appointment within defined time period, limited number of refills), and qualifications (eg, credentialing, licensure, national certifications)	4 months prior to go-live
15. Develop job descriptions for pharmacist and technician roles	Collaboration with Human Resources (HR) to determine job titles and pay grades. Delineate scope of responsibilities for each. Identify required and preferred qualifications and experience (eg, retail pharmacy experience, national certifications, residency training)	4 months prior to go-live
16. Hire staff	Develop recruitment, orientation, and training plan	3 months prior to go-live

CASE 3, TABLE 1. continued

Action Step	Considerations	General Timeframe
17. Identify key performance indicators and method for measuring and monitoring	Outcome metrics should include clinical (eg, A1C, BP), productivity (eg, PAs processed), efficiency/effectiveness (eg, PA turnaround time, financial assistance funds identified), satisfaction (patient and provider), and financial performance (eg, increased revenue capture). Measuring and monitoring should be automated as much as possible and include real-time data and drill-down functionality (eg, PowerBI or similar dashboard)	2 months prior to go-live
18. Go-live with pilot site	Assess metrics	
19. Expand as appropriate		

SUPPORTING MATERIALS

Following are some examples of documents that should be developed during the planning phase of MAP implementation:

- Business plan
- Action plan for implementation
- Workflow charts
- Collaborative practice agreements (if applicable)
- Organizational chart
- Job descriptions
- Onboarding, training, and credentialing requirements
- National certification requirements (if applicable)
- Presentation describing services to clinic/office staff and providers
- Promotional material

LESSONS LEARNED

Some key lessons learned through this process that should be addressed in program design and implementation include:

1. Physician and practice leadership collaboration and buy-in is essential.
2. Training and certifications need to be thoughtfully planned to ensure staff competencies and awareness of process, resources, and communication methods.
3. Software selection is a critical step and should be done in collaboration with the health system's IS department.
4. Benchmarking with health systems that have a more mature program is highly valuable, especially in process flow and software selection.

5. MAP team members should be provided with talking points, which include patient benefits, to assist them when offering the health system's retail or specialty pharmacy services.

6. Financial assistance resources and contact information should be maintained and readily accessible to all MAP team members.

7. Nuances to various insurance plans, medication coverage, processes, contact information, and other methods of success should be collated and readily accessible to all MAP team members.

8. Preformatted letter templates should be developed to enable timely and efficient response to denials.

9. Plan for the data science components: building business case (financial forecasting), data analytics (eg, Microsoft's PowerBI), dashboards, and other reports to predict, measure, and monitor operating performance.

10. Consider use of reports and artificial intelligence (machine learning) to identify missed opportunities, unmet needs, prescription leakage, and other opportunities for performance improvement.

REFERENCES

1. Sobeski LM, Schumacher CA, Alvarez NA, et al. Medication access: Policy and practice opportunities for pharmacists. *J Am Coll Clin Pharm* 2021;4:113–125.

2. Pharmaceutical Research and Manufacturers of America. Improving prescription medicine adherence is key to better health care. January 2011. **http://phrma-docs.phrma.org/sites/default/files/pdf/PhRMA_Improving%20Medication%20Adherence_Issue%20Brief.pdf.**

3. Mascardo LA, Spading KA, Abramowitz PW. Implementation of a comprehensive pharmaceutical care program for an underserved population. *Am J Health-Syst Pharm*; 2012;69:1225–1230.

4. Witters D. In U.S., an estimated 18 million can't pay for needed drugs. *Gallup*. September 21, 2021. **https://news.gallup.com/poll/354833/estimated-million-pay-needed-drugs.aspx.** Accessed December 12, 2021.

5. Rim MH, Thomas KC, Hatch B, et al. Development and implementation of a centralized comprehensive refill authorization program in an academic health system. *Am J Health-Syst Pharm*. 2018; 75:132–138.

6. Cutler T, She Y, Barca J, et al. Impact of pharmacy intervention on prior authorization success and efficiency at a university medical center. *J Manag Care Spec*. 2016. 22:1167–1171.

7. Rough S, Shane R, Armistead J, et al. The high-value pharmacy enterprise framework: Advancing pharmacy practice in health systems through a consensus-based, strategic approach. *Am J Health-Syst Pharm*. 2021; 78:498–510.

8. Leinss R Jr, Karpinski T, Patel B. Implementation of a comprehensive medication prior-authorization service. *Am J Health-Syst Pharm*. 2015; 72:159–163.

9. Rana I, von Oehsen W, Nabulsi N, et al. A comparison of medication access services at 340B and non-340B hospitals. *Research in Social and Administrative Pharmacy*. 2021;17: 1887–1892. **https://doi.org/10/1016/j.sapharm.2021.03.010.** Accessed December 12, 2021.

REMOTE AND TELEHEALTH SERVICES

Elaine Bedell, Patricia J. Killingsworth,
and Matthew Maughan

EXECUTIVE SUMMARY: PILOT BUSINESS CASE

A recent survey of hospitalists discovered that the primary concern and patient safety issue identified was the lack of a complete and accurate medication history prior to admitting orders being written for new patients being admitted into our hospitals.

Based on these findings, a multidisciplinary team of pharmacy, nursing, and hospitalist members, along with organizational leadership to provide oversight, was formed to develop a plan to improve this process. The team identified an inconsistent method for who, how, and when medication histories were completed. Literature also supports that during the process of completing a medication history, the "rate of unintentional discrepancies per medication" to be significantly lower when performed by a virtual pharmacy technician compared with other clinicians.[1]

As a result of this work, the team developed a plan to implement a virtual solution for obtaining an accurate medication history. Using this model, we could maximize efficiency with minimal staff additions, improve physician satisfaction, free up nursing resources to spend more time at the bedside, and decrease the number of medication errors associated with the medication history process.

The proposal was to start with phase one and pilot the program in one midsize hospital, using pharmacy technicians for a 10.5 hour shift, focusing on patients being admitted through the emergency department (ED). If successful, we would then expand this into all five hospitals and provide 19 hours of service per day.

We performed a thorough review of potential vendors that we could outsource this service to as an alternative solution. While there were vendors that could provide medication history services, we determined that there were no companies providing the level of service required, would not delay throughput in the ED, and would be available during the hours we needed to cover.

Financial Analysis/Overview

The cost of this program included both capital and operating expenses. Capital expenditures included hardware cost for wall-mounted smart TVs and mobile carts estimated at $73,500 and software cost for virtual connectivity at $10,000 for the initial site. These cost estimates were based on a 30 bed emergency department.

Operating costs for staffing the initial 10.5 hours of service with four pharmacy technicians would be $167,481.60, including benefits.

Additional operational costs to design and implement the program included IT costs for electronic medical record (EMR) build changes, hardware configuration, and deployment at $48,000, and project management support for six months at $96,000.

Implementation Plan

The time needed to finalize the phase one plan, hire staff and project manager, design and complete the IT build, purchase hardware, implement, and run a 60 day phase one pilot took a total of six months. While many of these tasks occurred concurrently, it was still an initial heavy lift and needed a dedicated team for six months to ensure success.

The start date for this project was determined once the project plan and funding had been approved and made available to begin phase one.

At the completion of phase one, the team gathered the data and concluded phase one was successful. An executive summary and budget to expand this program is being developed to align with our fiscal year budgeting cycle with a recommended start date during the 3rd quarter. (**Exhibit A**)

SERVICE DESCRIPTION/NEEDS ASSESSMENT

The manner in which we provide healthcare is rapidly changing. We have more ways to connect with our patients, caregivers, and members of the healthcare team, providing more options to our patients and customers for how best we can manage their care.

Pharmacy services can now reach our patients through face-to-face, telephonic, text, web-visit, and secure remote patient monitoring. The model of always having the patients come to us, while at times still necessary, can be supplemented through new modalities.

The American Society of Health-System Pharmacists (ASHP) high-value pharmacy enterprise framework includes recommendations to provide telehealth services, in addition to the telehealth-specific recommendations in the Pharmacy Advancement Initiative 2030.[2] These recommendations include explicit guidance for inclusion of telehealth to enhance pharmacy operations, comprehensive medication management, safety culture, pharmacy education, and workforce development.

Virtual care provides vital access to healthcare services and resources across populations regardless of barriers such as pandemic precautions, lack of transportation, distance, childcare availability, or inclement weather. Over the past year, our health system developed teams focused on discovering and implementing best practices for virtual care and then worked as a team of teams to establish a virtual care center of excellence. As one of these teams, pharmacy focused on implementing multiple new virtual programs to maintain and elevate healthcare services across the nation.

One of the priority pharmacy programs we still needed to develop was a virtual medication history program. A survey of our hospitalists identified a need to obtain accurate and timely medication histories when patients are admitted into one of our hospitals through our emergency department as the first critical step of medication reconciliation. This also aligned with our organization's key strategy of "do no harm":

- It is estimated that 1.5 million preventable adverse drug events (ADE) occur each year throughout the healthcare continuum.[3]

- Medication discrepancies contribute to adverse drug events within transitions of care.[4–6]

  - Estimated to occur in up to 70% of patients at admission and discharge.

  - Approximately 1/3 have the potential to cause harm.

  - Approximately 2/3 of potentially harmful medication discrepancies are attributed to errors in the medication history.

  - Estimated that close to 30% of prescribing errors are attributed to incomplete medication histories.

- Costs associated with ADE have been estimated at $3,244 to $5,857 per ADE.[7;8]

- Medication reconciliation is a key component of transitions of care and is defined as the "process of comparing the medication a patient should be using or is actively using to new medications that are ordered and resolving any discrepancies" with medication reconciliation and obtaining accurate medication histories being distinct processes.[9;10]

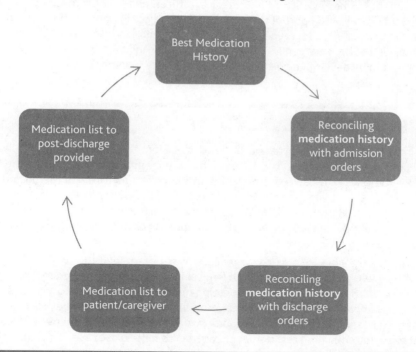

CASE 4, FIGURE 1. Medication history

- Obtaining accurate medication histories upon admission could be considered the pivotal gateway to the provision of good medication reconciliation.

- Utilization of pharmacy technicians to perform medication histories has quickly become a unique way to address resource limitations and improve the quality of data for medication reconciliation.[11–17]

- Studies have demonstrated significant reductions in medication errors, omissions, duplications, and drug interactions when utilizing pharmacy technicians to obtain medication histories.[11–17]

- Although pharmacy technicians based in the emergency department are becoming the standard of care for obtaining medication histories, the number of technicians that are needed to cover large EDs and/or multiple sites are resource intensive for large healthcare organizations. We have also found it is difficult to retain technicians to perform medication history work within the ED. Technological advances involving telepharmacy would address some of these challenges. Availability of telepharmacy services would allow for increased rates of medication history completion and expansion to other sites of care.[18]

- The organization and pharmacy overall strategy to "do no harm" was also a key driver for this program. Pharmacy continues to partner with other departments across the organization to find ways to provide more timely, safe, and accurate medication management. By providing a thorough review of the patient medications when a patient is admitted into our hospital, we are ensuring that the information the physicians have when writing the admitting orders is accurate, complete, and decreases the risks of a medication error.

- A key component to the success of this program was to include stakeholders that had strong interest, support, and were empowered to make this program successful. Including the Chief Pharmacy Officer, Chief Medical Officer, and Chief Nursing Officer was important to gain overall support of the program. Two critical champions of the program included the Director of the Emergency Department and the lead hospitalist. Their support and knowledge of the emergency department workflow and problem-solving skills allowed the program to be developed and well adopted by the emergency department staff.

OPERATING PLAN

In our hospitals, patients are admitted at all times, therefore this service needed to be evaluated for all 24 hours a day, 365 days out of the year. The primary goal was to complete the medication history before the physician had written the admitting orders as this was the hospitalists' chief complaint based on the survey results and would reduce the risk for medication errors to occur. In those cases where the patient was incapable of completing a medication history interview, the best information possible would be conveyed in the patient's medication history section of their electronic medical record.

When creating the plan for this new service, it was determined that establishing consistent hours of coverage was fundamental to long-term sustainability of the program. Providers needed to be able to rely on the accuracy of the medication history and be alerted to any gaps in the information. The program was designed as a telepharmacy program so it could efficiently address the variability of each hospital's admissions. In addition to the staffing requirements, a close evaluation was conducted to determine the technology requirements for this use case. These included that the technology be always available (at the bedside), did not require the patient, nurse, or caregiver to intervene in order to connect the pharmacy technician performing the medication history interview, and had a low need for maintenance. For these reasons, a wall-mounted solution that integrates with the patient's television (ie, smart TV) was selected for the majority of rooms, and mobile carts were used in areas where patient safety concerns or structural design prohibited a wall-mounted solution.

To achieve consistent hours of operation, the phase one pilot was implemented as 7-on, 7-off shifts for 10.5 hours. The daily staffing requirements matched the expected demand based on historical ED volume information and throughput. The peak times that patients are admitted to our hospitals through the ED are between 13:30 to 24:00. The hospital chosen for phase one had adequate ED admission rates during these peak times. Based on projected volumes, throughput, and an average completion rate of three medication histories per staff member per hour, two staff members per 10.5 hour shift were needed. Key metrics were gathered to validate the initial staffing plan:

- Number of ED beds being covered

- Number of admissions on average during the coverage time frame

- Average amount of time to complete a medication history

The purpose of phase one was to demonstrate the effectiveness, workflow, safety of the program, and validate the staff needed to complete 75% of medication histories for patients being admitted through the emergency department during the hours the service was provided. This was accomplished by looking for ways to refine the procedure for gathering the medication history, validating the technology and telecommunication platform, and determining the optimal staffing model, as well as refining the documentation and hand off communication procedures.

Key metrics were developed to measure each change in service to evaluate and to determine if the recent change improved or reversed progress. In this particular case evaluation of providing a full 24 hours of coverage versus the 10.5 hours that was originally chosen needed to be assessed. It was determined that 24 hours of coverage had the advantage of keeping the process the same for all patients, nurses, and physicians regardless of when they are admitted. However, the cost of providing that coverage along with the relatively low availability of patients from 03:00 to 06:00 gave sufficient pressure to move away from 24 hour coverage. Hours of operation were part of the pilot evaluation and then shifted as appropriate.

If approved, phase two will include an additional 10.5 hours 7-on, 7-off shift, from 05:00 to 15:30. This would provide a total of 19 hours coverage per 24 hour period with an overlap of two hours midday. Based on historical information, interviewing ED staff, and medication error reporting, medication history interviews are not reliably completed during the hours of 03:00 to 06:00. Prioritizing the patients admitted in chronological order would result in a higher likelihood that the patients admitted at 01:00 were alert and available for an interview starting at 06:00. This would also correspond to morning rounds. It would be important to consider how the work is prioritized and divided among the staff members during the hours of overlap to reduce any nonproductive time.

Further phases would continue to assess increasing the scope and complexity of the services offered. The expansion would include increasing hours to capture more than 19 hours of coverage, number of staff, number of hospitals, direct admissions, and other opportunities prioritized.

In the phase one pilot, the telepharmacy medication history key process steps included: identification of a patient; review of current medication list; review of outpatient-filled prescription data; interview of the patient to validate this information, including discussion of over-the-counter medicines (OTCs), nutraceuticals, and holistic products (in some instances, the pharmacy technician needed to contact the patient's physician(s), retail pharmacy(s), or caregiver to clarify information discovered during the medication history review process); documenting medication review in the designated communication tool; and communicating the results of the medication history to the next provider.

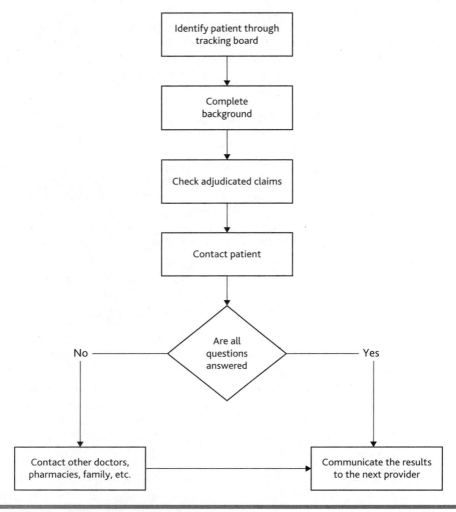

CASE 4, FIGURE 2. Workflow process: key steps

Certain steps in the process map were important measures of success, such as time between patient identification and completion of the interview. A full review of the process map with corresponding productive and unproductive time spent was valuable to evaluate the efficiency of the program, costs, and ability to scale the program. The dashboard for the telepharmacy medication history program appeared as follows (**Case 4, Figure 3**).

Percent of patients with a telepharmacy completed medication history (90%)	Percent of patients with a high alert medication that was added, deleted, or changed to the medication list (10%)	Average time between patient identification and completion of the interview (20 minutes)
Average number of **medications added** to the medication list (3)*	Number of **insulin** orders added or changed to the medication list (6/month)	Average time to complete the medication history interview (10 minutes)
Average number of **medications deleted** to the medication list (9)*	Number of **anticoagulation** orders added or changed to the medication list (8/month)	
Average number of **medications changed** in the medication list (5)*	Number of **pain** orders added or changed to the medication list (5/month)	

*Includes OTCs, nutraceuticals, and holistic products.

CASE 4, FIGURE 3. Dashboard: metrics of success

FINANCIAL PLAN

Capital

Based on the initial hospital with a 30 bed capacity in the emergency department and using a mixed model for technology, the following calculations demonstrate the financial requirements and rationale for application.

Capital requirements were based on a mixed model including wall-mounted technology for individual patient rooms within the emergency department as well as shared mobile carts for multi-use cases such as behavioral health patients or open bays with temporary partitions.

Five mobile carts ($3,500/device)=$17,500

20 wall-mounted solutions ($2,800/device)=$56,000

<u>Hardware total=$73,500</u>

In addition to the hardware components for the virtual technology, the software was another consideration. One critical functional need for the software was that it had "auto answer" capabilities. Auto answer prevented the need for the nurse, patient, etc. to touch the device or "accept" the call and improved the ability and efficiency for staff to connect with the patient.

After ensuring all legal requirements were met, the acquisition, installation, and maintenance of the virtual platform software was also considered. Virtual platform licensing fees are variable but in this case were approximately $400 per device. One other consideration for software licensing was whether the fees were one-time or annual fees. Many had a one-time installation fee but would also require an ongoing annual subscription fee as well.

25 virtual technology devices ($400 licensing fee per device)=$10,000

<u>Capital subtotal=$83,500</u>

Operational

Established goals for completion rates of medication histories drove the staffing model and hours of operation. For this example, we are showing a multiphase approach to initiate service with a plan for expansion.

The pilot phase covered peak hours in the emergency department from 13:30 to 24:00 and required two technicians. These two technicians covered 10.5 hour shifts of 7-on, 7-off, thereby requiring four technicians total for the pilot phase. Each shift included one meal break of thirty minutes.

Calculation for number of Full-Time Employees (FTEs)

10 hour shifts (7 days)=70 hours per two weeks for 0.88 FTEs per technician

Four Technicians (4×0.88=3.52 Technician FTEs)

3.52 Technician FTEs×($20.80/hour at 1,830 hours)=$133,985.28

$167,481.60 with benefits at 25%

Phase two would expand hours of coverage for a total of 19 hours per 24 hour period. This additional shift would cover 05:00 to 15:30 as a 7-on, 7-off 10.5 hour shift. One technician would be necessary for each rotation for a total of two additional technicians.

Calculation for number of Full-Time Employees (FTEs)

10 hour shifts (7 days)=70 hours per two weeks for 0.88 FTEs per technician

Two Technicians (2×0.88=1.76 Technician FTEs)

1.76 Technician FTEs×($20.80/hour at 1,830 hours)=$66,992.64

$83,740.80 with benefits at 25%

Additional consideration was given to the resources required for customization and configuration of technology solutions. For this program, we required new user roles to be created as well as a customized addition to the electronic emergency department tracking board by our information technology team. We budgeted 0.2 FTEs in phase one for this work.

Software build: 0.2 FTEs ($100/hour at 240 hours)=$24,000

Hardware configuration and deployment: 0.2 FTEs ($100/hour at 240 hours)=$24,000

IT total=$48,000

The last consideration for our budget was the utilization of a project manager for this program. Phases one and two were estimated to require 0.2 FTEs of project manager time for six months.

Phase one: 0.2 FTEs ($100/hour at 960 hours)=$96,000

Phase two: 0.2 FTEs ($100/hour at 960 hours)=$96,000

Project manager total=$192,000

Operational Total

Pilot

Personnel=$133,985.28; $167,481.60 with benefits at 25%

IT and PM=$144,000

Pilot total=$277,985.28; $311,481.60 with benefits at 25%

Phase Two

Personnel=$66,992.64; $83,740.80 with benefits at 25%

PM=$96,000

Phase two total=$162,992.64; $179,740.80 with benefits at 25%

Grand total=$440,977.92; $491,222.40 with benefits at 25%

To determine the number of staff required for phases one and two, we estimated the average number of medication histories to be completed. We based our calculations on the average number of admissions via the emergency department during the peak time and during the proposed phase two time period. As part of this evaluation, we also determined the average number of medication histories to be completed per technician each hour to be three. Calculations shown in **Figure 4**.

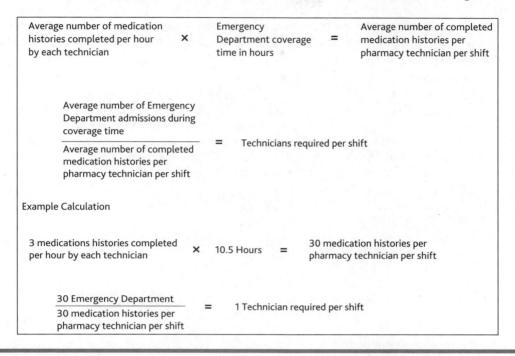

CASE 4, FIGURE 4. FTE calculation

LEGAL/REGULATORY CONCERNS

It was determined that an ongoing review of state regulations governing telepharmacy services, licensure requirements, and working across state lines will need to be vetted through our legal counsel as the program is expanded across state lines. Also, it will be critical to keep current as state laws regarding virtual pharmacy practice change.

Our operating model was to use pharmacy technicians that may not require licensure to perform the tasks for this job and may not fall within the scope of practice for state boards of pharmacy. We worked closely with our legal department to ensure we were following all state and federal laws.

A cursory review of current state requirements yielded no immediate concerns.

IMPLEMENTATION PLAN

The first phase of this project was a pilot phase that determined the viability of the proposed communication and documentation tools, the data that needed to be captured, and the measures of success for the program. This phase was staffed with two pharmacy technicians working remotely to cover one hospital from 13:30 to 24:00 in 7-on, 7-off shifts, allowing for coverage of peak admission times, which in turn provided enough patient volume to accurately test tools, gather data, and access results.

Continual analysis using weekly interviews with the pharmacy technician staff doing the work and members in the emergency department and weekly data review allowed for rapid iterative changes in communication and documentation tools as opportunities for improvement were uncovered. In order to determine the success of the pilot phase, we gathered and assessed the metrics outlined in **Figure 3**. Finally, we conducted a follow-up physician survey to obtain their feedback on the improved process.

The pilot phase revealed an average length of time for virtual medication history completion per admission to determine the number of staff needed for the implementation phase.

The virtual medication history program will move into phase two, or the implementation phase, when confidence in our process and tools is achieved. It was anticipated this would occur after 60 days or the completion of phase one. The implementation phase, phase two, would begin with training new staff and increasing hours of coverage to 05:00 to 24:00. Prioritizing the order of implementation in the five additional hospitals involved was determined during phase one.

Further phases would increase the scope and complexity of the services offered including direct admissions and other opportunities as they were prioritized.

Example Basic Equation (Based on Figure 4):

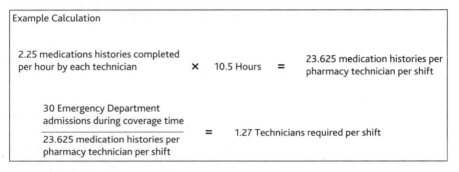

Example Calculation

2.25 medications histories completed per hour by each technician × 10.5 Hours = 23.625 medication histories per pharmacy technician per shift

$$\frac{30 \text{ Emergency Department admissions during coverage time}}{23.625 \text{ medication histories per pharmacy technician per shift}} = 1.27 \text{ Technicians required per shift}$$

Lessons Learned Post Pilot Phase:

1. While technology is not the sole limiting factor for the model, the type of technology available will drive the workflow, implementation, and cost of the program.

    a. Mobile carts will require emergency department staff to locate and move the carts as needed, while keeping in mind the need to monitor battery life and recharging.

    b. Mobile tablets are less cumbersome and, in our design, located in each room to reduce the staff burden of cart placement. However, these smaller devices will require additional security measures for inventory control. These smaller in room devices should also be evaluated for proper placement when new patients arrive due to possible displacement during the previous patient's visit.

    c. Wall-mounted solutions reduce multiple barriers such as placement and battery charging; however, these devices require a suitable structure for mounting. This can present a barrier in some emergency departments with nonpermanent partitions between rooms.

2. If medication histories are not currently completed by the emergency department staff prior to admission, then the virtual medication history program may not provide as significant a relief to nursing workflow as anticipated.

    a. Consider the current workflow prior to initiation and adapt goals as needed.

        i. For example: if medication histories are primarily completed by floor staff post admission, then the goal for time to completion may need to be extended to within 24 to 48 hours of admission and plans to virtually follow the patient to the floor would be appropriate.

3. Ensure the technology has other applications locked out to prevent patient access and utilization for personal use.

    a. For example: we identified a use to order Uber Eats for delivery to the emergency department.

4. Develop a security plan for the technology to prevent the removal of technology from the emergency department by patients/visitors.

    a. Potential hardware components for additional security would be:

        i. Locking frames for the smaller devices that mount to the cart or pole.

        ii. Equipment GPS tracking tags are another option for additional inventory management.

    b. Software to disable the device from additional functionality is another consideration to discuss with the local technology team.

5. Staffing satisfaction as a result of this program:

    a. Physician:

        i. They noticed a significant increase in the accuracy and quality of the medication histories.

        ii. Hospitalists noticed more medication histories completed prior to writing medication orders and completing the medication reconciliation on admission.

        iii. Physicians found they could utilize the medication history program to identify and manage high-risk patients by engaging pharmacy services to complete a full medication review.

    b. Pharmacy Technicians:

        i. The option for remote work has been well received by our pharmacy technicians and has become a strong component for job satisfaction and retention.

        ii. Recruitment for these remote positions has been simple and results in large numbers of highly qualified candidates.

    c. Nursing:

        i. Floor nurses found they had fewer numbers of medication histories to complete once patient was admitted to the floor.

        ii. Nurses found the discharge medication process easier because of initial accuracy, completion, and documentation of medication history.

REFERENCES

1. Gadallah A, McGinnis B, Nguyen B, Olson J. Assessing the impact of virtual medication history technicians on medication reconciliation discrepancies. *Int J Clin Pharm*. 2021;43(5): 1404–1411. PubMed

2. American Society of Health-System Pharmacists. PAI 2030. 2022. **https://www.ashp.org/ pharmacy-practice/pai?loginreturnUrl=SSOCheckOnly**.

3. Forster AJ, Clark HD, Menard A, et al. Adverse events among medical patients after discharge from hospital. *CMAJ*. 2004;170(3):345–349. PubMed

4. Leapfrog Hospital Survey. Factsheet: medication reconciliation. Revised April 1, 2022. **https:// ratings.leapfroggroup.org/sites/default/files/inline-files/2022%20Medication%20 Reconciliation%20Fact%20Sheet.pdf**. Accessed February 14, 2019.

5. Society of Hospital Medicine. MARQUIS Implementation manual: A guide for medication reconciliation quality improvement. October 2014. **https://www.hospitalmedicine.org/ globalassets/clinical-topics/clinical-pdf/shm_medication_reconciliation_guide.pdf**. Accessed August 29th 2017.

6. Cornish PL, Knowles SR, Marchesano R, et al. Unintended medication discrepancies at the time of hospital admission. *Arch Intern Med*. 2005;165(4):424–429. PubMed

7. Classen DC, Pestotnik SL, Evans RS, et al. Adverse drug events in hospitalized patients. Excess length of stay, extra costs, and attributable mortality. *JAMA*. 1997;277(4):301–306. PubMed

8. Bates DW, Spell N, Cullen DJ, et al. The costs of adverse drug events in hospitalized patients. *JAMA*. 1997;277(4):307–311. PubMed

9. The Joint Commission. National patient safety goals effective January 1, 2017. **https://www. jointcommission.org/assets/1/6/NPSG_Chapter_HAP_Jan2017.pdf**. Accessed September 6, 2017.

10. American Society of Health-System Pharmacists Council on Pharmacy Practice. ASHP statement on the pharmacist's role in medication reconciliation. Approved by the ASHP Board of Directors on April 13, 2012, and by the ASHP House of Delegates on June 10, 2012. *Am J Health Syst Pharm*. 2013;70(5):453–456. PubMed

11. Cooper JB, Lilliston M, Brooks D, Swords B. Experience with a pharmacy technician medication history program. *Am J Health Syst Pharm*. 2014;71(18):1567–1574. PubMed

12. Hart C, Price C, Graziose G, Grey J. A program using pharmacy technicians to collect medication histories in the emergency department. *P&T*. 2015;40(1):56–61. PubMed

13. Canadian Patient Safety Institute, Institut canadien pour la sécurité des patients. Best possible medication history. **http://www.patientsafetyinstitute.ca/en/Topic/Pages/Best-Possible-Medication-History.aspx**. Accessed November 18, 2016.

14. Remtulla S, Brown G, Frighetto L. Best possible medication history by a pharmacy technician at a tertiary care hospital. *Can J Hosp Pharm*. 2009;62(5):402–405. PubMed

15. Sen S, Siemianowski L, Murphy M, McAllister SC. Implementation of a pharmacy technician-centered medication reconciliation program at an urban teaching medical center. *Am J Health Syst Pharm*. 2014;71(1):51–56. PubMed

16. van den Bemt PM, van den Broek S, van Nunen AK, et al. Medication reconciliation performed by pharmacy technicians at the time of preoperative screening. *Ann Pharmacother*. 2009;43(5):868–874. PubMed

17. Alexander E, Butler CD, Darr A, et al. ASHP statement on telepharmacy. *Am J Health Syst Pharm*. 2017;74(9):e236–e241. PubMed

18. Pippins JR, Gandhi TK, Hamann C, et al. Classifying and predicting errors of inpatient medication reconciliation. *J Gen Intern Med*. 2008;23(9):1414–1422. PubMed

EXHIBIT A

Executive Summary Medication History Expansion Proposal for FY Funding

Summary

- The Virtual Medication History phase one pilot was developed as a result of the annual survey. In this survey physicians identified a gap in patient care and risk for medication errors when patients were being admitted into our hospitals with incomplete, inaccurate, or no existing medication history.

- The program was piloted in one hospital with a 30 bed emergency department. The results of the pilot were positive seeing KPIs including percent completion of medication histories, average number of medications added, deleted, or changed on the medication list, and average time to complete a medication history.

- Based on data gathered during phase one we averaged 90% completion of medication histories for patients in the ED during the 10.5 hours of service currently provided. This is 15% higher than we anticipated and was budgeted for in the phase one pilot.

- There are five additional hospitals that we need to implement but do not have bandwidth with the current staffing model. We also need to add a second 7-on, 7-off shift to expand our hours of coverage from 10.5 to 19 hours providing a more consistent program and completing more medication histories.

- There is economy of scale by providing this service centrally in a virtual model that allows us to maximize efficiency of staff and provide this service with fewer FTEs.

- Based on the success of the phase one pilot we are recommending that we expand this program to five additional hospitals and add a second shift to provide 19 hours of coverage.

Recommendation

- Approve $659,700 for equipment and software to expand program into five additional sites

- Approve 11.2 FTE Medication History Advocates to complete five remaining sites

- Approve an additional 6.54 FTE Medication History Advocates to add a second 10.5 hour shift, bringing closer to 24 hours of services

- Approve additional $96,000 in operational costs for Project Management and IT expenses

- Approve timeline for the program expansion

Estimated Equipment Needs and Costs

- We need an additional $578,900 to purchase hardware for expansion of program into five additional sites using combination of smart TV wall-mounted solutions and mobile carts.

Estimated FY Capital Equipment Costs: $659,700

Estimated Hardware: $578,900

Hospital	ED Bed Count	Device Count	Equipment Cost
Alabama	37	30 wall-mounted; 7 mobile carts	$108,500
Maryland	45	40 wall-mounted; 5 mobile carts	$129,500
Florida	35	32 wall-mounted; 3 mobile carts	$100,100
Michigan	54	50 wall-mounted; 4 mobile carts	$154,000
Tennessee	31	31 wall-mounted	$86,800
Total			$578,900

Note: mobile carts cost $3,500/device; wall-mounted cost $2,800/device

Estimated Software Costs: $80,800
- Auto Answer Software Cost ($400 licensing fee per device)
    - 202 Devices at $400/device=$80,800 annually

Estimated Operational Cost: $555,922

Estimated FY FTE Costs: $435,922 (with benefits)
- 11.2 FTEs to implement in the five remaining hospitals beginning Q3
    - 11.2×$20.80 for Q3 and Q4=$239,949($299,936 with benefits)
- 6.54 FTEs to implement the second 10.5 hour shift
    - 3.52 FTE in Q3 and Q4=$76,145 ($95,181 with benefits)
    - 3.02 FTE in Q4=$32,644 ($40,805 with benefits)

Estimated Project Management Costs: $96,000
- We budgeted 0.2 FTEs for six months in phase one. For this work we recommend the same for the expansion work.
    - 0.2 FTEs ($100/hour at 960 hours)=$96,000

Estimated IT Costs: $24,000
- All software builds occurred during the pilot phase. No additional resources needed for this expansion phase.
- Hardware configuration and deployment:
    - 0.2 FTEs ($100/hour at 240 hours)=$24,000

Timeline: Implementation and Costs
- Roll-out will occur in a phased approach, with phase one implementing three hospitals during Q3 and the first part of Q4.
- If capital and FTE dollars are approved, implemented in two remaining hospitals during the beginning of Q3 and ending Q4.

- If operational dollars approved, will expand hours of service with second 10.5 hour shift during Q3 and Q4.

New Request	Q1	Q2	Q3	Q4	Summary
			Alabama		
			Maryland		
			Florida		
				Michigan	
				Tennessee	
New Capital			$ 338,100	$ 240,800	Wall Mounted and Mobile Carts
New FTE's for 5 hospitals			$ 171,000	$ 128,936	Hired as hospitals are added
New FTE's for expanded hours			$ 95,181	$ 40,805	Expand second shift
New IT Dollars			$ 58,800	$ 46,000	Software license/hardware config/deployment
New PM Dollars			$ 48,000	$ 48,000	0.2 FTE Project Management Support
Totals			$ 711,081	$ 504,541	

Background

Previously submitted Pilot Business Case (See Above)

COMPOUNDED STERILE PREPARATIONS USING AUTOMATION – ROBOTICS

CASE
5

Kevin N. Hansen and Michael J. Freudiger

EXECUTIVE SUMMARY

The use of IV robotics can provide immense value to an organization through batch production of ready-to-administer (RTA) compounded sterile preparations (CSPs). Benefits realized are enhanced safety and quality, supply chain stabilization, and overall reduction of costs. While the current cost of IV robotics may seem high and out of reach for some organizations, with careful planning of CSP protocols and a strategic production schedule, an organization can easily offset the cost and gain a reduction in their overall drug spend. Further, the enhanced safety of autonomous compounding IV robots can provide manual labor relief during national shortages of premix sterile injectables. A successful business case is presented demonstrating approaches for calculating a return on investment (ROI) for an IV robotics program.

THE AUTONOMOUS PHARMACY

The "autonomous pharmacy" is a vision for the future of pharmacy that encompasses highly automated processes to enhance medication safety and efficiency. This vision will shift manual processes with a high reliance on human intervention and touch to automated processes, thus allowing personnel to shift their focus to value-added tasks and improving patient outcomes.[1] A "fully autonomous pharmacy" will have the goal of zero medication errors, waste, or human touches until delivery to patient. Further, this will allow pharmacists to focus 100% of their time on clinical activities, provide data and inventory visibility, and be compliant with regulations. The practice of sterile compounding has historically been a highly manual, human-driven process. This does not only bring about opportunities for deadly compounding errors, but also contamination, as humans are the main source of contamination of CSPs. The use of IV robotics elevates the practice of sterile compounding within the "autonomous pharmacy" infrastructure to achieve the highest quality and safety goals for CSPs.

In 2019, an international IV Robotics Summit was held at the Cleveland Clinic main campus in Cleveland, Ohio. The summit was held to evaluate the current state of IV robotic compounding and to develop a guide to continuously improve on the technology and expand the use for IV robotics in health systems in the future. The summit outlined that while the use of the current IV robotic technology is slower compared with manual compounding, they represent an important step to increase patient and employee safety. The enhanced benefits of improved precisions, accuracy, extensive documentation, safety features, and sterile advantages of using IV robotic systems was noted. Further, the cost of IV robots was identified as one of the main limiting factors preventing widespread adoption. Despite some limitations and opportunities for enhancements for the current IV robotic systems, the panel of experts had a call to action for both current and future users of IV robotics and outlined the importance of this technology for the future of pharmacy.[2]

Recommendations for Hospital Leaders (from International IV Robotics Summit[2])

- Adopt standard concentrations for specific populations (eg, neonates, pediatrics, adults) when appropriate.
- Adopt dose banding, if appropriate, to minimize preparation of custom doses.
- Develop specialized roles and advanced certifications for staff who maintain IV robotics systems.
- Develop adequate contingency plans for both planned and unplanned downtimes.
- Ensure adequate facilities to accommodate IV robotics in future expansion plans.
- Participate in end-user groups and publish available data to increase transparency and sharing of best practices.

BUSINESS/SERVICE DESCRIPTION

There were several main drivers for seeking an IV robotics program for our organization's health system, which is comprised of five acute care hospitals (over 1,200 acute care beds combined) and other facilities and services provided under the accountable care organization (ACO). The IV robot program was aimed to be incorporated into the flagship hospital of the health system, a 628 bed teaching hospital. Planning for the incorporation of an IV robotics program began during discussions of building a new inpatient pharmacy, located within the flagship hospital, in a dedicated cleanroom suite operation. The main drivers for seeking IV robotic automation included:

1. Ensure highest quality and safety of compounded sterile preparations

2. Provide RTA preparations where FDA premixes don't exist

3. Maintain a consistent supply chain of RTA preparations

4. Flexible product preparation to meet patient needs (concentration, bag size, etc.)

5. Flexible label production for safety and compliance

6. Cost savings to fund the above main drivers

While cost savings was included as a main driver, for our organization it was not the main focus; however, tracking cost savings was included to be fiscally responsible of resource utilization, offset the costs of the technology, and allow for future expansion of IV robots. Within the organization, if an FDA conventionally manufactured sterile product (ie, premix) was available, it was readily purchased and used throughout the health system. Within the perioperative service setting, the use of ready-to-administer (RTA) medication syringes were available in the anesthesia carts. RTA syringes have distinct advantages by improving anesthesia/anesthetist workflows and offering a reduction in drug waste, since unused RTA medications can be placed back in the cart if not used during the procedure. Many of these RTA syringes were obtained from 503B outsourcing facilities, as no conventionally manufactured products were available. The medication contents and layout of each anesthesia cart were standardized across the health system for all inpatient and outpatient surgical areas. Due to the ongoing quality issues and shipping delays with many 503B outsourcers, one goal of the IV robotics program was to stabilize the supply chain and ensure that RTA products are available at all times. Another goal is to expand the use of RTA syringes, since there are limited products offered by

503B outsourcers. Lastly, since the use of barcode medication administration (BCMA) scanning in the perioperative setting is not standard practice, the label design becomes a heightened focus, since many medications used in this setting can be mixed-up due to "look-alike/sound alike" issues. Having the ability to customize the labeling with anesthesia input was a strong desire.

ENVIRONMENTAL/NEEDS ASSESSMENT

The American Society of Health-System Pharmacists (ASHP) conducts a national survey every three years on pharmacy practice within hospital settings. One item within the survey is the use of robotic IV compounding devices for nonhazardous and/or chemotherapy preparations. In the 2020 survey, IV robots were used to prepare nonhazardous preparations in 3.4% of all hospitals surveyed (up from 2.3% in 2017), whereas IV robots were used to prepare chemotherapy preparations in 1.6% of all hospitals surveyed (up from 0.9% in 2017).[3] The adoption rate of IV robotics remains low. It is hypothesized that this slow adoption rate may be due to high costs for such technology or limited current operational capacity and throughput. To offset the costs, it is important to demonstrate financial value of the program, such that the nonfinancial benefits (eg, safety, quality) can be realized.

The Institute for Safe Medication Practices (ISMP) recommends that "to the maximum extent possible, commercially prepared, premixed parenteral products and unit dose syringes are used versus manually compounded sterile products."[4] Furthermore, the Centers for Medicare & Medicaid Services (CMS) recommends that healthcare providers take advantage of available technology in efforts to promote patient safety.

OPERATING PLAN(s)

With the efficiency of the current IV robot technology, an organization will have to choose wisely which compounds are prepared on the device and how many devices they would like to operationalize. Further, the number of robot technician operators and the hours/days of operation can impact the overall production capacity of a robot program. Four categories of compound types are proposed, each with their own cost savings strategy.

503B Product Substitution (ie, insourcing)

An IV robot can provide batch production of CSPs in high volume and in a safe manner. In the absence of an IV robot program many organizations may choose to outsource these types of CSPs to a 503B outsourcing facility. These outsourced preparations come at an increased price markup (compared with the cost of the ingredients used to prepare) and are not eligible for 340B savings. By using FDA conventionally manufactured sterile starting ingredients, an organization can insource these preparations and demonstrate cost savings through reduction in costly outsourcing, and if applicable, realize additional 340B savings.

Dose Optimization (ie, aliquot)

Some FDA conventionally manufactured sterile injectables are presented in a quantity or volume that greatly exceeds the typical dose, which may lead to excessive waste. Many of these products are labeled as single-dose vials, and as such, do not contain preservatives. When these vials are accessed at the bedside to prepare a dose, the remainder in the vial must be discarded. This presents an opportunity to use IV robots to aliquot the contents of single-dose vials into unit doses of smaller volumes such that costly waste is minimized. Further, this method can take products that may only be available in vials (requires some manipulation) and place them into syringes (RTA, no manipulation). This method requires careful planning to ensure the proper aliquot size is prepared and is made in quantities of the proper billing units for the given medication.

Displacement of Manual Admixtures

Another cost saving model for an IV robot program can be to reduce the manual admixtures prepared in batches in the pharmacy cleanroom. The cost savings opportunity for this model is based around reduction in manual labor, and opportunities for decreased waste, if extended beyond-use dates are utilized. With the preparation being automated, there may exist cost savings opportunities based on how the drug is currently being prepared manually in the organization compared with how the IV robot is able to produce the same CSP. For example, the cleanroom could be preparing a medication using a proprietary vial and bag system for safety and efficiency, whereas the IV robot may prepare the same final CSP from a sterile bulk ingredient vial. IV robots may be used to produce standard concentrations in standard size container-closure systems (syringes or bags) as intermediate preparations, to be further used in the preparation of patient specific doses. The utility of this type of workflow can be realized in pediatric hospitals which require unique concentrations of drugs that may not be used in adults or available from manufacturers. Preparations for neonatal and pediatric patients generally require multiple dilution steps to achieve a concentration, or the safest maximum concentration is necessary but not available. The use of preservative free products is also necessary and not typically available. Preparation of these solutions can require multiple steps and be more time consuming in the workflow of an IV room, and possibly prone to compounding errors. The solution to these listed limitations can be to use IV robots in the production of the necessary standardized concentrations in readily available forms (syringe and bags) for use in withdrawing patient specific doses. This not only improves efficiency in the IV room along with reducing drug waste, it also ensures each final preparation is made from standard concentrations produced in a system with minimal to no variation in concentrations or quality compared with a stock solution made by individuals each time a patient order is received. Compounds with frequently high volumes of use may be prepared using this workflow, freeing more time for compounding staff to focus on the manual compounding of other preparations.

Premix Drug Shortage Assistance

The last cost savings model is similar to displacement of manual admixtures, but specifically for when sterile injectable medications and premixes go on shortage. Some medication shortages can be in very high volume, requiring additional staff to manually prepare. An IV robot could be positioned with remaining capacity to be able to absorb this temporarily high workload.

In reviewing these five models, an organization should make a list of "potential" CSP protocols that they are interested in preparing with the IV robot program. The next phase will be to further evaluate the specific protocols to determine if they will be good candidates for the program. For each preparation, the organization should note the following:

1. **Beyond-Use Date (BUDs):** Will you utilize the default USP <797> beyond-use dates (no sterility testing), or extended beyond-use dates (with sterility testing)?

2. **Frequency of Use:** Determine the frequency of use for all areas that will be serviced. Consider standardizing the frequency denominator to weekly (for default BUDs) or monthly (for extended BUDs).

3. **Compounding Complexity**: Determine the complexity of the compounding process. Sterile repackaging of a medication would be considered low complexity, whereas a medication requiring reconstitution, dilution, unique standard concentrations, or bag volume adjustments would be considered higher complexity.

4. **Labeling**: Determine if the default label produced and placed by the robot on the final preparation will meet the organization's needs or if a customized or color label will be required. This may require additional workload depending on the IV robot system used.

5. **Protocol Efficiency**: With each of the above factors taken into account, the IV robot manufacturer can determine the efficiency of the specific CSP protocol. This is usually standardized in the number of preparations per hour. Compare this to the "average" efficiency for the specific IV robot to determine if it is a "fast," "average," or "slow" running protocol.

6. **Return on Investment**: Using one of the four cost saving models, apply the appropriate model to the specific CSP protocol to determine the ROI for the specific protocols.

The final selection of the CSP protocols will be dependent on the goals of the IV robot program set forth by the organization and the available budget for the appropriate number of IV robots. With the current efficiency of the IV robots on the market, it likely will not be feasible to prepare every CSP desired. Therefore, a balance should be provided that allows an organization to prepare the "needs" and the "wants." Some protocols may have a low or negative ROI, but can be offset by other protocols with a high ROI. For the low/negative ROI protocols, it is important to recognize that patient value can also be provided through an increase in quality, safety, and service. An organization should routinely review their "formulary" of IV robot CSP protocols to ensure benefits are realized continuously.

FINANCIAL PLAN

Example 1: Financial Savings with 503B Product Substitution (ie, insourcing)

For this model, we will be comparing the outsourcing cost of a given CSP to the insourcing costs. It is important to include the overhead costs for insourcing (eg, labor, automation, materials) as only comparing the drug costs will give an inflated return on investment. These types of analyses should always be carried out and verified by an organization, and not accept a vendor prepared ROI, for these reasons.

For this example, we will be using a fictitious "drug x" and use sample costs for demonstration purposes. To start, determine the details of the **FINAL** preparation, including the medication name, total drug and volume, concentration, and type (eg, syringe, bag). Next, evaluate the **INPUTS**, such as the size of the source ingredient vial, number of doses per vial, dilution and type of diluent (if applicable), and the anticipated volume of usage within the organization. The overhead **COSTS** should be determined, and which includes cost of drug and diluent per unit prepared, cost of syringes or other materials used, labor, automation, sterility testing, labels, and any other overhead costs associated with the insourced production. Analyzing this information then creates the **OUTPUTS**, allowing the organization to compare the total outsourcing cost per month to that of the estimated insourcing costs per month that will be used to determine the total savings per month. Here is a sample calculation using the methodology:

CASE 5, TABLE 1. Sample Calculation with 503B Product Substitution

FINAL	Medication	Drug X
	Final Product	25 mg/5 mL (5 mg/mL)
	Type	Syringe
INPUTS	Manufacturer Vial Size	100 mg/20 mL (5 mg/mL)
	Reconstitution or Diluent Needed?	No
	Dilution Volume	N/A
	Doses per vial	4
	# Doses per Month	1,000
COSTS	Cost of vial	$10.00
	Cost of each dose	$2.50
	Cost of diluent per dose	$0.00
	Cost of syringe per dose	$0.16
	Cost of syringe cap	$0.05
	Cost of labor, automation, sterility testing per dose	$10.00
OUTPUTS	Total Outsourcing Costs per Month	$25,000
	Total Insourcing Costs per Month	$12,710
	Insourcing Savings per Month	$12,290
	Insourcing Savings per Year	$147,480
	Percent Insourcing Savings	49.16%

When using the 503B outsourcing costs for a given preparation, it is important to ensure that you are choosing the appropriate costs. For example, some outsourcing facilities will offer the same preparation prepared using only sterile ingredients (ie, sterile-to-sterile), and another used from bulk APIs (ie, nonsterile-to-sterile). The purchasing cost may be drastically different for each of these, so it will be pertinent to ensure the chosen cost is with the preparation that aligns with how it will be prepared.

Example 2: Dose Optimization (ie, aliquot)

For this model, it will be important to analyze administration data at your specific institution to determine the opportunity to aliquot a certain medication. The cost savings model is accomplished through waste reduction with the current medication usage and vials stocked. In this example, we will explore a medication with a conventionally manufactured stocked single-dose vial size of 200 mcg/50 mL (4 mcg/mL) with a cost of $55.44 per vial ($0.28 per mcg). This medication is FDA approved and marketed as a continuous infusion; however, off-label IV push use of the medication is common, and the infusion vial is at the appropriate concentration (4 mcg/mL) for safe IV push administration. For the analyses we will assume that only a single dose is used from each vial, given the lack of preservatives, and hospital policy. For example, a 4 mcg dose would incur 196 mcg in waste. The dose's administered breakdown is as follows:

CASE 5, TABLE 2. Breakdown of Doses Administered

Total Doses Administered (one year):	2,790
Dose	Total Doses
2 mcg	4.4%
4 mcg	38.9%
8 mcg	31.1%
10 mcg	2.2%
12 mcg	9.2%
16 mcg	1.6%
20 mcg	6.1%
Odd doses ≤40 mcg	5%
>40 mcg	1.5%
Analysis	
Estimated Waste:	533,201.82 mcg
Estimated Waste Cost:	$149,296.51

Utilizing this administration data for this medication reveals at this institution that 98.5% of doses administrated as IV push are ≤40 mcg. Therefore, an appropriate aliquot dose for this medication could be 40 mcg/10 mL which will allow 5 doses from each 50 mL vial. Recalculating the estimated waste using a 40 mcg/10 mL dose (instead of the full 200 mcg/50 mL vial) reveals the maximum savings opportunity to reduce waste by 83.33%, resulting in a $124,409.60 drug cost avoidance. To further validate the appropriateness of the selected aliquot, it will be important to review the billing information for the given medication and ensure it is in quantities of the approved billing units.

Example 3: Dose Optimization (ie, aliquot)

In some cases, multiple vial sizes may be available for a given medication, however, the cost per each vial can be significantly different. For this example, a given medication is available as a 200 mg/2 mL (100 mg/mL) single-dose vial, and a 500 mg/5 mL (100 mg/mL) single-dose vial. The cost is $125.66 ($0.63 per mg) and $230.16 ($0.46 per mg), respectively. The larger 5 mL vial is 27% less expensive per mg than the same medication in the 2 mL vial presentation. Further, this medication is not available commercially or from a 503B outsourcing facility as a "ready-to-administer" syringe. Evaluation of the administration data by vial size reveals the following:

CASE 5, TABLE 3. Dose Administration Data by Vial Size

Total Doses Administered (one year):	19,827
Dose	Administrations
200 mg/2 mL (100 mcg/mL) vial	
≤200 mg	14,785
>200 mg	2,744
500 mg/5 mL (100 mg/mL) vial	
≤200 mg	602
>200 mg	1,696

Analyzing this administration data shows that a 200 mg/2 mL (100 mg/mL) syringe aliquot from a 500 mg/5 mL (100 mg/mL) vial could produce a drug cost reduction of over $523,158. Further savings could be realized by eliminating the 2 mL vials from the hospital formulary and only stocking the 5 mL vials and 2 mL prepared syringes. Further, outlining dosing guidelines for providers to use the 2 mL syringes for any dose ≤400 mg and use the 5 mL vial for doses >400 mg could further optimize savings by reducing drug waste.

Return on Investment (Overall)

To determine the full return on investment (ROI) for the IV robotics program, it will be pertinent to include operational data, programmatic costs, and cost savings (usually through cost avoidance). The ROI can be determined as a roll up for the entire program for a given period, or it can be detailed down to the drug protocol level. The latter may be beneficial for modification of the active drug protocol formulary to maximize the cost savings opportunities.

CASE 5, TABLE 4. Return on Investment

Operational Data	Units Produced	Total CSPs prepared by the IV robots
	Batches Produced	Total number of CSP batches produced by the IV robots. Will be important to have a definition for "batch" at your institution.
	Production Days	Number of operational days. Having IV robot days "off" allows for opportunities for preventative maintenance, certification testing, or "make-up" days from any planned or unplanned downtime.
	Downtime Hours	Tracking the total number of IV robot "downtime" hours, which can serve as an important quality metric.
	Operational Capacity	Determined from the actual production volume compared with the expected production volume on operational days, usually expressed as a percent.
Programmatic Costs	Robot(s)	Cost of the IV robots, lease, or subscription cost. Depending on the vendor, this cost may include contracted labor and maintenance costs.
	Maintenance	Cost of any planned or unplanned maintenance or repairs to the robot. May include parts and labor, if applicable.
	Drugs	Cost of drugs used to produce the final CSP utilizing the IV robot technology.
	Materials	Cost includes all consumables as part of the production process, including, but not limited to syringes, needles, caps, bags, labels, etc.
	Quality Assurance Testing	Depending on if the IV robot program is operationalized with the desired beyond-use dates, this cost should include any required testing to achieve such beyond-use dates. This could include sterility testing, method suitability, container closure integrity, and other associated tests.
	Production Labor	Any associated labor costs with the production of the CSPs using the IV robots (usually a pharmacy technician).
	Verification Labor	Any associated labor costs with the verification of the CSPs produced by the IV robots (usually a pharmacist).
	Waste	Tracking of any waste associated with the program. This could be due to failed production or defects, or expired CSPs prepared by the IV robots. Tracking waste will be an important metric to modify the production schedule for each protocol.

CASE 5, TABLE 4. continued

Cost Savings (Cost Avoidance)	Drugs	The summated cost savings using the applicable cost savings model for each drug protocol.
	Labor	Labor avoidance savings, if applicable to the specific protocols being used (usually for "Displacement of Manual Admixtures" or "Premix Drug Shortage Assistance").
	340B	Can be calculated retrospectively by evaluating how many CSPs produced by the IV robot were administered to 340B eligible patients.
Total Program Savings:		Summation of each of the elements under "cost savings."
Total Program Costs:		Summation of each of the elements under "programmatic costs."
Total Savings (ROI):		Subtracting the "Total Program Costs" from the "Total Program Savings" will provide the overall return. This can be performed prospectively over a period (usually five years) to determine the ROI, and performed prospectively after a given period (eg, monthly, quarterly) to determine program performance and savings achievements.

Return on Investment (Detailed)

A more detailed ROI can be determined by including the estimated performance of each protocol coupled with the target production volume. This allows a view into the overall production time that each protocol takes compared with the overall production capacity time. Adding a weighted overhead cost can demonstrate the ROI at the protocol level. In some cases when performing this analysis, it may indicate that a certain protocol is costing more than it is saving. This will be highly dependent on the selection of formulary protocols, production volume, and how the program is operationalized. Having a detailed understanding of the ROI for each protocol can help an organization to prioritize certain protocols when making any protocol formulary modifications.

IMPLEMENTATION PLAN

For a successful implementation, it will be pertinent to determine in advance the desired production capacity, initial protocol formulary, and allocated space for the IV robots. Once the initial protocol formulary is determined, the vendor can supply the anticipated production performance of each. Next, a determination of the hours of operation and number of operators will need to occur. For some IV robot devices, additional personnel can improve the performance through minimizing any downtime in the workflows (eg, retrieving stock, labeling, loading, unloading), and one personnel may have the ability to run multiple IV robotic devices simultaneously. When calculating the annual operational capacity in totality, it is vital to reduce the operational run time due to planned and unplanned downtime, staff callouts, vacations, etc., which can be used to determine the "true run time," representing a more realistic number for production capacity. Depending on the budget, it may be prudent to develop an initial plan and then a future expansion plan. The initial plan can be used as a "proof of concept" which may allow additional financial support for expanding the program.

CASE 5, TABLE 5. Example Implementation Plan

Evaluation	Protocols	Capacity	Requires	ROI
Current	13	100,000 units/year	Robots: 2 Techs: 2	>$850,000
Expansion and Optimization	20	160,000 units/year	Robots: 3 Techs: 4	>$1,600,000

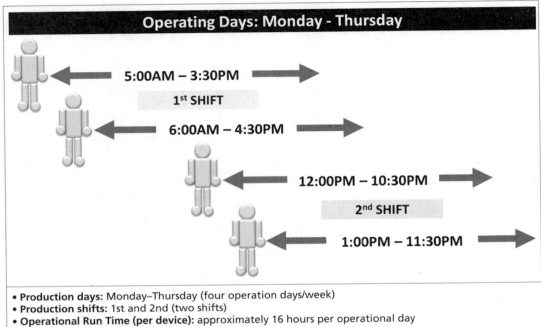

Operating Days: Monday - Thursday

5:00AM – 3:30PM
1st SHIFT

6:00AM – 4:30PM

12:00PM – 10:30PM
2nd SHIFT

1:00PM – 11:30PM

- **Production days:** Monday–Thursday (four operation days/week)
- **Production shifts:** 1st and 2nd (two shifts)
- **Operational Run Time (per device):** approximately 16 hours per operational day
- **True Run Time (minus downtime, holidays):** 2,750 hours/year
- **Number of Robots:** three
- **Average Production Performance:** 19.5 preps/hour
- **Operational Production Capacity:** ~160,000 total preps/year

CASE 5, FIGURE 1. Example of production optimization

A rate limiting step for the IV robotics program may be available space within a cleanroom suite for proper placement. Each robot may require specific requirements, such as power, compressed air, water, and may even have a weight capacity that could require floor reinforcements. The architectural requirements should not be understated during the initial planning phases for implementing IV robots.

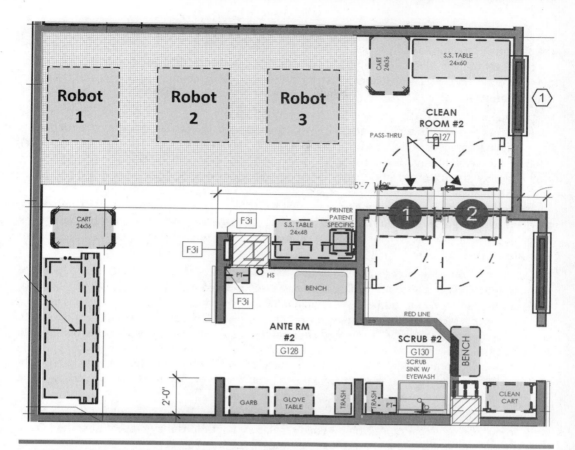

CASE 5, FIGURE 2. Example cleanroom space planning

LEGAL OR REGULATORY CONCERNS

The use of IV robots for compounding allows for the production of preparations in standardized sizes and concentrations, and more importantly, in large quantities. The production of preparations in ever larger quantities may have certain legal implications that must be explored. The FDA's Guidance on Essential Copies for 503A Pharmacies states a drug product must be compounded by a licensed pharmacist or physician who does not compound regularly or in inordinate amounts any drug products that are essentially copies of a commercially available drug product, among other conditions.[5] A compounded preparation may be an essential copy of a commercially available product if it has the same API (active pharmaceutical ingredient), a similar or an easily substitutable dosage strength, and can be used by the same route of administration. Exceptions include the allowance to compound a similar preparation if the compound is for an individual patient and the prescribing practitioner has determined that the change will produce a significant difference for the patient. Examples of these changes include compounding without dyes or excipients due to a patient's allergies, producing liquid forms for patients with swallowing difficulties, and producing dosage sizes that are not achievable with conventionally manufactured products (needing 6 mg tablets when only 5 mg tablets exist). When an FDA approved product is not available due to a shortage, compounding a copy of the original product is acceptable when there is documentation of the drug being on the shortage list and when the list was checked. Furthermore, in order to not be an essential copy, the pharmacy must not be compounding the preparation regularly or in inordinate amounts, meaning they cannot be compounded regularly (at regular times or intervals) and not very often. These definitions within the FDA guidance must be considered when compounding preparations in an IV robot program.

Compounding pharmacies within 503A definitions are those which are compounding for their own patients pursuant to a physician order, with the allowance of certain amounts of anticipatory compounding based on their usual use. In comparison, compounding pharmacies defined under 503B (outsourcing pharmacies) must be registered with the FDA and generally are compounding preparations without a prescription, with the purpose of selling the preparations to healthcare facilities. 503B pharmacies have their own FDA's Guidance on Essential Copies for 503B Pharmacies, which include not compounding preparations that are copies of commercially manufactured drugs, only compounding copies when they are on the drug shortage list, and only compound using bulk substances that are on the FDA Bulk Drug Substances List.[6] This sets 503B compounding pharmacies apart from manufacturers.

In the case of using larger sized single-dose vials to produce smaller aliquots of ready-to-use syringes, the definitions of compounding must also be considered. The United States Pharmacopeia, General Chapter <797> for Sterile Compounding defines "compounding" as "combining, admixing, diluting, pooling, reconstituting, repackaging, or otherwise altering a drug or bulk drug substance to create a sterile medication."[7] Whereas the FDA's definition of compounding excludes activities such as reconstituting, or other such acts that are performed in accordance with directions contained in approved labeling provided by the product's manufacturer and other manufacturer directions consistent with that labeling. This is an important distinction when evaluating the requirements within FDA compounding guidance documents.

When IV robots are introduced into healthcare systems and begin to be utilized for the large-scale production of preparations, the outlined regulatory limitations may present operational and legal challenges that facility directors must evaluate.

FUTURE OF IV ROBOTICS

The use of IV robotic devices to prepare CSPs will allow pharmacies to achieve zero patient harm from compounding errors or contamination and is an important element in the autonomous pharmacy framework to attain the status as a high reliability organization (HRO). Over time, barcode scanning technology has become the minimum standard for ensuring the right medication, dose, and patient for medication administration within healthcare settings. Unfortunately, no technology standards exist today for preparing CSPs, and thus patients remain vulnerable. As manufacturers continue to improve on the speed, reliability, safety features, and cost of IV robotics, the technology could be positioned and widely adopted to be the minimum standard for preparing CSPs.

LESSONS LEARNED

- Proper formulary selection of IV robotic protocols is essential to ensure a robust ROI can be realized.

- The current performance of IV robots on the market may not allow for production of all CSP needs within an organization, thus a hybrid approach of automated, semiautomated, and manual compounding may ensue.

- Careful evaluation of each robot and vendor on the market will ensure a successful implementation that will meet the organization's established goals with the defined budget and allocated cleanroom space.

- Continuous evaluation of IV robot protocols will ensure the maximum value and benefit is being provided by the IV robot program.

- The ROI of IV robotics can be used to further expand the IV robotics program to increase the amount of CSPs prepared using full automation.

- IV robots are not "plug and play" devices, and require careful planning, coordination, maintenance, and care for continued successful production.

- An IV robotics program can provide immense value to patients and an organization through reducing drug spend through waste reduction and avoidance of outsourcing, in addition to providing the safest method of sterile preparation.

REFERENCES

1. Flynn AJ, Fortier C, Maehlen H, et al. A strategic approach to improving pharmacy enterprise automation: Development and initial application of the Autonomous Pharmacy Framework. *Am J Health Syst Pharm*. 2021;78(7):636–645. PubMed

2. Long J, Calabrese S, Al-Jedai A, et al. Cleveland Clinic International IV Robotics Summit. *Am J Health Syst Pharm*. 2021;78(9):800–805. PubMed

3. Pedersen CA, Schneider PJ, Ganio MC, Scheckelhoff DJ. ASHP national survey of pharmacy practice in hospital settings: Dispensing and administration-2020. *Am J Health Syst Pharm*. 2021;78(12):1074–1093. PubMed

4. Institute for Safe Medication Practices. ISMP Guidelines for Safe Preparation of Compounded Sterile Preparations. 2016. **https://www.ismp.org/guidelines/sterile-compounding#:˜:text=The%20ISMP%20Guidelines%20for%20Safe%20Preparation%20of%20Compounded,prevent%20errors%20during%20pharmacy%20preparation%20of%20parenteral%20admixtures**. Accessed March 16, 2022.

5. U.S. Food & Drug Administration. Compounded drug products that are essentially copies of a commercially available drug product under section 503A of the Federal Food, Drug, and Cosmetic Act guidance for industry. January 2018. **https://www.fda.gov/regulatory-information/search-fda-guidance-documents/compounded-drug-products-are-essentially-copies-commercially-available-drug-product-under-section**. Accessed March 16, 2022.

6. U.S. Food & Drug Administration. Bulk drug substances used in compounding under section 503B of the FD&C Act. February 20, 2022. **https://www.fda.gov/drugs/human-drug-compounding/bulk-drug-substances-used-compounding-under-section-503b-fdc-act**. Accessed March 16, 2022.

7. Unites States Pharmacopeia. General Chapter <797> pharmaceutical compounding – sterile preparations. **https://www.usp.org/compounding/general-chapter-797**. Accessed March 16, 2022.

PHARMACY BENEFIT MANAGEMENT COST CONTAINMENT: IS IT A MISSED OPPORTUNITY?

Ginny Crisp and Caron Misita

EXECUTIVE SUMMARY

Healthcare systems are very often self-funded employers facing increasing healthcare costs due to the introduction of the Affordable Care Act (ACA). The provision of comprehensive and affordable healthcare for employers, while costly, is manageable with the right cost containment strategies. Understanding the current pharmacy benefit landscape is critical to successfully providing access to healthcare while containing costs. The following chapter will provide key strategies to navigating rising healthcare costs with a focus on the pharmacy benefit.

INTRODUCTION

The ACA of 2010 brought about many changes to the healthcare system. The primary goals of healthcare reform were to make healthcare affordable and accessible to everyone, despite preexisting conditions, while supporting innovative medical care delivery methods which focus on lowering healthcare costs.[1] The employer shared responsibility provision (also known as the employer mandate) is included in the ACA and requires large employers (at least 50 full-time employees) to provide comprehensive and affordable healthcare coverage, which should include full coverage of preventative care.[2]

Generally speaking, employer groups offering health coverage (hereafter referred to as plan sponsor or sponsor) choose between being fully insured or self-funded. When fully insured, the plan sponsor contracts a medical carrier to provide and fund all aspects of employee health coverage, in return for which the sponsor pays a premium to the carrier. Based on the plan performance, the premium may be adjusted with each contract renewal cycle. In contrast, when self-funded, the plan sponsor contracts a medical carrier or a third-party administrator (TPA) to administer the plan for certain agreed upon fees. Under the self-funded arrangement, the plan sponsor is ultimately responsible for the costs accrued to provide the health coverage (including both medical and pharmacy expenses) for its employees and dependents. In 2021, 64% of employees were enrolled into a plan that was self-funded by their employer.[3] More specifically, the healthcare sector had a significantly higher enrollment, with 82% of employees enrolled into a self-funded plan. Almost all (99%) of employees were enrolled into a plan which provided prescription coverage.[4]

In the self-funded space, especially given the increasing costs around medications, plan sponsors may seek creative solutions to optimize pharmacy benefit coverage while controlling plan spend. Many health systems have a large employer-sponsored health plan which may or may not engage the pharmacy department in the management of the plan. Health systems, when engaging the pharmacy department, are uniquely situated to manage these costs due to their access to clinical and pharmacy expertise. There are several areas that can be targeted to achieve these lower plan costs. While an exhaustive list is beyond the constraints of this discussion, several of the more common areas will be addressed in the following sections.

PHARMACY BENEFIT MANAGERS

With the rising cost in medications, Pharmacy Benefit Managers (PBMs) play a key role in helping plan sponsors reduce pharmacy expense. It is estimated that for every $1 spent on PBM services, the PBM can reduce drug spend by $10 and save payers and members up to 50% of usual medical and prescription costs.[5] PBMs are successful in reducing healthcare costs through a variety of venues which include negotiating rebate contracts with manufacturers and drug discounts with pharmacy networks, providing mail order and specialty pharmacy services, encouraging the safe and effective use of generics and affordable brand medications, reducing waste, improving adherence, and preventing drug interactions.[5] The following sections will describe these tools in further detail as well as provide guidance on how to navigate a successful PBM relationship.

PHARMACY BENEFIT CONTRACTS

While not the most obvious place to start, cost containment strategies should have plan sponsors start with the current administrative services agreement (ASA) in place with their PBM. Depending on the arrangement selected for medical administration, the pharmacy ASA may be bundled into the medical agreement or a stand-alone ASA (preferred). While there are many PBMs offering pharmacy benefit management services, in 2020, the three largest PBMs held 77% of the total market share of prescriptions.[6] ASAs provide important details regarding the administration of the plan as well as the responsibilities of the PBM. Close attention should be paid to all of the financial sections to ensure the most cost-effective arrangement is currently in place.

Contract Arrangement Methodologies

In general, PBMs administer the prescription plan using one of two drug pricing methodologies. The traditional approach is the longest standing and is quickly falling out of favor as plan sponsors are becoming educated around PBM services. This methodology allows the PBM to pay pharmacies for prescriptions filled under the plan using the PBM-Pharmacy Administrative Contract. The PBM can then charge the plan sponsor an amount that is different than the amount that the PBM pays to the pharmacy for the same prescription (**Figure 1**). In the PBM industry, this is referred to as spread pricing.

Typical language in the ASA which points to this type of arrangement might include the following: "Under the Traditional Pricing Model, plan sponsor shall pay the effective retail pharmacy rates as set forth in this agreement and these rates may differ from the amounts paid to the retail pharmacies and PBM A may retain the difference." The traditional pharmacy model is not ideal for the plan sponsor, given that in most cases, the exact amount of the "spread" withheld by the PBM is not disclosed. This "spread" is considered proprietary since it would disclose the proprietary pharmacy contract terms with the PBM. For these reasons, discovering the financial impact of this arrangement on the plan sponsor's drug expense is difficult.

Figure was developed by authors.

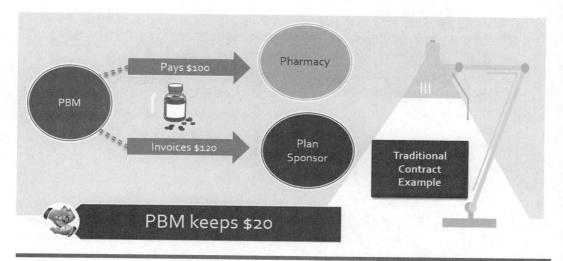

CASE 6, FIGURE 1. Traditional pharmacy pricing model example

The second and preferred contract methodology is the pass-through pricing model. In this model, for each prescription the plan sponsor pays the PBM the same amount that the PBM paid to the pharmacy. Rather than charging the plan sponsor "spread pricing," the fees for administrative services are typically charged as either a per claim fee (average range $2 to $8) or a Per Member Per Month (PMPM) fee. This model is preferred as the plan sponsor can audit the fees being paid, compare market fees, and understand the plan sponsor's true drug expense.

Drug Pricing

At this time, and for the past four decades, the most widely accepted drug pricing modality in the PBM space is Average Wholesale Price (AWP). The AWP is only a benchmark and does not represent the actual drug price.[7] This inflated rate is the basis for agreed-upon reimbursement rates by a PBM to a pharmacy for a prescription. Understanding this is important from the plan sponsor's perspective as it ultimately impacts the plan's drug expense.

As it relates to drug pricing, there are several terms that should be included in the ASA. First, brand and generics must be defined in the definition section of the ASA. Since drug pricing is impacted by a PBM's definition of a brand and a generic, the most favorable definition is that brands and generics are defined by a third-party vendor using its multisource code (eg, Medi-Span®). Single source generics should be included in the generic rate guarantees. Second, the ASA should provide information around the expected discounts off of AWP for brand, generic, and specialty drugs filled at either retail or mail order locations and for 30 days (commonly includes one to 83 days) versus 90 days (commonly 84+ days) prescription fills (**Table 1**).

A PBM's drug pricing is expressed as a percentage discount off the drug's published AWP price. The higher the discount, the lower the drug expense. The gold standard is to have these discounts clearly stated in the ASA and guaranteed at the plan sponsor level rather than at the PBM's book of business level. An annual discount reconciliation should be performed and any shortfalls of meeting the guarantees should be paid to the plan sponsor by the PBM within a defined timeline.

Rebates

Rebates are often offered by manufacturers to PBMs for certain single source brand drugs in exchange for preferential placement of their drug on the PBM's drug formulary. Since a self-funded plan is

CASE 6, TABLE 1. AWP Discount Pricing Example Categories

Dispensing Location & Day Supply	Drug Pricing Guarantees Expressed as % off AWP	
	Brand	Generic
Retail 30		
Retail 90		
Mail Order		
Specialty		

responsible for the plan's drug expense, the plan sponsor should receive rebates back for the portion of rebates obtained by the PBM that represents the plan's share. This may be net a small administrative fee charged by either the PBM or the PBM's rebate aggregator.

As with drug pricing, the ASA should clearly define the rebate program including which drugs would be excluded from rebates. Rebate programs can be defined and administered in many ways. The gold standard is to have 100% pass-through of rebates to the sponsor with rebate guarantees provided based on drug type, day supply, and dispensing location (**Table 2**).

CASE 6, TABLE 2. Rebate Guarantee Example Categories

Dispensing Location & Day Supply	Rebate Minimum Guarantees* Expressed as per claim amount
	Brand
Retail 30	
Retail 90	
Mail Order	
Specialty	

*Greater of a) 100% of rebates received [net a potential small administrative fee] or b) minimum per claim guarantee.

Overall Terms

PBM ASAs should disclose all fees being charged, as this can be used to review market competitiveness. The ASA may include an addendum with a fee schedule which describes fees charged, for example for reporting, drug coverage appeals, drug utilization, or clinical program management. A careful review of these should be completed to ensure an understanding of what is being charged and these can be negotiated during a renewal cycle. Additionally, close attention should be paid to the term and termination section of the ASA. Ideally, the ASA would allow for termination *without cause* as long as a reasonable notice is provided (typically 60 to 90 days). Termination language should also outline the timely provision of a claims file at no charge to the plan sponsor and earned but unpaid rebates being paid to the plan sponsor upon termination. Considering the discussed aspects of PBM contracts, [the authors' experience has shown that] a pass-through contract with clear and improved terms may result in 20% or more in drug expense savings for plan sponsors.

FORMULARY AND UTILIZATION MANAGEMENT PROGRAMS

Compared with being fully insured, a self-funded plan has more flexibility over the prescription benefit. Plan sponsors utilize PBMs to provide several services and rely on their expertise to design drug coverage in the most cost-effective way. One vital service is the creation and maintenance of the drug formulary. While the plan sponsor will decide the applicable member cost share based on the formulary design, the PBM will establish the formulary.

Formulary Management

There are many design approaches to formularies. With the introduction and quick growth of the specialty market, many PBMs are offering 3 or 4 tier formulary options. In 2021, 92% of employees were enrolled into a plan with drug tiers, with 52% having 4 or more tiers.[5] The most common tier structure is generics (tier 1), preferred brands (tier 2), nonpreferred brands (tier 3), and specialty drugs (tier 4). An effective formulary management strategy to lower drug expense is to create a member cost share differential between tiers with the expectation that members (along with their prescribers) will select the lowest cost alternative across the tiers. This provides a cost savings to plan sponsors as long as the formulary has been designed by the PBM with the *lowest net cost approach* rather than the *rebate driven* approach.

The lowest net cost approach takes all factors into consideration when placing drugs on the formulary and when selecting the applicable tier. This would include the drug cost (AWP), availability, clinical effectiveness, safety, and lastly rebates. In contrast, the rebate driven approach is going to place drugs on the formulary and at preferred tiers using the rebate yield as the main consideration. This is especially rampant with PBMs that retain a portion, or all, of the rebates obtained on behalf of the self-funded plans.

A PBM utilizes a Pharmacy and Therapeutics (P&T) Committee to establish and maintain the formulary. This typically will include a medical director, clinicians (pharmacy, nursing, social work, physicians, specialty physicians), and representatives from underwriting. While the PBM maintains the formulary, many self-funded plans with clinical expertise may request a formulary customization which aligns with the plan's drug experience and can result in drug expense reduction.

Utilization Management Programs

Once the formulary is created, the PBM will overlay utilization management programs to provide further structure. Some of these programs are financially driven while others may be for member safety. Examples of these programs include prior authorizations, step therapy, quantity limits, and dose optimization. Prior authorizations usually require a specific diagnosis and documented previous treatment failures with preferred agents. Step therapy requires prior use of one or more clinically equivalent but more cost-effective preferred therapies with documented treatment failure(s). Prior authorization approvals generally last up to one year whereas step therapy in most cases must only be documented once. Quantity limits and dose optimization are used to ensure safe use of a drug (eg, controlled substance) or to ensure adequate dose optimization before considering adjunctive therapy.

PLAN DESIGN

The majority (75%) of employer groups providing health coverage offer employees only one type of health plan. However, when looking specifically at employer groups based on volume of employees, this statistic changes, with 59% of larger employer groups (those with ≥200 employees) offering more than one plan type.[8]

Plan types can be broadly categorized into those with a typically co-pay based prescription cost-sharing structure (such as health maintenance organization [HMO] plans, preferred provider organization [PPO] plans, etc.) and those with a typically deductible-based prescription cost-sharing structure (including both high-deductible health plans [HDHPs] that qualify for a health savings account [HSA] and those that may be associated with an employer-based health reimbursement arrangement [HRA]).[8,9] For the purposes of this discussion, HSA-qualified HDHPs as well as non HSA-qualified HDHPs and HDHPs associated with an HRA will be collectively referred to as HDHPs.

Plan Cost Share vs. Member Cost Share

Over the years, one of the cost containment strategies that employers have implemented has been cost shifting the plan spend from the plan sponsor to the members. One such strategy is through the type of plan offerings. For example, over the past 15 years (2006 to 2021), the percentage of employers offering a HDHP has increased from 7% to 22%. Notably, worker enrollment in HDHPs has followed suit, increasing from 4% being enrolled in HDHPs in 2006 to 28% being enrolled in HDHPs in 2021.[10] It should be noted, however, that a shift from a prescription co-pay based plan to a HDHP does not necessarily result in increased member cost share, given that the move to a HDHP could be accompanied by HSA/HRA-type benefits or incentives that limit member cost share.

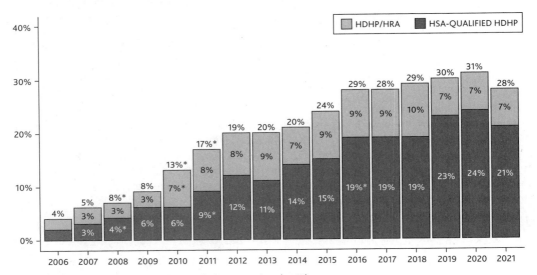

* Estimate is statistically different from estimate for the previous year shown (p < .05).
NOTE: Covered workers enrolled in an HDHP/SO are enrolled in either an HDHP/HRA or a HSA-Qualified HDHP. Values may not sum to totals due to rounding.
SOURCE: KFF Employer Health Benefits Survey, 2018-2021; Kaiser/HRET Survey of Employer-Sponsored Health Benefits, 2006-2017

CASE 6, FIGURE 2. Percentage of covered workers enrolled in an HDHP/HRA or HSA-Qualified HDHP, 2006-2021

However, plan type is not the only cost-sharing strategy, as expense can be shifted from the plan to the members through various other means, including premiums, coinsurance, and adjustments to co-pay structure. As pharmacy benefit performance is routinely analyzed and the need to optimize plan spend is identified, assessment of plan versus member cost-sharing, and adjustment of plan design accordingly, is one potential action to consider.

Pharmacy Network

As previously mentioned, the PBM establishes PBM-Pharmacy Administrative Contracts with various dispensing pharmacies, which guide the pricing paid by the PBM to the dispensing pharmacy for the prescriptions dispensed (both ingredient costs and dispensing fees). Some of these contracts will be more competitive than others. Through routine pharmacy benefit performance monitoring, if specific pharmacies are noted to be carrying a higher volume of plan spend in comparison with the volume of prescriptions/prescription types dispensed, it may be valuable to consider limitation of the pharmacy network to exclude dispensing pharmacies with less competitive pricing under the PBM-Pharmacy Administrative Contracts. However, such a step can be challenging for two reasons. First, appropriate member access to pharmacies must be maintained. Second, the PBM-Pharmacy Administrative Contracts are proprietary.

Where this can be an especially effective cost control measure is in the health system space, in which the plan sponsor, through its in-house Department of Pharmacy and dispensing pharmacy, has access to both the PBM-Pharmacy Administrative Contract details and also the sponsor ability to adjust incentives or cost shares to encourage member utilization of an in-house pharmacy. The potential benefits of this option will depend heavily on alignment of the in-house Department of Pharmacy and plan sponsor. If these two groups are aligned, their combined efforts can be used to adjust the PBM In-House Pharmacy-Specific contract to optimize pricing. At the same time, the plan sponsor can utilize various tools to influence member utilization and encourage movement to the in-house pharmacy. Examples include:

- Co-pay incentives—lower co-pay at in-house pharmacy
- Co-pay disincentives—higher co-pay at external pharmacy
- Pharmacy convenience programs:
    - Mail-order or home delivery of prescriptions
    - Prescription courier to employee-specific workplace
    - Parking vouchers if parking for in-house pharmacies is a challenge
    - Expanded pharmacy hours/locations to meet employee needs

Preventive vs. Expanded Preventive List

The ACA enacted in 2010 included a requirement that nongrandfathered health plans cover the following preventive services without any cost sharing requirement on the part of the member:

- Evidence-based items or services having a United States Preventive Services Task Force (USPSTF) recommendation of "A" or "B"

- Immunizations recommended by the Advisory Committee on Immunization Practices (ACIP) of the Centers for Disease Control and Prevention

- Evidence-based preventive care and screenings supported by the Health Resources Services Administration (HRSA)

- Women's preventive care and screenings supported by the HRSA (not otherwise addressed by the USPSTF recommendations)[11]

Though HDHPs are traditionally required by law to not provide coverage for services until the member has met his/her deductible, the "no cost share" requirement of the preventive services section of the ACA allows for these preventive care services to be provided to members prior to the deductible being met.

Subsequently, the Internal Revenue Service, in July 2019, published guidance intended to expand upon the list of preventive services that a HDHP could provide to members prior to a deductible being met, adding the following list of preventive care items or services (**Table 3**).[12] It should be noted that while this list expands the preventive services that can be provided to members at zero cost share prior to the deductible being met, this list is not added to the *required* or *mandated* list of services that must be provided to members at no cost share per the ACA.

CASE 6, TABLE 3. July 2019 IRS-Expanded ACA Preventive Services

Preventive Care for Specified Conditions	For Individuals Diagnosed with
Angiotensin Converting Enzyme (ACE) inhibitors	Congestive heart failure, diabetes, and/or coronary artery disease
Antiresorptive therapy	Osteoporosis and/or osteopenia
β-blockers	Congestive heart failure and/or coronary artery disease
Blood pressure monitor	Hypertension
Inhaled corticosteroids	Asthma
Insulin and other glucose lowering agents	Diabetes
Retinopathy screening	Diabetes
Peak flow meter	Asthma
Glucometer	Diabetes
Hemoglobin A1c testing	Diabetes
International Normalized Ratio (INR) testing	Liver disease and/or bleeding disorders
Low-density Lipoprotein (LDL) testing	Heart disease
Selective Serotonin Reuptake Inhibitors (SSRIs)	Depression
Statins	Heart disease and/or diabetes

The USPSTF also made HIV pre-exposure prophylaxis (PrEP) a Grade A recommendation in June 2019.[13] Hence, with plan years beginning on or after June 30, 2020 (one year after the Grade A recommendation), HIV PrEP became a part of the list of preventive services to be covered at no member cost share.[14]

Given these various guidelines, below is a compilation of generally accepted ACA-mandated preventive medications to be covered at no member cost share (**Table 4**).

Some plan sponsors choose to expand the preventive medication list beyond what is generally accepted as the ACA-mandated list. This can be referred to as an Expanded Preventive Drug List. Expanded Preventive Drug Lists vary widely across PBMs and plan sponsors, but they may often include some of the medications and/or medication classes referenced in Table 3, such as:

- Mental health medications (both antidepressants and antipsychotics, going beyond just SSRIs referenced by the July 2019 IRS guidance)

- Diabetes medications (including insulins)

- Antiresorptive therapies for osteoporosis / osteopenia

- ACE inhibitors

- β blockers

CASE 6, TABLE 4. Sample ACA-Mandated Zero Member Cost Share Preventive Medication List*

Drug Class	Comments / Limitations
Aspirin	
Prenatal Vitamins / Folic Acid supplementation	
Pediatric oral iron replacement	
Pediatric fluoride supplementation	
Bowel preparations	Ages 50 to 75 years
Statins	Ages 40 to 75 years
Breast cancer preventives: anastrozole, exemestane, letrozole, raloxifene, tamoxifen	Females; Ages 35 and older
HIV PrEP: emtricitabine-tenofovir disoproxil fumarate, emtricitabine-tenofovir alafenamide	Preventive use only; Must try generic first
Prescription and Over-the-Count Tobacco Cessation	
ACIP-Recommended Vaccines	
Contraceptives (oral, patch, injectable, emergency, diaphragms, intrauterine devices, implants, condoms)	Females only (with exception of condoms); If generic available in class, generic only

*Dose or product specific limitations may apply.

- Nonstatin hyperlipidemia medications
- Miscellaneous cardiovascular medications (eg, diuretics, calcium channel blockers, anticoagulants, antiplatelets, nitrates/nitroglycerin, digoxin)
- Asthma/chronic obstructive pulmonary disease medications
- HIV medications
- Transplant antirejection medications

If a plan sponsor elects to utilize an Expanded Preventive Drug List, additional decisions remain, including:

- Are generics and brand names covered within the classes on the Expanded Preventive Drug List?
- Are specialty medications covered within the Expanded Preventive Drug List?
- For HDHPs, do prescriptions for Expanded Preventive Drug List medications bypass the deductible?
- Do prescriptions for Expanded Preventive Drug List medications utilize a standard member cost share (ie, standard co-pay or coinsurance) or is there a different (typically lower or zero) co-pay?

When utilizing an Expanded Preventive Drug List, especially in combination with bypassing of a deductible and lower member cost share, the impact can be an increase in plan spend. However, this does not account for any potential improvement in medical spend due to possible improved preventive medication adherence and improved chronic medical condition control that may result. Plan sponsors should consider and strive to understand the variability in the ACA-mandated preventive drug list and the expanded preventive drug list coverage options in comparison with their goals when making these plan selections.

DRUG SOURCING

In 2020, specialty drug spend accounted for around 50% of self-funded drug expense.[15] With product mix continuing to shift to specialty and orphan drugs, many plan sponsors are seeking creative solutions to provide access to specialty drugs for their members while limiting their potential drug expense exposure. In the past several years, the development of specialty solutions has been at the forefront of PBM strategies to address current plan sponsor concerns as well as create a marketplace differentiator compared with other PBMs. Several of these solutions will be discussed in more detail in the following section.

Variable Co-pay Programs

Many PBMs offer variable co-pay programs and may include both maximization as well as accumulator functionality. These programs leverage available manufacturer co-pay programs for high-cost specialty drugs to reduce the out-of-pocket costs for members. With the maximization approach, a PBM will set up the member's cost share for a particular drug to mimic the annual (or monthly) limits available for that drug. By maximizing the annual amount available, some of the drug expense shifts from the plan to the member and is then covered by the manufacturer. The accumulator portion of these programs are set up to address the concern that a member will receive undue credit toward their out-of-pocket expense (ie, deductible and max out-of-pocket limits) which has been paid on the member's behalf using the manufacturer co-pay card program. In recent months, many states have created laws that prevent plan sponsors from denying a member's ability to use co-pay program dollars toward their out-of-pocket expenses.[16] While not currently enacted, federal legislation was put forward to also limit this program aspect for self-funded employers.[17] If both features are available for a variable co-pay program, a plan may experience around 20% specialty expense reduction for applicable drugs.

Alternative Funding Programs

PBMs offering alternative funding programs may provide an internal solution, which is developed and managed directly by the PBM, or as a bolt-on service by a third-party vendor. In cases where it is through a third-party vendor, integration and cooperation by the PBM is critical for the program's success. Plan sponsors often find these programs are more readily available and comprehensive through smaller PBMs focusing on plans with up to 20,000 employees. The largest PBMs with the highest market share do not typically offer these programs for a variety of reasons, with the primary reason being the loss of rebates as well as potential loss of specialty revenue by their owned specialty pharmacies.

These programs differ from variable co-pay programs in that they exclude coverage of certain high-cost specialty drugs. The program has member advocates who assist members with finding outside drug funding. The source of funding may include manufacturer programs, disease state programs, and private foundations. The advocate works with the member to identify a program, submit the appropriate paperwork to support eligibility, and ensure the member receives direct shipment of the drug to the member's home. When managed appropriately, these programs can offer significant savings to a plan sponsor.

International Drug Importation

Probably one of the most controversial cost containment strategies is international drug importation. This refers to the practice of procuring drugs at the member level from a country other than the United States. At this time, there are many regulatory agencies trying to navigate through this complex issue to provide more cost-effective options for the residents of the United States, where costs for the same medication may be 10 times higher. The National Association of Boards of Pharmacy has created a task force to evaluate the regulatory environment and how it will impact states' ability to regulate drug importation. Additional goals are to provide support and education materials to states creating and overseeing drug importation programs.[18]

SUMMARY

With persistent rise in drug costs, plan sponsors will continue to be concerned over the increased expense and seek creative ways to contain costs. A plan sponsor should stay up-to-date on many different facets of the pharmacy benefit, including the pharmacy administrative services agreement, formulary and pharmacy network selection, utilization management programs, and specialty cost containment programs. Health systems may be perfectly situated to assist in the management of their employer-sponsored plan by leveraging outpatient pharmacy services, discounted drug pricing, as well as the availability of clinical expertise.

It should be noted that the pharmacy benefit management cost containment arena is one that is constantly changing. The statements and examples in this discussion were true at the time of writing.

CASE 6, TABLE 5. Terminology Referenced Within Chapter

Administrative Services Agreement (ASA)	A contract or agreement which provides details around how a pharmacy benefit is administered (also known as pharmacy agreement, pharmacy contract).
Annual Discount Reconciliation	The practice of measuring the average discount off AWP for each guaranteed category. Typically, over performance of a guarantee may be used to offset underperformance. If an overall underperformance is found, the PBM will owe the plan sponsor the amount of the underperformance.
Drug Utilization Management Program	Programs focused on the most cost-effective, safe, and therapeutically effective use of drugs. These programs often include prior authorizations, step therapy, and quantity limits.
Member	A covered individual on an employer-sponsored health plan and can include the employee, spouse, or dependents.
PBM-Pharmacy Administrative Contract	A contract between a PBM and a dispensing pharmacy (eg, retail, mail order, specialty) which describes reimbursement by the PBM for dispensed drugs by the pharmacy.
Rebate Aggregator	A third party which is often PBM-owned or affiliated that subcontracts with other smaller PBMs to aggregate drug purchasing volume and distributes rebates to PBMs.
Renewal Cycle	The time period when an ASA is nearing the end of its term and allows for renegotiation of the ASA.

REFERENCES

1. U.S. Department of Health and Human Services. What is the Affordable Care Act? https://www.hhs.gov/answers/health-insurance-reform/what-is-the-affordable-care-act/index.html. Accessed December 28, 2021.

2. Internal Revenue Service. Determining if an employer is an application large employer. https://www.irs.gov/affordable-care-act/employers/determining-if-an-employer-is-an-applicable-large-employer. Accessed December 28, 2021.

3. Kaiser Family Foundation. 2021 Employer health benefits survey: Summary of findings. November 10, 2021. **https://www.kff.org/report-section/ehbs-2021-summary-of-findings/**. Accessed December 28, 2021.

4. Kaiser Family Foundation. 2021 Employer health benefits survey. Section 10: Plan funding. November 10, 2021. **https://www.kff.org/report-section/ehbs-2021-section-10-plan-funding/**. Accessed December 28, 2021.

5. Visante. The Return on Investment (ROI) on PBM Services. February 2020. **https://www.pcmanet.org/wp-content/uploads/2020/02/ROI-on-PBM-Services-FINAL_.pdf**. Accessed January 24, 2021.

6. Kaiser Family Foundation. 2021 Employer health benefits survey. Section 9: Prescription drug benefits. November 10, 2021. **https://www.kff.org/report-section/ehbs-2021-section-9-prescription-drug-benefits/**. Accessed December 28, 2021.

7. Mikuli M. Market share of the top pharmacy benefit managers in the U.S. prescription market in 2020. June 16, 2021. **https://www.statista.com/statistics/239976/us-prescription-market-share-of-top-pharmacy-benefit-managers/#statisticContainer**. Accessed December 29, 2021.

8. Gencarelli DM. Average wholesale price for prescription drugs: Is there a more appropriate pricing mechanism? Issue brief: National Health Policy Forum; June 7, 2022; Washington, DC. **https://www.ncbi.nlm.nih.gov/books/NBK561162/**. Accessed January 1, 2022.

9. Kaiser Family Foundation. 2021 Employer health benefits survey. Section 4: Types of plans offered. November 10, 2021. **https://www.kff.org/report-section/ehbs-2021-section-4-types-of-plans-offered/**. Accessed January 8, 2022.

10. Kaiser Family Foundation. 2021 Employer health benefits survey. Section 8: High-deductible health plans with savings option. November 10, 2021. **https://www.kff.org/report-section/ehbs-2021-section-8-high-deductible-health-plans-with-savings-option/**. Accessed January 8, 2022.

11. U.S. Department of the Treasury, Internal Revenue Service. Coverage of certain preventive services under the Affordable Care Act. 80 Fed. Reg. 41318 (July 14, 2015) (to be codified at 26 CFR part 54). **https://www.govinfo.gov/content/pkg/FR-2015-07-14/pdf/2015-17076.pdf**. Accessed December 30, 2021.

12. Internal Revenue Service. IRS expands list of preventive care for HSA participants to include certain care for chronic conditions. IR-2019-129. July 17, 2019. **https://www.irs.gov/newsroom/irs-expands-list-of-preventive-care-for-hsa-participants-to-include-certain-care-for-chronic-conditions**. Accessed December 30, 2021.

13. U.S. Preventative Services Task Force. USPSTF issues grade A recommendations for PrEP & HIV testing. June 11, 2019. **https://www.hiv.gov/blog/uspstf-issues-grade-recommendations-prep-hiv-testing**. Accessed December 30, 2021.

14. U.S. Departments of Labor, U.S. Department of Health & Human Services, U.S. Department of the Treasury. FAQs about Affordable Care Act implementation, part 47. July 19, 2021. **https://www.dol.gov/sites/dolgov/files/EBSA/about-ebsa/our-activities/resource-center/faqs/aca-part-47.pdf**. Accessed January 8, 2022.

15. Evernorth. 2020 Drug trend report executive summary. 2021. **https://d17f9hu9hnb3ar.cloudfront.net/s3fs-public/2021-03/Evernorth%202020DrugTrendReport%20ExecutiveSummary_0.pdf**. Accessed on January 3, 2022.

16. Aimed Alliance. Copay accumulators enacted laws. **https://aimedalliance.org/copay-accumulators-enacted-laws/**. Accessed on January 3, 2022.

17. Department of Health and Human Services. Patient protection and affordable care act; HHS notice of benefit and payment parameters for 2020. April 25, 2019. **https://www.federalregister.gov/documents/2019/04/25/2019-08017/patient-protection-and-affordable-care-act-hhs-notice-of-benefit-and-payment-parameters-for-2020**. Accessed on January 3, 2022.

18. National Association of Boards of Pharmacy. Report of the task force on state oversight of drug importance. September 20-21, 2021. **https://nabp.pharmacy/wp-content/uploads/2021/12/Report-of-the-Task-Force-on-State-Oversight-of-Drug-Importation.pdf**. Accessed December 30, 2021.

PHARMACY & THERAPEUTICS COMMITTEE FORMULARY REVIEW BIOSIMILAR FINANCIAL ANALYSIS

CASE 7

Joel Hennenfent and Candy Tsourounis

BUSINESS CASE

Health System A is having significant financial issues with skyrocketing labor costs, overtime, and contract labor due to a global pandemic. In response, the System Chief Medical Officer (CMO) has asked the System Vice President of Pharmacy (VP of Pharmacy) and the Chief Pharmacy Officer (CPO) of a major academic medical center for ways to reduce costs. Both the System VP of Pharmacy and the CPO report to the System CMO. The system is looking for opportunities to capture savings and prevent the need to reduce patient care services and staff. The CPO and System VP identify a significant financial savings opportunity by rapidly adopting biosimilars in the outpatient oncology infusion centers. Health System A has had limited success with biosimilar adoption for multiple reasons. In fact, the significant savings opportunity was presented to the oncology providers numerous times over three years; however, there was considerable hesitation in converting to biosimilars even though the American Society of Clinical Oncologists Statement supports the adoption and conversion to biosimilars. The System CMO is fully onboard to support the biosimilar conversion, however, they were not willing to expend the political capital to force the conversion in the past. Given the new financial situation, the entire C Suite supports advancing the initiative. For this case, we will walk you through the thought process and provide an example financial analysis for a biosimilar conversion.

EXECUTIVE SUMMARY

The first biosimilar product to come to the European market was in 2006, followed by the first biosimilar product launching in the U.S. market in 2015. Since then, the growth and adoption of biosimilar products in the U.S. have grown rapidly. Given their long history of use, biosimilars represent a significant value opportunity for health systems nationwide. Despite the significant value that the biosimilars provide, integration and adoption issues remain from multiple perspectives.

Medication formulary management is extremely complex, even for those with significant experience managing formularies. Biosimilars have been a learning opportunity like no other with new literature, provider adoption challenges, and payer plan product steering. By bringing brilliant clinicians, specialized pharmacists, nurses, and providers together across many different clinical areas, there is an opportunity to transform biosimilar adoption.

DOI 10.37573/9781585287130.017

Sharing the team's financial success with all stakeholders makes it essential to track cost savings and revenue generation from incorporating biosimilars into the formulary. Health systems are now making progress adopting biosimilar utilization and creating processes to rapidly incorporate new biosimilar products in the future.

BUSINESS/SERVICE DESCRIPTION

Health systems in the U.S. were slow to adopt biosimilars compared with their European counterparts, with few health systems transitioning to biosimilars from branded products. The introduction of biosimilars in the U.S. began around 2015, and adoption accelerated around 2020. Many organizations started adopting biosimilars when the biosimilar for filgrastim launched in 2015. Since then, over thirty biosimilar products have entered the U.S. market with the potential to provide significant savings for the institution. As the market for biosimilars continues to grow rapidly, health systems are developing strategies to stay on top of the rapid growth, the changing drug purchasing costs, and the significant impact these therapies have on revenue. Some health systems have adopted a yearly review strategy that focuses on a comprehensive assessment of payer coverage, utilization patterns, purchasing cost, safety, and efficacy to establish or re-establish the biosimilar, which represents the best opportunity for patients and health systems.

Many health systems focused their efforts on biosimilar use within the outpatient setting (in clinic/infusion center) as this is driven by payer coverage. The initial health system strategy of implementing biosimilars was focused on initiating therapy "new starts," as this simplified the ordering process and provided clinicians some assurance in knowing that they didn't have to switch every patient. This strategy also provided clinicians some additional time to gain experience prescribing the biosimilar agents and it allowed each service or specialty area to develop familiarity with using a biosimilar. With time, each service would identify select patients to switch from the reference product to the biosimilar. It also increased awareness around the best time to make the once yearly review during the reprior-authorization time frame. Some health systems allowed clinicians to opt out of using biosimilars for select disease states. For example, patients with stable metastatic disease in whom the reference product was being used could continue to receive the reference product. Another example is in patients with neuromyelitis optica where a lack of efficacy during the transition could be medically devastating for a patient if their condition progresses to vision loss. As of 2022, health systems have experienced a significantly positive biosimilar experience and have freely transitioned patients between biosimilar products as their cost, coverage, and revenue change.

Many health systems have moved beyond the outpatient setting and have established a preference for a specific biosimilar agent in the inpatient setting. This preference has been set by leveraging the review and approval of the organization's Pharmacy & Therapeutics (P&T) Committee. Clinician specialists identify the biosimilar of choice by working with prescribers and nursing staff to create inpatient use criteria for biosimilar use. Larger health systems have established formal biosimilar subcommittees whose focus is on reviewing existing utilization trends, monitoring current and future biosimilar opportunities, and making recommendations to the P&T Committee.

ENVIRONMENTAL/NEEDS ASSESSMENT

An institution's P&T Committee serves as an essential review and approval pathway for biosimilar adoption primarily because it is a medical staff committee that oversees the medication use process for a healthcare organization. The P&T Committee plays a vital role in establishing medication use policy particularly because it emphasizes a critical review of the primary literature and published real world evidence, collaborates across multiple disciplines in all practice areas and service lines, and establishes protocols to help implement decisions. Another important role of the P&T Committee is to serve as an impartial review step that evaluates all available evidence and helps to counterbalance the information on the reference product(s) that sales representatives may be sharing. This practice is called "counter detailing." The P&T Committee, in this case, would provide a balanced, unbiased review, including the advantages and disadvantages associated with adopting a specific biosimilar over the reference product or other competitor biosimilars. Another important consideration when assessing the appropriateness of a biosimilar is the use of guidelines or position statements from a national or international organization. Incorporating the recommendations described in guidelines or position statements within a specific specialty area can be instrumental in the success of an organization adopting biosimilars. For example, within the oncology specialty area, the American Society of Oncology Statement: Biosimilars in Oncology fully supports biosimilar adoption. As more data regarding conversion to biosimilars is published, other professional organization guidelines that fully support biosimilar adoption in other disease states will be published, and this will help rapidly advance adoption in current and future disease states.

The biosimilar landscape is changing rapidly and requires effective real-time communication and information coordination. Communication challenges exist in healthcare and during times of added uncertainty that can stress the healthcare system. These challenges extend across multiple service lines (inpatient, outpatient, infusion area) and clinical staff (nursing, pharmacy, medical staff, operations staff). Another challenge is that some biosimilars are used in adult and pediatric patients across multiple service lines and clinical indications. This requires updating pharmacy purchasing and distribution processes, clinical pathways/order sets, IT and safety systems, and takes the coordination of many care providers as well as integration of the IT infrastructure. This can be an arduous yet necessary undertaking as paying attention to details and outlining the institution's process map matter. One crucial requirement is having a targeted education campaign, including organization email announcements, in-services, presentations at grand rounds, and specialists' meetings to socialize the initiative.

OPERATING PLAN(s)

Health system leadership support of biosimilars conceptually and practically is essential for success. Gaining the endorsement of the executive suite, medical directors, and relevant department chair representatives is critical for quick adoption, implementation, and realization of cost savings. Once leadership has endorsed the biosimilar approach, the traditional Pharmacy & Therapeutics Committee process may be followed, like how other medications are reviewed and approved for use. As you work with the key stakeholder, it is essential to highlight the FDA-approved language that biologics have "no clinically meaningful difference from the reference product" and that the biosimilars have a long history of safe and effective use in other countries. Document biosimilar experiences from similar institutions to your organization that have adopted the biosimilar of interest or any biosimilar and share their experience and patient outcomes. To assist the ordering process, some health systems have established "interchangeability" policies and processes for biosimilars that help guide prescribers in selecting the biosimilar of choice.

FINANCIAL PLAN

The rapid adoption of biosimilars within health systems creates an opportunity to improve the financial bottom line, which is even more critical now with the negative economic impact of the global pandemic. A comprehensive financial evaluation is important during the presentation for formulary consideration, and this evaluation can be extremely complex. The financial plan should include estimates based on reasonable targets appropriate within the health system. These estimates should be scaled over time, recognizing that not all reference product use can be converted all at once. The plan should also include existing reference product utilization and all possible biosimilar options for the target diagnoses and patient populations.

Category

Identify the originator and all available biosimilar products in the product category. Additionally, include biosimilar products expected to enter the market within the next quarter of the fiscal year.

Drug Purchasing Cost

The originator and biosimilar product costs vary by contract and 340B program participation. For each product, collect your health system's ASP, WAC, 340B, and GPO pricing information for your financial evaluation. Work closely with your contracting partner to evaluate the contract market basket, market share, volume requirements, rebates, and special requests (eg, the need to add the biosimilar to the formulary, order set inclusion). Note that 340B price changes quarterly, and GPO pricing changes quickly in a highly competitive environment.

Reimbursement

The originator and biosimilar products payer reimbursements vary by site of care (eg, hospital out-patient department (HOPD), physician office). For each product, collect the CPT Codes, E/M Codes, HCPCS Code, JG Modifier, TB Modifier, JW Modifier, Revenue codes (eg, 0260 IV therapy, 0500 outpatient service general, 0510 clinic general), New Technology Add-On (NTAP), etc. Evaluate your current utilization in physician offices, hospital outpatient department (HOPD) sites of care, Medicare Administrative Contractors (MACs), and private commercial payers.

Patient Assistance Program

As with all very costly biologics that are infused chronically, a manufacturer's patient assistance program is essential. Each patient assistance program can vary widely on the amount of assistance it offers to patients in need. Depending on your patient mix and potential patient enrollment, a robust patient assistance program may change the financial value delivered and the direction of the formulary product selection. For each biosimilar used, consider the degree of financial assistance offered and confirm that the manufacturer's patient assistance program does not promote the white-bagging process as your state regulations and Boards of Pharmacy may not allow white bagging.

Key Stakeholders

Identifying the key stakeholders can be accomplished by reviewing the ordering and authorizing providers for the reference products within the health system. The pharmacy drug information specialist or the medication formulary manager can work closely with the key stakeholders of each specialty area to present the biosimilar opportunity and develop a strategy for selection, implementation, and monitoring.

Example Financial Analysis

The following financial analysis is composed of two parts. The first is the organization's costs associated with the reference product and the biosimilar options noted as A, B, C, and D, **Table 1**.

Cost Assumptions:

Cost does not include intravenous supplies, chair time for infusion, ancillary medications, or nursing time.

CASE 7, TABLE 1. Drug Purchasing Costs

Drug	Strength (vial)	WAC Cost/Unit	Inpatient Cost/Unit (GPO)	Outpatient Cost/Unit (340B)
Reference Product	100 mg/5 mL	$1,300	$1,132	$260
Biosimilar A	100 mg/5 mL	$750	$515	$275
Biosimilar B	100 mg/5 mL	$600	$530	$170
Biosimilar C	100 mg/5 mL	$580	$475	$175
Biosimilar D	100 mg/5 mL	$530	$430	$223

The second essential component involves a utilization report from your organization that indicates how many units of each product your organization currently uses. This is essential to compare your health system's current spending to the expected spending over time to estimate how much the health system would save if the switch occurred at a given percentage. Each organization's goal may be different than another organization and predicting when the target percentage will be achieved may be difficult as adoption rates vary. Setting a goal for your organization at one year is a reasonable target. In the example below, the target conversion goal to the preferred biosimilar was set at 50% based on the organization's payer mix and biosimilar coverage, **Tables 2 and 3**. Although biosimilar D appeared to have the lowest cost for the organization and offered the greatest savings, in this example, biosimilar D did not have adequate payer coverage by insurance. Biosimilar C offered the most widespread payer coverage and offered a significant cost savings.

CASE 7, TABLE 2. Payer Coverage Criteria

Insurance Plan	Prior Authorization Required	Failed Reference Biologic	Confirmed Diagnosis	Preference for Biologic A	Preference for Biologic B	Preference for Biologic C	Preference for Biologic D
Federal/State Government Plan	√		√	√		√	
Commercial Health Plan 1	√		√	√		√	√
Commercial Health Plan 2	√	√	√		√	√	
Commercial Health Plan 3	√		√			√	

CASE 7, TABLE 3. Current Spend and Projected Savings

Drug Name	Purchases 12/1/20-11/30/21 ($ spent for 100 mg vial units)	Projected cost with 50% reference product, 50% Biosimilar C (94% 340B, 6% GPO)	Projected savings from a 50% switch to Biosimilar C
Reference Product	$3,085,215 10,983	$3,915,826	$495,531
Biosimilar A	$1,473,031 4519	$3,740,535	$670,821
Biosimilar B	$156,6 10	$2,981,273	$1,430,084
Biosimilar C	$24,25 5	$2,992,375	$1,418,981
Biosimilar D	$0 0	$3,321,864	$1,089,493
TOTAL	$4,411,356		

IMPLEMENTATION PLAN

The financial analysis is an essential piece of the decision-making process on formulary inclusion and can help inform the implementation plan.

SUPPORTING MATERIALS

For those looking for best practices, example tools, webinars, podcasts, and expert insights on formulary management, please visit www.formularytoolkit.org. The authors of this case were on the ASHP Foundation Steering Committee creating the toolkit, which was designed to share best practices for health system formulary monographs and can be used for small community hospitals as well as tertiary care medical centers.

No single drug monograph format can meet every health system's needs; however, certain core elements are essential to include when evaluating a new drug therapy. Individualization is important as each health system is unique. The level of technology available at each type of institution may impact the level of detail included in the drug monograph (eg, intravenous smart pumps, clinical decision support, clinical intervention software, etc.). Other important considerations include the special populations the organization serves, such as pediatrics, transplant, oncology, etc. The formulary toolkit serves to assist anyone preparing a drug monograph or PowerPoint presentation for formulary consideration.

LESSONS LEARNED

- Provide published and historical evidence to support the efficacy and safety of biosimilars

- Include FDA-approved language that biologics have "no clinically meaningful difference from the reference product"

- Document biosimilar experiences from similar institutions to your organization that have adopted the biosimilar of interest

- Understand your organization's top payers (federal/state government and commercial)

- Review the coverage for the reference drug and all available biosimilars

- Review the Patient Assistance Program for each biologic and biosimilar

- Gather the WAC, GPO, and 340B costs for the reference biologic and the available biosimilar

- Consider your organization's historical use of the reference biologic and/or biosimilar(s)

- Calculate your organization's yearly spending on the reference biologic and/or biosimilar(s)

- Gather stakeholder feedback whether service lines agree to implement the biosimilar of choice for new starts, reauthorizations, or all patients

- Establish a target switch threshold per year for your organization, recognizing that the target may be achieved slowly over a defined period and that each organization may have their own unique target threshold

- Estimate the costs and savings if your organization were to convert from the reference biologic and/or current biosimilar to the target biosimilar

- Identify the biosimilar of choice for your organization based on insurer coverage, drug purchasing cost, patient assistance program, and estimated use based on a reasonable target

- Work with your key stakeholders from appropriate service lines to gain support for the recommendation

- Outline a plan to implement the biosimilar of choice, which includes education, updating ordering tools, establishing a go-live date, and a monitoring plan

- Establish a re-review frequency and best time of year for the re-review to ensure that the biosimilar of choice remains appropriate over time, including an assessment of clinical efficacy, safety, switch opportunity, reimbursement/payment

REFERENCES

1. Dalpoas SE, Socal M, Proctor C, Shermock KM. Barriers to biosimilar utilization in the United States. *Am J Health Syst Pharm*. 2020;77(23):2006–2014 10.1093/ajhp/zxaa297. PubMed

2. American Society of Clinical Oncology Statement. Biosimilars in Oncology. **https://ascopubs.org/doi/10.1200/JCO.2017.77.4893**

HOSPITAL OUTPATIENT (RETAIL) PHARMACY

CASE 8

Eric Reimer

EXECUTIVE SUMMARY

This facility has recently reached a size and patient volume to support a hospital outpatient pharmacy. The attached pro forma using comparable facilities from other parts of this health system shows that an outpatient pharmacy would be a profitable endeavor. The ability to fill discharge prescriptions for our patients would maximize the profit from a patient encounter. Further ability to support the patient with complete medication reconciliation and ongoing refills would add to the predicted prescription volume, increasing profit to the hospital. As a 340B covered entity, having an entity-owned pharmacy would increase the amount of profit currently received from contract pharmacies. In the spirit of the 340B program of increasing access to care, this additional revenue could be used to fund further expansion of the hospital's capabilities. The revenue opportunity is outlined in the financial plan below. Two outpatient pharmacies in our system with a similar payer mix and patient volume have been used to estimate the increase in profits for this pharmacy. During this time when capital is limited in this health system, projects like this that are financially profitable in the short term should be prioritized.

A second benefit to an outpatient pharmacy would be a more robust Transition of Care (TOC) program. The needs assessment below shows how that would greatly benefit this facility by reducing readmissions. It would also help provide a higher standard of care for patients by ensuring treatment success.

Building a new pharmacy will require a collaborative effort between the Hospital Pharmacy, Facility Maintenance, Human Resources, Legal Affairs, and Contracting departments. The contributions of each team are outlined in the operating plan, implementation plan, and legal sections below.

By bringing these teams together to support this project, this hospital can acquire one of the most valuable tools in the modernization of healthcare.

BUSINESS DESCRIPTION

The facility served by this new pharmacy is a 600 bed hospital operating as a 340B Disproportionate Share Hospital (DSH). Currently, the hospital has 340B agreements in place with several community contract pharmacies to serve the discharge prescription needs of the patients. The proposed pharmacy will be an Outpatient Pharmacy Department wholly owned by the hospital.

DOI 10.37573/9781585287130.018

It will operate as a 340B covered entity-owned pharmacy. While the focus will be on filling discharge prescriptions for patients of the hospital and surrounding clinics, it will be open to the public for all retail prescription needs.

Having a pharmacy that is open to the public allows for the filling of prescriptions written by prescribers outside of this health system. This will allow our hospital to provide better transitions of care upon discharge. It will also allow for ongoing monitoring and medication therapy management (MTM) as patients follow up with primary care providers in the weeks and months following discharge.

As outlined in the Needs Assessment section below, hospital administration has prioritized reducing readmissions in the five year strategic plan. This pharmacy will play a key role in achieving that goal by improving the discharge process and transitions of care. Readmission rate reduction will be a key metric in gauging the success of the new pharmacy. Readmission rates of pharmacy patients will be tracked and compared with previous rates, as well as rates of patients who choose to use a different pharmacy upon discharge. Based on the studies cited in the needs assessment, the goal for this project will be a hospital-wide reduction of readmissions by 15% within one year. To ensure proper credit for the absolute risk reduction, a second goal of 50% relative risk reduction for Outpatient Pharmacy patients versus patients who choose to use an external pharmacy will be set.

NEEDS ASSESSMENT

All hospitals across the nation, including this one, have struggled with patient readmissions. CMS has been reducing payments to hospitals with excessive readmissions for almost a decade now. Within the last two years, further legislation has increased the scrutiny on hospital readmission performance relative to other hospitals.[1]

A recent study showed that pharmacist-led transitions of care programs reduced 30 day readmissions in a large health system in Florida.[2] Other studies have shown that bedside delivery of discharge medications resulted in a significant reduction in 30, 60, and 90 day readmission rates.[3;4]

Outpatient pharmacists are uniquely positioned to support patients through transitions of care during the discharge process and beyond, ensuring treatment success. Not only does this reduce the impact of reimbursement reductions to the hospital, it is also the new best practice to support the patient.

An added benefit of a pharmacy-driven transitions of care program is pharmacy access services. These services should be a collaboration between pharmacy technicians, prescriber staff, and social workers. Since many of these positions already exist within the hospital, a well-designed program need not add many employees. The addition of a pharmacy technician and the collaborative efforts of the aforementioned positions will reduce demands on prescriber time. The ultimate goal of this team is to make the prescription affordable to the patient. To meet this end, the team will assess insurance coverage and pursue any additional help necessary. This may include insurance prior-authorization work, enrolling the patient into Medicaid, finding manufacturer discount programs, applying for assistance from external foundations, and determining eligibility for internal charity programs. During open enrollment periods, this staff can assist patients with finding optimal plans based on their prescription needs. This may include working with an affiliated health plan to provide better coverage to patients.

The performance of the 340B program at this hospital has been limited by the filling fees paid out to contract pharmacies. When a hospital contracts with a separate business entity for 340B pharmacy services, the covered entity will receive all the revenue for the prescription in exchange for the cost of the drug and a filling fee. This places a burden on the covered entity in several ways. First, filling fees vary by contract and a covered entity with multiple contract pharmacies must dedicate excessive administrative time to properly bill and audit the payments to both parties. There are many software solutions that streamline this process, but some manual auditing and billing is still required. If a software solution is implemented, fees for licensing cut into the profit margin from

340B revenues. Additionally, there may be switch or interface fees involved to properly integrate the software with the electronic medical record and pharmacy workflow software. An entity-owned pharmacy will keep most of the margin from 340B-qualifying prescriptions in house, increasing the performance of the program. Software may still be needed to ensure accuracy if the pharmacy does not have the space to keep a separate stock for nonqualifying prescriptions, but the interface with an in-house pharmacy will be simpler and less expensive to implement. Increases in revenue will help the hospital serve two purposes. First, they will be able to pass savings along to the patient to make their discharge prescriptions more affordable. Second, the hospital will be able to use these funds to expand services and infrastructure to better serve the patients of this community.

The hospital is home to a growing Pharmacotherapy Clinic. This pharmacist-run clinic started with anticoagulation but has grown to include monitoring and medication management of several disease states. The management of this clinic is interested in implementing a community-facing immunization program but lacks the space to accommodate walk-in patients. By adding outpatient pharmacists to the existing collaborative practice agreement held by the pharmacotherapy clinic staff, this program can be expanded to the benefit of both departments.

OPERATING PLAN

The pharmacy will open with a pharmacy manager designated as the Pharmacist in Charge (PIC) with the State Board of Pharmacy. One other pharmacist, two technicians, and one clerk will make up the rest of the full-time staff. One per diem pharmacist and technician will provide coverage for vacations and sick calls. The PIC will be hired first and will manage the construction of the new pharmacy, selection and placement of furniture, fixtures, and equipment (FF&E). The PIC will be responsible for all required licensing of the new pharmacy with the assistance of the hospital legal team. The PIC will also serve as the hiring manager for the rest of the staff and work with the Human Resources department to conduct recruiting, onboarding, and training.

FINANCIAL PLAN

The following pro forma shows an estimate that an investment of four hundred thousand dollars to build this pharmacy will lead to break even in one year with significant profits in the following years. During this time when this health system has a tight supply of funds for projects, profitable plans like this one should be prioritized.

CASE 8, TABLE 1. Sample Pro Forma

Annual Data Unless Otherwise Noted	Comparable #1	Comparable #2
Prescribing Facility Size (Licensed Beds)	650	425
Facility Prescriptions Generated	270,633	360,819
Capture Rate of Facility Prescriptions by Outpatient Pharmacy	43%	27%
Prescription Volume	116,372	97,421
Number of Pharmacy Full-Time Equivalent (FTE=Staffed Employee Hours/2080)	6	5
Labor Costs (Wages and Benefits)	$953,881	$790,901
Cost of Goods Sold (COGS)	$6,982,320	$3,559,969
Other Overhead Costs (Non-Drug Supplies, Licensing, Equipment Maintenance)	$52,981	$42,813
Building Lease	$71,400	$35,525

CASE 8, TABLE 1. continued

Annual Data Unless Otherwise Noted	Comparable #1	Comparable #2
Rentable Square Feet	2,040	1,015
Revenue	$11,025,006	$4,986,524
Gross Margin	$4,042,686	$1,426,555
Earnings Before Interest, Depreciation, and Amortization (EBIDA)	$2,964,424	$557,316

Annual Inflation and Growth Trends	
Prescription Volume	3%
Revenue	2%
COGS	3%
Labor Costs*	3%
Lease Costs	3%

*Includes raises for experience, cost of living, and achievements

Startup Costs	
IS Installations (Workflow Software, Phone System, Point of Sale, Hardware)	$150,000
Furniture, Fixtures, and Equipment (FF&E)	$50,000
Construction	$160,000
Hiring and Training	$20,000
Other Startup Costs (Licensing, Advertising, etc.)	$10,000
Total	$390,000

	Startup Year	Full Year 1	Year 2	Year 3	Year 4
EBIDA Estimates	2022	2023	2024	2025	2026
Facility Prescription Generation	124,299	256,056	263,737	271,649	279,799
Capture Rate	27%	35%	43%	43%	43%
Outpatient Pharmacy Volume	33,561	89,619	113,407	116,809	120,314
COGS	$1,620,010	$4,455,807	$5,802,734	$6,145,971	$6,504,580
Revenue	$2,448,666	$6,800,398	$8,605,418	$9,034,034	$9,480,622
Gross Profit	$828,656	$2,344,591	$2,802,684	$2,888,063	$2,976,042
Gross Margin	34%	34%	33%	32%	31%
Labor Costs	$872,391	$898,562.73	$925,519.61	$953,285.20	$981,883.76
Building Lease Costs	$42,700	$43,981	$45,300.43	$46,659.44	$48,059.23
Other Overhead Costs	$15,014	$41,295.69	$53,778.79	$55,392.15	$57,053.91
IS Maintenance and Support	$20,000	$20,600.00	$21,218.00	$21,854.54	$22,510.18
Total Non-Drug Expenses	$950,105	$1,004,439.42	$1,045,817	$1,077,191.33	$1,109,507
EBIDA	−$511,449	$1,340,151.62	$1,756,867	$1,810,871.68	$1,866,535

Abbreviations:	
COGS	Cost of Goods Sold
EBIDA	Earnings Before Interest, Taxes, Depreciation, and Amortization
FTE	Full-Time Equivalent (Calculated as staffed employee hours/2080)
IVR	Interactive Voice Response (Phone tree, voicemail, keypad prescription refill requests)
FF&E	Furniture, Fixtures, and Equipment
IS/IT	Information Systems/Information Technology

LEGAL AND REGULATORY CONCERNS

Once hired, the PIC will be responsible for ensuring all pharmacy licensing is in place. Needed licenses and permits will include the following:

1. State Pharmacy License (obtained from the State Department of Health/Board of Pharmacy)

2. DEA License (obtained from the Federal Drug Enforcement Administration)

3. State Business License (obtained from the State Department of Revenue)

4. Local Business License (obtained from the City/County Department of Revenue)

5. Reseller permit (obtained from the State Department of Revenue)

The hospital contracting department will apply for a liability insurance plan for the pharmacy and provide the PIC with a certificate for third party enrollment.

As the PIC hires staff, HR will assist in ensuring each staff member is appropriately licensed. The PIC will collect physical copies of staff licenses for display in the pharmacy.

The PIC will apply for a National Provider Identifier (NPI) number and National Council for Prescription Drug Programs (NCPDP) number. Then the PIC will work with the hospital contracting department to enter the pharmacy into contracts with various third-party payers. These will include Medicaid for this and the surrounding states, as well as state Labor and Industries work injury compensation plans. The new outpatient pharmacy will utilize the same wholesaler currently contracted to the inpatient pharmacy. After outpatient wholesale accounts are set up, the pharmacy will utilize the Pharmacy Service Administrative Organization (PSAO) operated by the wholesaler to contract with commercial third-party plans. These will include Medicare Part D Plans. This wholesaler is one of the largest in the country. By joining their PSAO, the Outpatient Pharmacy will have the benefit of negotiating power that far exceeds that of the health system alone. Careful discernment including an assessment of reimbursement should precede any independent contracting outside of the PSAO.

Certain medications needed for organ transplants conducted in this hospital, as well as immunizations, diabetic supplies, and durable medical equipment all require billing Medicare Part B. The PIC will work with our contracting department to enroll in Medicare and obtain the appropriate Provider Transaction Access Number (PTAN). The PIC and all staff will spend a training day working through the applicable modules on the Centers for Medicare & Medicaid Services (CMS) website.

The workflow software purchased for the pharmacy will include a point of sale (POS) system, cash registers, and credit card devices. Accounting will work with the PIC to set up merchant identification numbers for the devices. Information Services will ensure the connections for adjudication and credit card processing are secure and compliant with the Health Insurance Portability and Accountability Act (HIPAA). Accounting will ensure that the POS is charging sales tax appropriately for items sold over the counter. The PIC will create an account with the state Prescription Monitoring Program and the workflow software data export process will be implemented.

The PIC will work with the Facility Maintenance Department to ensure all pharmacy signage is compliant with state and local laws. Because the pharmacy is not open 24 hours a day, signage at the entrance to the hospital and on the front of the pharmacy will need to display pharmacy hours in compliance with the differential hours regulations set forth by the Board of Pharmacy. The Facilities team, as well as the Marketing and Communications department, will be asked to facilitate the development of signage.

Once all licensing is in place, the 340B administrator will register the pharmacy with the Health Resources and Services Administration (HRSA).

IMPLEMENTATION PLAN

Upon approval, the following steps will be carried out in order as detailed above:

1. Accounting department will open a new department on the general ledger.

2. Pharmacy Director will work with HR to hire the PIC.

3. PIC will begin the licensing process.

4. Construction of the space and installation of FF&E will begin.

5. Software, telephone, and network installation will follow the IT hardware installation.

6. Wholesale accounts will be created.

7. Staff will be hired and trained.

8. Drugs, vials, and other supplies will be ordered.

9. Opening day will be finalized and a grand opening celebration planned.

10. The Hospital Marketing and Communications department will assist the PIC with advertising. A press release will be issued to the local media outlets. Cafeteria tray liners will be printed with pharmacy advertising for use with meals delivered to patient rooms. Posters will be hung strategically throughout the hospital in elevators, waiting rooms, and high-traffic hallways.

11. Testing of all systems will take place in the week prior to opening day.

The space selected is on the main floor of the hospital just inside the main entrance. The space is currently occupied by a gift shop, florist, and coffee bar. These three separate businesses are all owned by the hospital and will be rolled together into one space as a front end for the pharmacy. Allowing these businesses to utilize the pharmacy point of sale system will streamline retail operations for the hospital and serve all of the retail needs for patients, visitors, and employees. By helping existing staff of these businesses achieve their pharmacy assistant/clerk license, they can be utilized to cashier and run deliveries for the pharmacy. By integrating these businesses, a career ladder is created to guide new employees into healthcare.

LESSONS LEARNED

During implementations of projects like the one outlined above, the key lesson learned is to maintain a flexible timeline. Local weather-related disasters or large-scale disasters like a pandemic can cause significant delays. These can include delays in the processing of applications for licenses and third-party contracts. There could also be supply chain issues delaying construction materials, FF&E, or even product to be sold. During the COVID-19 pandemic, federal agencies like the DEA were taking twice as long to process applications as they did before the pandemic. State agencies were taking five times longer in some cases. If something goes awry with the application, finding help within these agencies was almost impossible as everyone was working remotely. Telephone call hold times were unworkable, and emails took weeks to receive a response.

Construction project timelines and costs can vary greatly depending on the availability of materials. Supply chain issues in the early 2020s have resulted in lumber and other materials fluctuating in cost three to fourfold. Contractors that bid a project will suddenly find themselves without labor as employees are out sick or are recruited away by more competitive job opportunities.

Labor shortages are not limited to construction. As the COVID-19 pandemic progressed, experienced pharmacy technicians became extremely hard to find. As of this writing, sign on bonuses for technicians now far exceed anything offered to pharmacists. Applicants will accept a job offer only to back out at the last minute to take a better offer from a different company. Hiring managers and HR personnel need to use extremely aggressive recruiting tactics to find and keep good pharmacy labor. Since this technician shortage is coinciding with a glut in the pharmacist market, the old standard pharmacist to technician ratios should be abandoned and pharmacists now need to be trained to cover many technician duties. Many companies are creating technician training programs to provide an internal career path for employees taking entry-level positions like assistants or clerks.

The key to a successful project is to surround the PIC with support from teams that are highly experienced in human resources, information technology/systems, legal review/contracting, and facility maintenance and construction. With good support from a solid team of specialists, a profitable outpatient pharmacy department is an achievable goal for any mid to large size hospital.

REFERENCES

1. Hospital readmissions reduction program (HRRP). Centers for Medicare & Medicaid Services. **https://www.cms.gov/Medicare/Medicare-Fee-for-Service-Payment/AcuteInpatientPPS/ Readmissions-Reduction-Program**. Accessed January 7, 2022.

2. Miller D, Ramsey M, L'Hommedieu TR, Verbosky L. Pharmacist-led transitions-of-care program reduces 30-day readmission rates for Medicare patients in a large health system. *Am J Health Syst Pharm*. 2020;77(12):972–978. PubMed

3. Lash DB, Mack A, Jolliff J, et al. Meds-to-beds: The impact of a bedside medication delivery program on 30-Day readmissions. *J Am Coll Clin Pharm*. 2019;2(6):674–680. doi: 10.1002/ jac5.1108.

4. Witcraft EJ, Norris AM, Fudzie SS, et al. Impact of medication bedside delivery program on hospital readmission rates. *J Am Pharm Assoc (2003)*. 2021;61(1):95–100.e1. doi: 10.1016/j. japh.2020.09.023. PubMed

HOSPITAL-BASED INFUSION CENTER

Lisa Mascardo, Zachary Pollock,
and Scott Sterrett

EXECUTIVE SUMMARY

This report discusses an option for managing ongoing infused therapies for patients within the health system.

If there is one project that can add significant quality, safety, and revenue rewards for a health system, it is the creation of an infusion center. Hospitals or health systems discharge patients from acute admissions in need of ongoing infused therapies or run ambulatory oncology or other specialty clinics where infused therapies are the treatment standard. This typically requires that the provider send treatment orders to community infusion centers or home infusion companies.

While many community infusion centers exist, they may be limited to medium to large metropolitan areas and require patients to travel to another location for treatment. Coordination of information between the provider and infusion center may be fragmented. Community infusion centers do not have access to the patient's electronic health record (EHR), and thus have no baseline knowledge of a patient's allergies, lab values, and disease course. This may prevent the infusion team from being alerted to pertinent clinical information such as whether a patient has a fistula and should not have an IV started on one side. If an unexpected event happens during treatment, details may not get back to the patient's provider.

The patient must make additional effort to set up their appointment(s) with a community infusion center and coordinate with necessary lab test scheduling. If insurance issues are identified and prior authorizations are required, there may be delays in communicating with the provider to get appropriate therapy approved.

Creating a hospital-based infusion center allows the health system and more specifically, providers, to maintain close supervision of the patient's treatment. All information is readily available to the full team involved in the patient's care. Revenue attributed to drug margin and administration fees is captured. Most importantly, the patient benefits from fully coordinated care with seamless transitions, one designated location for appointments, and assurance that all information and communication is documented within one EHR.

DOI 10.37573/9781585287130.019

BUSINESS/SERVICE DESCRIPTION

Hospitals or health systems that provide oncology or specialty services likely rely on infusion therapies such as biologics and antineoplastics as part of their treatment plans. A hospital-based infusion center would allow comprehensive services to be provided to patients in a location where safety can be monitored, adjunctive therapies easily added, and the complete experience documented in the same electronic health record utilized by the entire healthcare team.[1]

An infusion center is a complex operation that involves many departments within a health system, including specialty departments that prescribe the therapies, nursing, pharmacy, information technology (IT), finance, marketing, registration, and scheduling. Additionally, ancillary services such as pathology and radiology present dependencies that impact patient scheduling and flow. There is not one specific location that hospital-based infusion centers must reside in the overall organizational structure. Oversight may come from a department responsible for the majority of infusion orders, such as internal medicine or oncology, within an ambulatory infusion and home care division, or in another dedicated place in the organization's structure.

The infusion center supports elements of the health system's mission, vision, and strategy in three areas: improving access to services that may otherwise have to be obtained elsewhere, improving quality of care with a multidisciplinary approach, and improving revenue capture. Additionally, if the institution treats uninsured or underinsured patients, there is an opportunity to provide patient assistance programs to improve affordability.

ENVIRONMENTAL/NEEDS ASSESSMENT

Hospitals or health systems that provide specialized treatments for cancer, congenital diseases, immune deficiency disorders, anemia, or autoimmune disorders should evaluate the opportunity to have an infusion center, as these conditions often rely on infusion therapies. While each specialty clinic could potentially have a small number of chairs or beds for their respective patients or rely on outside community infusion centers to treat their patients, having one dedicated location for all the system's patients should be considered.

An infusion center on a health system's campus where the specialty clinics are located allows for patients to see their providers and receive therapy in the same location. Additionally, colocating lab and radiology services would further decrease patient stress around coordinating appointments and potentially improve adherence. The ability to manage scheduling labs, radiology, clinic appointments, and infusions within one system provides for an overall more seamless experience. Patients can be closely monitored during first doses and throughout therapies prone to reactions. If unforeseen circumstances or infusion reactions do occur, appropriate follow-up, documentation, and rescheduling can occur. The patient also has confidence that their provider is aware of any issues and can tailor future therapies accordingly.

Hospitals and health systems may also enroll patients in and manage clinical trials. Having an infusion center and corresponding pharmacy services with staff familiar with investigational study protocols is an asset to investigators.

Traditionally, infusion therapies are covered under medical insurance benefits, and health systems purchase the medications from wholesalers and bill the patient's insurance. This process is called buy and bill. Some insurance plans are moving biologics to the pharmacy benefit and requiring that the medication be provided by a specific specialty pharmacy, a process called white bagging. It is important to evaluate payer mix and determine which payers use which billing strategy. Many health systems have policies against white bagging, and therefore it may not make sense to undertake the effort and expense of an infusion center without the revenue from the medications themselves. Some payers also only cover specialty infusions administered in an ambulatory or office-based place of service. This has not traditionally been the case for chemotherapy agents for oncology diagnosis, especially if the providers are part of an NCI-designated cancer center.

Due to the substantial cost of many infused medications, some patients may benefit from financial assistance through drug manufacturers and other programs. The infusion center needs a team of experienced people who do benefits investigation and prior authorization for patients prior to them starting therapy to ensure therapies are covered. It is also wise to have financial counselors available to discuss the expected costs with patients to ensure there won't be affordability issues. Patients receiving investigational medications are not charged for those infusions but are required to receive care at the institution. Special billing processes would be established to charge expenses to study grants and sponsors. The unique billing and financial support activities that can be provided from the same system where the infusion orders originate and are prepared are potential competitive advantages beyond what stand-alone community or office-based infusion providers offer.

Establishing a hospital-based infusion center will require support from multiple departments. First, providers who prescribe infused therapies should be engaged to ensure they support the concept and are willing to send their patients to an internal infusion center. Once provider support is confirmed, design engineers from Capital Management should be engaged to identify suitable space. Factors to consider include proximity to clinics most likely to send patients to the center, proximity to appropriate pharmacy services for compounding the infusion medications, ease of patient access and future expansion potential. A capital project will likely be necessary to build out identified space for appropriate workflows and patient aesthetics. Most institutions have a schedule for considering and approving capital projects for upcoming years, which should be considered for planning purposes.

IT will have several teams involved in launching a new infusion center. The new area will require department and schedule builds to add to the existing organizational architecture. If any new workflow modules within the electronic health record are to be utilized, the interface team will participate. Clinical applications teams may build order sets and medication records, which flow into the pharmacy system. It is standard practice to include elements of the care plan, necessary labs, and ancillary therapies into each treatment protocol, and these should be reviewed by pharmacists and other members of the healthcare teams who write the orders. It is also now considered best practice to utilize IV workflow technology for safe medication compounding and smart infusion pumps for safe medication administration.[2] These would require pharmacy informatics, the team responsible for building the smart pump libraries, and biomedical engineering to assist.

Patient check-in/check-out and scheduling staff will be needed to start and end patient visits. Nursing staff will manage patients throughout the visits. Volunteer services and Food and Nutrition may be engaged to improve the patient experience. Environmental Services/Housekeeping will need to add a new location to their service area. Pharmacy staff will review orders for appropriateness and prepare medications. Central Stores will restock supplies in the new area. Billing and coding staff will ensure charges are appropriate, and Finance staff will oversee the revenue cycle. Based on the projected revenue and new work added to each of the services, new staff will likely need to be approved, recruited, hired, and trained.

OPERATING PLAN(s)

This operating plan is meant to serve as a basic example of how a health system may design the operations of their infusion center and in no way is fully representative of all options or approaches. Volumes and resources can be scaled or adjusted based on the unique characteristics of each health system.

The days and hours of operation should be determined based on how best to fit with specific clinics, projected patient volumes and patient access considerations. In this example, the hospital-based infusion center will begin by operating 11 hours a day from 0700 to 1800 Monday through Friday. These specific hours are determined based on a review of the number and type of orders for patients suitable for the infusion center. A full twelve months of data are reviewed to consider therapies with varying intervals of recurrence as well as any variation in volume throughout the year due to other unknown factors. In addition to the orders review, clinic appointment volumes and timing can be reviewed to facilitate appointment scheduling. A survey of patients and their families about when they would desire to receive infusion services can also be conducted to determine optimal operating hours. Using these survey results at baseline and repeating throughout operation is helpful to gauge whether the service is meeting the preferential needs of its patients.

The number of orders serves as a foundational metric to build other operating statistics to project patient volumes, determine capital needs related to space and equipment and arrange for staffing. **Table 1** outlines the operating statistics derived from this information that are used to inform further planning and the pro forma in the financial plan. The health system leadership team can engage its strategic planning team to best understand the organization's growth strategy to forecast infusion growth over a specific time horizon. This includes outlining the organization's plans for expansion of specialty services that prescribe infusion therapy, recruitment in those areas, and current and available market share opportunities.

CASE 9, TABLE 1. Volume Metrics

Volume Metric					
	Year 1	Year 2	Year 3	Year 4	Year 5
Annual Infusion Visits	6,072	6,983	8,030	9,235	10,620
Daily Infusion Visits	24	28	32	37	42
Average Length of Infusion (hr)	3	3	3	3	3
Chair Utilization	3	3	3	3	3
Daily Chair Demand	8	9	11	12	14
Operating Hours/Days	11/5	11/5	11/5	11/5	11/5

The Design and Construction team with Capital Management creates a physical layout that meets the needs of the service with input from all key stakeholders. This model calls for an initial infusion center footprint that includes sixteen treatment spaces divided into four pods, appropriate clean/soiled utility, storage, nurse triage, reception/waiting, and a USP 797/800 compliant cleanroom. The pods will be designed so that one treatment space each in two of the pods will be single rooms with beds. The beds allow for therapy that may need to be administered in the prone position, relief for patients unable to tolerate a chair for the duration of therapy, or for isolation in the event such precautions are needed for individual patients. The footprint to be completed in the initial phase of construction allows for growth over a five year time horizon. It is also built in an area that allows for expansion to double its capacity when the service grows beyond the initial projections.

Each health system will choose to adopt their own staffing models with ratios pertinent to the complexity of care they are providing. Infusion suite staffing ratios for nursing vary anywhere from one nurse per patient in the clinical research setting up to four patients per nurse and beyond. The staffing model in this operating plan is arranged based on the proposed layout of treatment spaces in **Table 2**.

CASE 9, TABLE 2. Nursing Staffing

Nursing Staffing Ratio					
	Year 1	Year 2	Year 3	Year 4	Year 5
Annual Infusion Visits	6,072	6,983	8,030	9,235	10,620
Daily Infusion Visits	24	28	32	37	42
Staff Nurse (FTE)	4.3	6.0	8.9	8.9	10.4
Nursing Assistant (FTE)	1.4	1.7	1.9	2.2	2.5
Nurse Manager (FTE)	0.5	0.5	0.5	0.5	0.5

CASE 9, TABLE 3. Pharmacy Staffing

Pharmacy Staffing Ratio					
	Year 1	Year 2	Year 3	Year 4	Year 5
Annual Infusion Visits	6,072	6,983	8,030	9,235	10,620
Daily Infusion Visits	24	28	32	37	42
Dispenses per Visit	1.3	1.3	1.3	1.3	1.3
Pharmacy Preptime per Dispense (hr)	0.5	0.5	0.5	0.5	0.5
Technician Staffing (FTE)	2.2	2.6	3.0	3.4	3.9
Pharmacist Staffing (FTE)	2.9	2.9	2.9	2.9	2.9
Pharmacy Manager (FTE)	0.5	0.5	0.5	0.5	0.5

The order volumes also drive pharmacy preparation and dispensing metrics. **Table 3** outlines these operating statistics which inform pharmacy staffing ratios and hood space. USP 797/800 regulations must be implemented within the planning and design. This accounts for appropriate hood space to prepare hazardous and nonhazardous medications, anteroom, drug storage, and staff workspace. The operating model calls for the infusion pharmacy to be constructed within/adjacent to the infusion suite so that medications can be taken directly to the specified treatment space once verified by pharmacy. This adjacency eliminates the need for additional staff to distribute prepared medications to the infusion area, promotes greater communication and collaboration among clinical staff, and allows for the clinical pharmacists to be able to deliver their expertise directly to patients in the infusion area through counseling and education as well as supporting the nursing and provider staff with medication expertise.

At the time of publication, the Centers for Medicare & Medicaid Services (CMS) required general supervision of the hospital outpatient-based infusion services.[3] The adopted practice model for this infusion center will depend on provider coverage to come from the providers in adjacent clinics who are prescribing the infusion therapy. Order questions will be sent to them directly and a coverage plan for responding to the infusion center for patient evaluation is arranged. As the infusion center grows and hours of operation expand, there will likely be the need to revisit having a licensed independent practitioner (LIP) stationed within the infusion center. As it stands, no additional LIP staffing is accounted for in the original financial plan. Other staffing for the infusion center includes scheduling staff to check patients in and out as well as taking incoming calls and scheduling patients on demand. This staffing is done in direct correlation with hours of operation and patient volume. The day-to-day operations of the infusion suite are jointly managed by a nurse manager and pharmacy manager. The charge nurse has responsibility to review orders for each visit; compare with protocols, lab results, and vitals; and release the orders to pharmacy. The charge nurse is also responsible for approving add-on patients, guiding patient flow and chair assignment along with offering back up support to the nursing staff directly caring for patients in the pods. The pharmacy manager supervises the pharmacy operations and staff and informs infusion treatment order builds in the electronic medical record.

Pricing for the services provided is developed through the health system chargemaster process. Working closely with finance and coding and compliance personnel, institutional charges are developed based on benchmarks with local and national providers and payer data. To aid in setting up charges, pertinent charge codes are mapped to standard definitions to allow for a standard productivity metric referred to as unit of service (UOS) in this example. The UOS can be aligned with Healthcare Common Procedure Coding System (HCPCS) for standardization. The HCPCS Level II codes or J Codes are used for the pharmaceutical charge for injectable medications that cannot be self-administered, including chemotherapy. When setting up the treatment plans and vial sizes of medications used, the coding team will have to give careful consideration to the appropriate number of units being billed based on dosage delivered. These charges will drive inputs for the pro forma outlining profitability of the service. The percent markup applied may vary based on the extent of the cost of the drug or technical service provided. Appropriate markups based on cost should be reviewed closely. Given the fact that highly expensive drugs are likely being administered, it may be beneficial to review charges more frequently than what is often an annual process.

Infusion services will require a benefits investigation with patients' insurance plan and likely some level of prior authorization. A team of revenue cycle specialists will be notified of each new infusion therapy plan entered. A predetermined workflow will be followed to complete the benefits investigation for each plan and gain the appropriate authorization for the infusion suite to buy and bill the medication(s) to be administered prior to the patient appointment. Some models may require this process to be completed before a patient is scheduled. Due to the high cost of therapy, it is also beneficial to have financial navigators available to provide financial counseling to patients so that they better understand their financial responsibility. This team can also work to identify patient assistance programs that offer copay assistance, medication replacement, or other forms of assistance to offset the financial toxicity to patients and their families. The operational expenses of this team will be included in the Overhead assumptions of the financial plan's pro forma in this model.

The operational performance of the infusion center is monitored in a dashboard of key performance indicators (KPIs). While they can vary, they may look something like those in **Table 4**.

CASE 9, TABLE 4. Infusion Operational KPIs

Infusion Center Operational KPIs	
Appointment Volume	Pharmacy Products per Visit
UOS Volume	Clean Room Dispenses
UOS: Appointment Ratio	Infusion/Appointment Duration Mix
Unsigned Orders	Patient Wait Time
Appointments by Service	Duration by Day of Week

There may be some therapies that are not conducive to the hospital-based infusion center environment for a variety of reasons including type or length of therapy, patient condition, or site of service constraints. These service needs will be met through collaborations with the health systems' home care service or services in the region that provide effective opportunities to promote continuity of care within the organization without discharging the patient from a service.

FINANCIAL PLAN

The foundational metric of orders for infusion therapy already existing within the health system are used as the starting point for the pro forma that outlines the financial implications and profitability of the proposed service. Key assumptions can be determined by reviewing much of the information already established in the institution. The key assumptions for this model are illustrated in **Table 5**. Note that drug cost and subsequent net income are largely dependent on whether the hospital

CASE 9, TABLE 5. Key Assumptions

Operating Statistics and Assumptions					
	Year 1	Year 2	Year 3	Year 4	Year 5
Infusion UOS	13,966	16,060	18,470	21,240	24,426
Infusion Visits	6,072	6,983	8,030	9,235	10,620
Infusion UOS/Visits	2.3	2.3	2.3	2.3	2.3
Supply Cost per UOS	$11.25	$11.59	$11.94	$12.29	$12.66
Drug Cost per UOS	$ 1,240.00	$ 1,277.20	$ 1,315.52	$1,354.98	$1,395.63
Gross Technical Revenue per UOS	$ 562.50	$ 562.50	$ 579.38	$ 579.38	$ 596.76
Gross Drug Revenue per Infusion UOS	$ 5,995.00	$ 5,995.00	$ 6,354.70	$ 6,354.70	$ 6,735.98
Visit Growth Rate	15%	15%	15%	15%	15%
Collection Rate	38.5%	39.0%	39.5%	40.0%	40.5%
Drug/Supply Inflation Rate	3%	3%	3%	3%	3%
Charge Increase Adjustment	—	—	3%	—	3%
Overhead	20% of net revenue annually inclusive of capital plan and equipment, administrative, regulatory, financial, IT, marketing				

is 340B eligible.[4] Advantageous 340B pricing requires that medications are ordered by providers employed by the 340B hospital for patients whose care is provided at a qualified hospital clinic and documented in the hospital's electronic health record. Physician-owned and other non-340B practice sites cannot achieve the same positive gross margin, resulting in decreased profitability and long-term success.

Combining these assumptions generates the pro forma in **Table 6** projecting the financial performance of the hospital-based infusion service.

CASE 9, TABLE 6. Pro Forma

Hospital Based Infusion Pro Forma					
	Year 1	Year 2	Year 3	Year 4	Year 5
Revenue					
Gross Technical Revenue	$ 7,855,650	$ 9,033,998	$ 10,700,770	$ 12,305,886	$ 14,576,321
Gross Pharmacy Revenue	$ 83,723,772	$ 96,282,338	$ 117,368,170	$ 134,973,395	$ 164,532,569
Contractual and Other Adjustments	$ (56,321,345)	$ (64,242,965)	$ (77,481,709)	$ (88,367,568)	$ (106,569,790)
Total Net Operating Revenue	$ 35,258,077	$ 41,073,371	$ 50,587,231	$ 58,911,712	$ 72,539,101
Operating Expenses					
Salaries and Wages	$ 986,715	$ 1,136,849	$ 1,441,438	$ 1,472,940	$ 1,614,149
Fringe Benefits	$ 409,333	$ 473,010	$ 596,318	$ 612,541	$ 673,226
Subtotal Personnel Expenses	$ 1,396,048	$ 1,609,859	$ 2,037,756	$ 2,085,481	$ 2,287,375
Supplies	$ 157,113	$ 186,100	$ 220,436	$ 261,106	$ 309,280
Drugs	$ 17,317,344	$ 20,512,394	$ 24,296,931	$ 28,779,714	$ 34,089,572
Repairs, Maint, Minor Equip	$ 2,500	$ 2,875	$ 3,306	$ 3,802	$ 4,373
Other Operating Expenses	$ 1,500	$ 1,725	$ 1,984	$ 2,281	$ 2,624
Subtotal Non-Personnel Expenses	$ 17,478,457	$ 20,703,094	$ 24,522,657	$ 29,046,904	$ 34,405,848
Subtotal Operating Expenses	$ 18,874,505	$ 22,312,953	$ 26,560,413	$ 31,132,385	$ 36,693,223
Overhead	$ 7,051,615	$ 8,214,674	$ 10,117,446	$ 11,782,342	$ 14,507,820
Total Expenses	$ 25,926,120	$ 30,527,627	$ 36,677,859	$ 42,914,728	$ 51,201,043
Operating Income (Loss)	$ 9,331,957	$ 10,545,744	$ 13,909,372	$ 15,996,985	$ 21,338,057
Net Income (Loss)	$ 9,331,957	$ 10,545,744	$ 13,909,372	$ 15,996,985	$ 21,338,057

LEGAL OR REGULATORY CONCERNS

There are multiple legal and regulatory issues involved with creating a hospital-based infusion center. In order to participate in and bill Medicare and Medicaid programs, the infusion center must meet the conditions for coverage and conditions of participation from CMS.[5] This has already been established if the infusion center is created within a hospital that has deemed status.[6] Organizations with authority to accredit on behalf of CMS include the Joint Commission, Det Norske Veritas (DNV) and Accreditation Commission for Healthcare (ACHC).

The sterile compounding process necessary to prepare the medications in an infusion center is also a highly regulated process. A hospital pharmacy license is required by the state, and the pharmacy must comply with USP 797[7] and USP 800[8] guidelines for safe compounding of sterile and hazardous medications.

IMPLEMENTATION PLAN

CASE 9, TABLE 7. Implementation Timeline

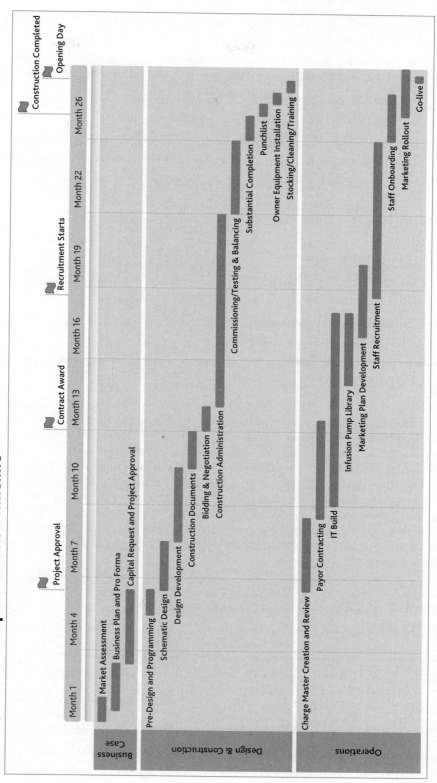

SUPPORTING MATERIALS

The following list of materials are considered necessary for planning and implementing hospital-based infusion services:

- List of departments for collaboration, or key stakeholders (IT teams, Finance, Capital Management, Pharmacy, Nursing, Patient Access/Scheduling, Specialty Departments)

- Pharmacy license

- Accreditations

- Position descriptions for key roles including infusion nurse, nursing assistant, nurse manager, pharmacist, pharmacy technician, pharmacy manager, and scheduling staff

- Policies and procedures (examples may include):

  ○ Protocol build, review, and maintenance

  ○ Clinical staff training and competency assessment

  ○ Sterile compounding processes and staff competencies

- Emergency protocols

- IT build requirements

- Architectural design plans and renderings

LESSON LEARNED

Hospitals that have implemented infusion centers have realized there is value in providing a mix of both hazardous and nonhazardous infusions. When considered with patient scheduling, it is possible to optimize throughput of products coming from the compounding pharmacy and decrease patient wait time. Products that are not dependent on the patient meeting lab or other clinical criteria should be prepped ahead of time when the beyond use date supports it. With therapies changing rapidly due to the identification of more biologics, hospitals should consider whether they have specialty pharmacy services in place to capture shifts from IV to PO treatment. Patient infusion scheduling should also be coordinated with or around other appointments the patient may have in the hospital, which is a primary benefit of keeping infusions within the system. Note that providers and clinics who prescribe infusion therapies less frequently may need additional support for entering treatment plans into the system.

Finally, the hospital should engage marketing and communication resources to publish materials well in advance of the infusion center opening to ensure appointments are scheduled as soon as available. The organization's providers and patients should be aware that the service is/will be opening and how to access it.

REFERENCES

1. American Society of Health-System Pharmacists. *Navigating and Optimizing Infusion Services when Hospital-based Care is Not an Option*. **https://www.ashp.org/-/media/assets/practice-management/docs/Site-of-Care-Challenges-81919.pdf**. Accessed January 21, 2022.

2. Institute for Safe Medication Practices. 2021-2022 Targeted medication safety best practices for hospitals. February 9, 2021. **https://www.ismp.org/guidelines/best-practices-hospitals**. Accessed February 10, 2022.

3. Centers for Medicare & Medicaid Services. *January 2020 Update of the Hospital Outpatient Prospective Payment System (OPPS) Transmittal 266.* **https://www.cms.gov/files/document/ r266bp**. Accessed December 7, 2021.

4. Health Resources & Services Administration. 340B eligibility. **http://www.hrsa.gove/opa/ eligibility-and-registration/index.html**. Reviewed May 2018. Accessed December 10, 2021.

5. Centers for Medicare & Medicaid. Conditions for Coverage (CFCs) & Conditions of Participation (CoPs). **http://www.cms.gov/regulation-and-guidance/legislation/ CFCsAndCoPs**. Updated December 1, 2021. Accessed December 10, 2021.

6. American Society for Healthcare Engineering Website. Status D. **http://www.ashe.org/ advocacy/orgs/deemedstatus**. 2021. Accessed December 10, 2021.

7. U.S. Pharmacopeia. General Chapter <797>: Pharmaceutical compounding–sterile preparations. **https://www.usp.org/compounding/general-chapter-797**. Accessed December 10, 2021.

8. U.S. Pharmacopeia. General Chapter <800>: Hazardous drug–Handling in healthcare settings. **https://www.usp.org/compounding/general-chapter-hazardous-drugs-handling-healthcare**. Accessed December 20, 2021.

HEALTH SYSTEM MAIL ORDER PHARMACY

Alfred E. Lyman Jr. and Polly Fox

EXECUTIVE SUMMARY

The purpose of this business case is to implement a health system mail order pharmacy service. Capital funding for $3.6 million is being requested to procure automation equipment to lower overall dispensing costs. The 10 year net present value (NPV) for this business case is $6.2 million. The scope of the project includes finding adequate space to house the mail order pharmacy all the way to full implementation with moving prescription volume from retail to mail order.

Strategic objectives for mail order are to reduce overall costs, improve customer satisfaction by delivering prescriptions to the home, improve safety, and improve adherence. Additionally, improving productivity and efficiency in workflows by having prescriptions filled through automated equipment can help drive overall affordability and keep costs down. Some of the key benefits of shifting prescriptions to mail order include decreasing the overall rate of rise in retail labor dispensing costs and allowing retail pharmacy staff to focus more on clinical activities. Shifting more prescriptions to mail order over time also will help lower dispensing labor costs. By year five, we expect at least a break-even point, assuming a starting mail order volume of 8% on a total prescription volume of 1.5 million prescriptions in year one. The break-even point may be reached sooner by increasing mail order utilization or having more than a 2% annual growth rate.

As part of the location requirements, a 4,500 square foot space will need to be leased or secured. This will allow adequate room for automation equipment and potential expansion as volume increases over time. Costs for a leased space are factored into our operational plan at $8.50 per square foot. Vendor selection will be a key factor in getting the appropriate equipment to allow for a capacity of 2,000 prescriptions per day in a four hour production shift to be filled via mail order.

BUSINESS/SERVICE DESCRIPTION

Over the past several years, consumers have prioritized more convenience and easy access to healthcare services, including pharmacy services. While many consumers have access to retail outpatient pharmacies, there are still several who may be in more rural areas, have transportation issues, or simply prefer home delivery as an option to receive medications. Decreasing profits, demands on staffing, and many other factors make it increasingly difficult to provide retail pharmacy services in a cost-effective manner. Building or obtaining a mail order pharmacy facility can help reduce demand on retail pharmacies, improve medication adherence rates, reduce cost to fill, improve customer satisfaction, and improve safety by reducing manual fill errors. In one recent publication, adherence to diabetes medications, in particular metformin, improved.[1] The purpose of this business case is to build a new mail order pharmacy.

In a recent publication from 2018, prescription cost to fill in a retail setting was $12.40.[2] Through mail order fulfillment, our primary objective is to reduce overall cost to fill. This will continue to deliver on the mission of providing high-quality, affordable healthcare. Secondary objectives include improving adherence rates, providing high customer satisfaction, and reducing labor costs.

Our analysis determined that with capital investment of $3.6 million, there is an opportunity to reduce dispensing costs by $2.1 million annually by year 10 with improvements in fulfillment automation. The implementation timeline is one year to go live and one and a half years for full implementation.

ENVIRONMENTAL/NEEDS ASSESSMENT

A mail order facility will provide state-of-the-art technology in automation to allow prescriptions to be filled efficiently and accurately. With rising labor costs and more demands on retail pharmacies (eg, providing clinical services), mail order pharmacy can take much of the dispensing function to provide prescriptions at a lower cost. Customer satisfaction can also be improved by delivering prescriptions directly to the home, thus improving access, adherence, and convenience.

Services may be provided to multiple different insurers or plans to increase overall mail order volume. It will be important to drive enough volume to mail order to ensure financial viability. Offering co-pay incentives (eg, 90 day supply of medications for two co-pays instead of three) and high-cost or specialty medications through mail order should be considered.

It is important to ensure adequate space for the mail order facility. One advantage for a mail order pharmacy is it does not need to take up valuable space within an institutional healthcare facility and location is less important compared with a retail walk-in pharmacy. Leased space is generally preferable with enough square footage to house all equipment and drug inventory, allowing for efficient dispensing, packaging, and mailing processes.

Other factors to consider may include adjacency to shipper for prompt pick-up of packages, licensing/regulatory for what states you plan to ship prescriptions to, web portal for ease of ordering, front-end (FE) work such as call center functions, back-end (BE) work including fulfillment and shipping, and how to market the service to consumers and other key stakeholders, including physicians.

OPERATING PLAN

The new mail order facility will open with 4,500 square feet of operating space. Opening design will support 2,000 prescriptions per four hour shift with a throughput of approximately 500 prescriptions/hour. The mail order pharmacy will be open five days per week, eight hours per day. Production will only occur four hours per day with the remaining time spent on FE work, answering telephone calls, etc. Consideration in the future of expanding hours or opening a weekend shift may be addressed as needed. Current layout and structure will have the ability to offer 1,000 NDCs to customers of the mail order pharmacy.

Orders can be received by telephone via interactive voice response (IVR), online order via web, mobile application, or staff entry. Initial setup will include two semiautomated filling stations and six manual filling stations. Semiautomated filling stations will house 150 bins with some duplication of NDCs for fast moving items. The majority of prescriptions will be auto-labeled and then travel on a conveyor system using radio frequency identification (RFID) technology to land in the appropriate station where they will be filled via semiautomated machines or manually. Orders are routed to stations based on NDC. Prescriptions of similar NDCs can be grouped in manual filling stations allowing staff to fill them in batches. This process allows for quicker processing as staff do not have to walk aisles continually. These prescriptions also do not need to take up valuable space on the conveyor line. Nongrouped orders will be filled, labeled by staff, placed on the conveyor belt, and finally coupled with any other prescriptions before being routed to packing. Orders are packed, labeled, and marked with prepaid postage then staged for pickup by contracted shipping vendor.

Table 1 outlines the total staffing plan, which includes four and a half FTE to open in year one, growing to 15 FTE.

CASE 10, TABLE 1. Mail Order Staffing Plan

Mail Order Role	Type	YR 1	YR 2	YR 3	YR 4	YR 5	YR 6	YR 7	YR 8	YR 9	YR 10
Dispensing FTE	Technician	1.0	1.0	1.5	2.0	2.0	2.5	2.5	2.5	3.5	4.0
Product Verification FTE	Pharmacist	1.0	1.0	1.0	1.0	1.0	1.0	1.0	1.0	1.0	1.0
Packaging/Shipping FTE	Technician	0.5	0.5	0.5	1.0	1.0	1.0	1.5	1.5	2.0	2.0
Production Support FTE	Technician	—	—	2.0	2.0	2.0	2.0	2.0	2.0	3.0	3.0
Call Center FTE	Technician	2.0	2.0	3.0	3.0	4.0	4.0	4.0	5.0	5.0	5.0
	Total FTE	4.5	4.5	8.0	9.0	10.0	10.5	11.0	12.0	14.5	15.0

Due to the small number of staff, management support will come from the current staffing structure. This will be reassessed in future years as needs/demand changes. The staffing plan of 15 FTE by year 10 can support up to 624,000 mail order prescriptions annually in a four hour production run time. Due to low volumes and uncertainty of demand to shift to mail order, we have assumed a small staffing model upon opening. Assuming a volume growth of 3% per year and a 2% shift in mail order utilization, our analysis indicates capacity would be running at 84% by year 10 and reassessment would need to occur to continue ensuring packages reach customers within acceptable time constraints. The goal of mail order turnaround times in our business case is five days from the time of order receipt to time of delivery to the home.

Volume growth, retail store and mail order volume, retail store and mail order dispensing cost/Rx, labor cost/Rx, nonlabor cost/Rx, and total mail order cost/Rx are depicted in Table 2.

Since staff are shared between call center functions and production floor, run time hours can be expanded by adding more staff to cover call center work and staggering shift start times. At a full production run time of eight hours and 15 FTE, this model is capable of handling over a million prescriptions annually. The sharing of staff between the production floor and call center allows for the utilization of part-time staff, aids in staff satisfaction by allowing some job role variety, and allows the business to gradually add staff to production floor over time as demand rises.

Financial break-even status begins to materialize in year five. If mail order penetration started at 16% in year one with the same consistent growth of 2% per year, break-even status can be achieved by year two. Some ways to enhance mail order utilization may include strong partnership with physicians as many patients tend to use mail order when recommended by their provider. Large marketing campaigns to raise awareness of the new service and potential co-pay discounts when applicable (eg, 90 day supply for the cost of two co-pays) may also further improve mail order utilization.

Pharmacy technicians and pharmacists will be involved in the FE call center work, answering patient questions, taking prescription orders, addressing problems, and counseling if patients have

CASE 10, TABLE 2. Mail Order Pharmacy Key Performance Indicators

	YR 1	YR 2	YR 3	YR 4	YR 5	YR 6	YR 7	YR 8	YR 9	YR 10
Total Volume –3% growth	1,545,000	1,591,350	1,639,091	1,688,263	1,738,911	1,791,078	1,844,811	1,900,155	1,957,160	2,015,875
Store Volume	1,421,400	1,432,215	1,442,400	1,451,906	1,460,685	1,468,684	1,475,849	1,482,121	1,487,441	1,491,747
Mail Order Volume	123,600	159,135	196,691	236,357	278,226	322,394	368,962	418,034	469,718	524,127
Mail Order %–2% growth	8%	10%	12%	14%	16%	18%	20%	22%	24%	26%
Total Store Dispensing Cost/Rx	$8.43	$8.43	$8.42	$8.41	$8.40	$8.38	$8.36	$8.33	$8.30	$8.27
Mail Order Labor Cost/Rx	$2.73	$1.39	$1.69	$1.72	$1.49	$1.42	$1.37	$1.23	$1.44	$1.39
Mail Order Non-Labor Cost/Rx	$9.84	$11.38	$9.37	$7.95	$6.88	$6.06	$5.41	$4.87	$4.43	$4.06
Total Mail Order Cost/Rx	$13.31	$13.36	$11.79	$10.29	$9.09	$8.11	$7.33	$6.73	$6.45	$5.98
Total Program Cost/Rx	$9.49	$9.76	$9.84	$9.85	$9.85	$9.84	$9.83	$9.82	$9.85	$9.82
Baseline Cost/Rx	$9.10	$9.28	$9.47	$9.66	$9.85	$10.05	$10.25	$10.45	$10.66	$10.88
Difference	$0.39	$0.48	$0.37	$0.19	$0.00	–$0.21	–$0.42	–$0.64	–$0.81	–$1.05

questions about their medications. They will also be involved in back-end production work, although this will primarily be pharmacy technicians. Pharmacists will be needed on the production floor for any data verification of prescriptions, drug utilization review (DUR) screening, and final verification of products. Technicians will primarily be responsible for stocking of canisters, fulfillment, etc. Pharmacy technicians or pharmacy clerks/shipping clerks would finalize packages for mailing. In this business case, we recommend utilizing pharmacy technicians only as it gives more flexibility with a small number of staff to cover all the areas. For example, a pharmacy technician who is helping with shipping packages could be moved to help with call center work, whereas a shipping clerk may not be licensed to perform these duties.

Key performance indicators (KPIs) will include total daily prescription volume, prescriptions filled per hour, overall mail order utilization rate, percent of prescriptions mailed within five days (order receipt to delivery), and total cost to fill. Total cost to fill can be further broken down into FE labor costs, BE labor costs, and nonlabor costs (ie, supplies, shipping, credit card fees, and a category for other). FE costs include any call center functions. BE costs include only those costs associated with the production floor and packaging.

FINANCIAL PLAN

Since revenue is the same regardless of fulfillment type, we have excluded revenue considerations from this analysis. Costs were assessed over 10 years. Capital outlay is $3.6 million with a 10 year net present value (NPV) of $6.2 million. Base assumptions on an annual basis include 3% prescription volume growth, 2% mail order volume growth, 2% wage inflation, 3% shipping cost inflation, and 2% nonpayroll cost inflation. Savings are realized as cost avoidance in future years. By year 10 at 3% growth, assuming no mail order services, retail stores would need an additional 52 FTE and $8.0 million in operating costs to support the 30% increase in prescription volume. This plan assumes lease costs are included in operating costs at an average rate of $8.50 per square foot of space and maintenance costs are added beginning in year two post implementation. Capital requirements for store expansion or retrofit based on future volume projections were not included in this analysis which would further improve NPV outcomes.

By year 10, the mail order service would need to add 10.5 FTE for a total of 15 FTE to support the 30% additional volume. In addition, shipping costs and packaging costs would also need to be added. Total operating cost additions are $3.1 million over 10 years. Break-even begins to occur at year five; however, if utilization patterns and demand are more favorable than this analysis would suggest, break-even can occur much faster. If, for example, mail order penetration was at 16% in year one and grew 2% per year, the break-even point could occur by year two of implementation.

We have not included any estimate for charges to customers due to shipping costs nor any additional charges for choosing to use the mail order pharmacy. We believe the benefits to the program and the benefits to the customer outweigh passing along additional costs. Providing shipping for free also creates "no barriers" to incentivize customers to try mail order services, which in turn can assist in growing demand. This decision can be reassessed in future years.

This financial plan relies heavily on a balance between reductions to store staffing while increasing staff within the mail order pharmacy. The management team in all areas of the program will need to monitor and evaluate staffing needs regularly to ensure appropriate staffing levels are maintained based on volumes in all pharmacies. Holding or delaying hiring in stores when staff turn over may need to be considered in balancing workload between the two entities.

Table 3 highlights estimated cost structure changes from baseline to year 10 of implementation.

CASE 10, TABLE 3. Cost Structure Changes from Baseline to Year 10

	Current State		With Mail Order	
	Base Line	Year 10	Year 10	Change
Total Volume	1,500,000	2,015,875	2,015,875	—
Mail Order Volume	—	—	524,127	524,127
Mail Order %	—	—	26.0%	26.0%
Total Program FTE	151	204	166	(38)
(In Millions)				
Payroll Cost	$12.8	$20.2	$16.0	-$4.2
Non-Payroll Cost	1.1	1.7	3.9	2.1
Total Operating Cost	$13.8	$21.9	$19.8	−$2.1
Store Dispensing Cost/Rx	$9.23	$10.88	$8.27	−$2.61
Mail Dispensing Cost/Rx			$5.98	$5.98
Total Dispensing Cost/Rx	$9.23	$10.88	$9.82	−$1.05
Capital Expenditure			$3,558,000	
NPV Difference:10 Year			$6,192,749	

Without mail order implementation, projected dispensing cost/Rx would increase by $1.65 or approximately $3.3 million per year by year 10. With the implementation of the new mail order store, dispensing cost/Rx would increase by $0.60 or approximately $1.2 million per year, resulting in an annual cost avoidance of $2.1 million.

Table 4 contains a breakout of capital equipment needs. These projections do not include additional remodeling or retrofit of buildings which may include electrical work, opening of walls, generator additions, etc. Assessment will occur upon determination of site location.

Dispensing area includes two semiautomatic dispensers, an area designated for filling controlled-substance prescriptions (ie, C-IIs), and six manual dispensing stations. Packaging includes one semiautomated packing station and three manual packing stations. Software and IT costs may vary depending on final vendor selection. We have provided high level estimates for this analysis based on early conversations with vendors under consideration.

CASE 10, TABLE 4. Capital Equipment Costs

Capital Equipment	
Software	$1,000,000
Servers/IT and hardware costs	$500,000
Labeler/capper/sorter/conveyor	$1,160,000
Two semiautomatic filling stations	$400,000
Six manual filling stations	$66,000
One semiautomatic packing station	$400,000
Three manual packing stations	$21,000
One pharmacist workstation	$11,000
Total	$3,558,000

LEGAL AND REGULATORY CONCERNS

Individual state Pharmacy Practice Acts are an important consideration as most have specific rules and regulations related to mail order pharmacy. For example, some states require a licensed Pharmacist-in-Charge for a particular state if you are going to mail prescriptions into that state. Having pharmacist and institutional licenses in multiple states may be a barrier to regulatory compliance, especially in trying to keep up with the ever-changing regulatory landscape. Additionally, some states also have regulations to allow for consideration of waivers for certain automated dispensing functions that require less pharmacist verification time, which can help to improve efficiency and overall workflow. Consideration should also be given to reviewing requirements in the United States Pharmacopeia chapter 1079 ("Good Storage and Distribution Practices for Drug Products").[3]

IMPLEMENTATION PLAN

Several factors need to be considered for implementation. In **Figure 1**, we have outlined the major components for the new mail order facility from securing space to staffing and go-live.

The implementation plan assumes a partial go-live in month 13 at 30% of the anticipated mail order volume with full implementation occurring in month 19. Staff will begin onboarding starting in month seven of the project with the pharmacist first and then technicians shortly thereafter with all staff trained and ready for partial go-live within two months. Installation of equipment is expected to span four months with staff onsite to review any details, questions, or concerns with the vendor prior to go-live date.

LESSONS LEARNED

Identifying and securing adequate space is critical for the success of a mail order pharmacy with a production floor. The location or facility must include ample room for automated equipment and have the space and design for appropriate drug storage. It is also important to factor in any anticipated growth over time as it can be very costly to retrofit a space or find new space once you have implemented.

Selecting a vendor is a key step in choosing the equipment, layout, and overall workflow design for any mail order pharmacy. There are vendors who do not recommend or have allegiance to specific equipment. It may also be good to consider a consultant or other expert when choosing compatible software and equipment. Partnering either with a vendor or engineering within the health system is also important to ensure you have technical assistance with any equipment failures.

Marketing and promoting your mail order service is an important step even prior to implementation and post-implementation. Identifying and engaging key stakeholders, including prescribers, early on can help gain buy-in and promote the service to patients. Flyers, automated messaging in the electronic health record (eg, including mail order pharmacy service in after-visit summaries), and having staff promote to patients at retail pharmacies are all potential strategies to boost mail order utilization.

Having faster mail order turnaround times can improve overall utilization and customer satisfaction with the service. A key step in this process is choosing the shipping vendor and ensuring you have adequate service delivery agreements. Packages that arrive late and/or are not received within the promised turnaround time can degrade utilization and lower overall customer confidence in the service. Sending test packages to various zip codes can help identify shipping times and set expectations for what is realistic. Along those lines, it is important to consider how you will deal with lost packages and have a plan for when this occurs.

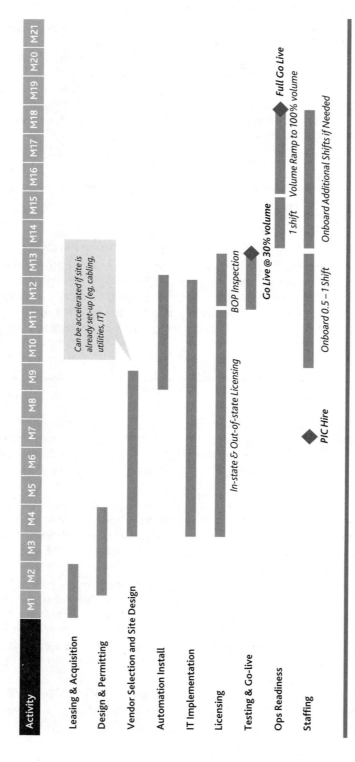

CASE 10, FIGURE 1. Implementation plan and timeline

Staffing models should include an ability to flex from FE call center type work to production floor and vice versa. If one area has a particular bottleneck or increased demand, it is imperative to address the workflow issue to either move prescriptions over to production or slow down production to clear telephone queues. This also provides some variety in the work for staff to be able to shift between the two different areas. Utilizing pharmacy technicians rather than pharmacy or shipping clerks can also give greater flexibility. In general, creation of the mail order pharmacy affords both technicians and pharmacists opportunities to pursue different roles within the health system.

Monitoring and reporting out on key metrics are essential for staff and key stakeholders. While certain financial metrics may not always need to be included for frontline staff, it is important to regularly report out on overall mail order utilization, turnaround times, and any customer satisfaction metrics, such as survey results. Sharing any patient stories or quotes can also help enhance the service over time. While positive stories are always helpful, it is also essential to look at any opportunities for improvement and share feedback with staff and stakeholders.

Business continuity is a key factor to consider in the event the mail order pharmacy is not operational for any given time period. Whether you will send prescriptions back to retail pharmacies or have an alternate mail order provider is important to think through. It is best to have these plans outlined in the event there is some type of equipment or facility failure before it happens.

Identifying how you will collect co-payments for prescriptions is essential. Whether this will be through secure telephone lines or through other types of secure systems, it is important to confirm these are compliant solutions to protect consumer financial information.

As the mail order pharmacy volume increases and grows over time, consideration should be given to centralizing call center or FE type work. This can help to improve overall time to answer calls and provide resolutions to problems or answer patient questions. Providing ongoing customer service training and using process improvement to refine workflows can help over time as volume and demands change.

Centrally filled prescriptions could also be considered as another business strategy to reduce labor in the store operations and overall cost/Rx. Prescriptions ordered for next day or later pick up could be filled at the mail order facility and delivered back to the stores within a 24-h period. This would be an additional way to maximize the use of the mail order facility and to offset volumes in the stores. Software enhancements to allow patients to select the pharmacy pickup location and route the order to the refill facility would need to be included, as well as transportation to deliver the medications.

Continuous capital needs planning should occur annually and reassessment of new equipment, new technology, or expanded capabilities should be reviewed regularly. Failing to plan for the replacement of aging equipment can result in unexpected downtimes. In contrast, not planning for unexpected volume increases properly can impact the ability of mail order to achieve turnaround commitments and degrade customer satisfaction. Turnaround time and throughput issues can be doubly painful as call volumes escalate (eg, customers reaching out to locate prescriptions) as well as longer production run times to catch-up resulting in overtime pay rates. Failing to evaluate product mix changes over time can hide new opportunities for enhancing savings (eg, purchasing more ATD units to shift additional NDCs from manual filling to automated tablet dispensing could reduce FTE or converting manual stations to semiautomatic tablet dispensing for faster moving products).

It will be important to investigate future capabilities to keep up with rapidly changing industry and consumer demands. For example, with more telehealth services and more companies having a full online presence, customers expect they will be able to receive both prescription and OTC medications through mail delivery. E-commerce shows no signs of slowing down, as many consumers are now accustomed to convenience and expect lower cost. Delivering more than pharmaceuticals could be beneficial to the health system overall. Consideration should be given to looking at e-commerce platforms that incorporate these options. The future of mail order pharmacy seems to be moving toward the ability to deliver medications with faster turnaround times while providing additional OTC medications to meet consumer needs. Another service that consumers may be look-ing to in the future includes medication synchronization via mail order. This may also add to con-sumer convenience where fewer interactions are needed for patients to obtain medications.

REFERENCES

1. Ramachandran B, Trinacty CM, Wharam JF, et al. A randomized encouragement trial to increase mail order pharmacy use and medication adherence in patients with diabetes. *J Gen Intern Med*. 2021;36(1):154–161. PubMed

2. Abt Associates. Shoemaker-Hunt S, McClellan S, Bacon O, et al. Cost of dispensing study: January 2020. **https://www.nacds.org/pdfs/pharmacy/2020/NACDS-NASP-NCPA-COD-Report-01-31-2020-Final.pdf**. Accessed December 9, 2021.

3. The United States Pharmacopeia. *39th rev., and The National Formulary*. 34th ed. Rockville, MD: United States Pharmacopeial Convention; 2016.

POPULATION HEALTH

Sarah LeMay and Jennifer Wood

EXECUTIVE SUMMARY

Population health management is an important opportunity to engage patients in primary care, improve access to the primary care team, and improve the overall health of a group of patients. The goals of the quarterly focus on population health are to decrease barriers to population health management, leverage data to standardize pharmacist practice, improve patient care, and promote health equity. This is accomplished with a rotating population health focus. Every three months, pharmacists working with patient aligned care teams (PACTs) utilize materials disseminated by a project lead pharmacist to simultaneously focus on a unique health metric or chronic condition.

Organization

The program will have a project lead pharmacist who manages administrative aspects of the workflow including reporting data to the pharmacy department. The project lead will work collaboratively with a population health subcommittee to identify current primary care metric gaps and create needed materials. The patient aligned care team (PACT) pharmacist structure will remain unchanged.

Finances

The main cost of the program to the pharmacy department is the full-time equivalent (FTE) hours required for the project lead to create and maintain the program. The program operates on cost containment within a government-based healthcare system, the Veterans Health Administration (VHA).

SERVICE DESCRIPTION

Practice Site

The William S. Middleton Memorial Veterans Hospital (Madison VA) in Wisconsin is part of the Veteran's Health Administration (VHA). The mission of the VHA is to "fulfill President Lincoln's promise to serve and honor the men and women who are America's Veterans."[1] Five core values demonstrate the VHA's mission to Veterans and are shown in **Figure 1**.

DOI 10.37573/9781585287130.021

Integrity	Act with high moral principle. Adhere to the highest professional standards. Maintain the trust and confidence of all with whom I engage.
Commitment	Work diligently to serve Veterans and other beneficiaries. Be driven by an earnest belief in VA's mission. Fulfill my individual responsibilities and organizational responsibilities.
Advocacy	Be truly Veteran-centric by identifying, fully considering, and appropriately advancing the interests of Veterans and other beneficiaries.
Respect	Treat all those I serve and with whom I work with dignity and respect. Show respect to earn it.
Excellence	Strive for the highest quality and continuous improvement. Be thoughtful and decisive in leadership, accountable for my actions, willing to admit mistakes, and rigorous in correcting them.

CASE 11, FIGURE 1. VHA values "I CARE values"[1]

At the Madison VA and associated community-based outpatient clinics (CBOCs), pharmacists are widely integrated in primary care clinics within patient aligned care teams (PACTs). Each PACT team includes a primary care provider (PCP, a physician or advanced nurse practitioner), nurse care manager (RNCM), medical support assistant (MSA), and pharmacist. The team is also supported by a nutritionist, a social worker, and the Integrated Care team (IC, mental health integrated with primary care).

The PACT team functions in a patient centered model which includes population health management and is responsible for the overall healthcare of approximately 1,200 patients. Each pharmacist generally works with three PACT teams or 3,600 patients. The pharmacist provides comprehensive medication management for conditions including diabetes, hypertension, gout, hyperlipidemia, chronic obstructive pulmonary disease (COPD), and many others, co-managing chronic disease states alongside the PCP. Pharmacists have a broad scope of practice and independently lead appointments and order medications and laboratory tests.

Service

The quarterly focus on population health is a framework and set of resources provided to pharmacists working with PACT teams. The resources are supplied by a population health committee made up of frontline pharmacists. This pharmacist-run population health management program was created in alignment with the VHA mission and core values including commitment to quality care, advocating for Veterans' interests, and striving for excellence and continuous improvement. The program focus is to maximize proactive outreach with the intention of decreasing the need for costly hospitalizations, emergency room visits, and negative outcomes of poor disease control in a variety of chronic disease states.

NEEDS ASSESSMENT

Population health management is the practice of utilizing healthcare analytics to proactively target specific clinical interventions aimed at improving quality of care across a patient population.[2;3] This is a key component to the PACT model because a population health approach to managing chronic disease within a primary care clinic can reduce poor health outcomes, save patients and institutions money, and improve quality of life.[4;5]

There are many opportunities for population health management in the primary care setting at the Madison VA and pharmacists in the PACT team have always been well situated to focus on population health management. Quality standards which align closely with the Healthcare Effectiveness Data and Information Set (HEDIS) metrics are set at the national and regional level providing goals for the care team.[2;4;5] Population health data surrounding these metrics is readily available in the form of data warehouses and population health dashboards. These resources include information about diabetes, hypertension, chronic obstructive pulmonary disease (COPD), ischemic heart disease, and many other chronic disease states.

Historically, completion of population management efforts was left to the discretion of each pharmacist and team. With so many available opportunities, it became difficult for each pharmacist to know what areas to prioritize. It was also difficult to set goals and find time to complete interventions. Other challenges included a lack of standardization leading to care that was not equitable between PACT teams, time needed to find data, and time needed to report data and show the effects of interventions. These challenges led to pharmacists feeling overwhelmed by population health management.

The quarterly focus on population health provides a focus area so that pharmacists know how to prioritize population health management. Manageable weekly goals are provided. Resources are provided to decrease the time needed to find tools and data. Finally, data tracking through the subcommittee increases efficiency of reporting.

OPERATING PLAN

Overview

The population health subcommittee chooses one area of population health management each quarter and pharmacists across the healthcare organization are encouraged to focus on that area during the quarter. Focus areas are chosen to meet facility, regional, and national performance metrics. The committee creates a one page document that includes goals, suggested interventions, links to resources such as note templates, and directions to access needed population health data, the data or metrics that the committee will collect, and answers to frequently asked questions if needed. Two specific facility data-driven areas for improvement will be described in Examples 1 and 2 below.

Workflow

A cyclical workflow is used for ongoing focus areas and the cycle is described in **Figure 2** below. The steps of the workflow are:

1. Identify a quarterly focus area that:

    a. Aligns with organizational and/or department goals

    b. Addresses a known gap in care such as a metric falling below goal or an area where a healthcare disparity exists

    c. Has easily accessible data for patient identification and outcome measurement

2. Create one page outline such as in **Figure 3** and gather resources

3. Present quarterly focus to frontline staff

4. Frontline staff completes interventions to target the quarterly focus area

5. Data are collected by the population health subcommittee

6. Lead pharmacist relays quarterly accomplishments to frontline staff and leadership

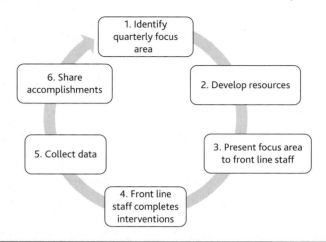

CASE 11, FIGURE 2. Quarterly population health management workflow

Roles and Responsibilities

Population Health Project Lead

The population health project lead is a frontline pharmacist working in the PACT setting. This pharmacist should have a special interest in population health. They will present the quarterly focus to the frontline pharmacists working in PACT. Full-time equivalent (FTE) hours are dedicated to researching current needs, creating materials, and providing resources to other frontline pharmacists. This pharmacist is also responsible for collecting data on the quarterly interventions and sharing that data with the frontline pharmacists, the pharmacy supervisor, and leadership. This data consists of comparing a specific outcome measure at baseline and post-intervention. The project lead confers with the pharmacy supervisor and population health subcommittee periodically to ensure program goals are met. Within the workflow described in **Figure 2**, the project lead is responsible for steps three, five, and six.

Population Health Subcommittee

This is a workgroup made up of several frontline pharmacists working in PACT. The work group is responsible for identifying focus areas and choosing one each quarter. They develop documents and gather resources to be used during the quarterly focus. Throughout the three months, the workgroup answers questions and provides support as needed. If needed the one page document will be updated to reflect clarifications that were needed during the quarter.

Front Line Pharmacy Staff Working with PACT Teams

The involvement of a project lead creates a streamlined process where each PACT pharmacist can easily integrate the population health management workflow into their weekly responsibilities without the need for additional FTE hours as shown in **Figure 2** steps one through three. Individual pharmacists will use resources sent by the project lead to extract data from the identified dashboard or data warehouse. They will develop workflow plans, often in accordance with resident and student learners on their team. A pharmacy technician could also be integrated into this workflow by managing administrative responsibilities such as scheduling, collecting data, and other duties within their scope of practice. Pharmacists will review each identified patient in the electronic health record (EHR) to determine if an outreach is indicated. For example, they may determine that a patient is due for a laboratory test. The pharmacist or learner may call the patient during time set aside for unscheduled patient care. Alternatively, they may identify another member of the PACT

Population Health Quarterly Focus: Alcohol Use Disorder (AUD)

Quarter 1

Goal

- Make at least 1 AUD related intervention per week

Suggested Interventions

- Complete brief alcohol interventions during clinic visits
- Review patients with AUD who are not on medication treatment who have upcoming visits and intervene at visit
- Reach out to patients with AUD who are not on medication treatment
- Focus on patients who are not already connected to MH

Resources

Link to Patient Reports

- URL link to patient reports
- Directions on how to access patient reports

AUD References and Templates:

- URL link to templates

Documenting in Electronic Medical Record

- Screenshots of electronic medical record showing how to document interventions

Metrics

- URL link to location of data that will be used
- # and % of interventions for AUD Apr-Jun 2020 vs Jul-Sep 2020
- # and % of patients with AUD diagnosis who are not on medication treatment before and after intervention period

*This information is included as FYI only. The population health committee will collect this data.

AUD Quarterly Focus FAQ

Where does the patient list come from?

ICD9 and 10 codes in patient chart

Do we need to do an AUDIT-C with the patient over the phone?

This is recommended, but not required. It can give you a better picture and allow you to fit the Veteran into recommended interventions more easily.

Why are patients on gabapentin on this list?

Veterans on gabapentin are on the list because they may be on gabapentin for other indications at potentially ineffective doses and because it is not considered first line in the VA/DoD guidelines for AUD treatment. These patients will require chart review.

Do I start the patient on therapy or refer them to mental health professionals?

Depends on the patient case and your comfort level.

CASE 11, FIGURE 3. Example outline disseminated to frontline staff for "Quarterly focus on alcohol use disorder"

and ask them to reach out to the patient. For example, the MSA or a pharmacy technician could call the patient to schedule a lab test. If indicated, a potentially billable encounter is created and future appointments are scheduled as needed.

Pharmacy Supervisor

Pharmacy leadership will supervise the program and ensure success is marketed to relevant stake-holders within the hospital system. The pharmacy supervisor also gives guidance to the workgroup on national, regional, facility, and department priorities. Feedback is gathered from pharmacists and other team members to identify further process improvements.

EXAMPLE 1. EQUITY-FOCUSED DIABETES CARE

This population management strategy focused on health equity through use of a population health dashboard called the "primary care equity dashboard." This tool provides data about disparities in healthcare outcomes based on race or gender and identifies patients who may be in need of an intervention. This strategy represents a single quarterly focus. Background information and materi-als shown in **Table 1** were provided to front line pharmacists. After receiving materials, pharmacists identified patients with A1c >9 or with no A1c in the past year. After a review of the EHR, a variety of strategies were taken to coordinate care. Examples of interventions are collaboration with primary care provider ahead of scheduled appointments to recommend therapy change or calling patients to establish re-establish care with appropriate PACT team member pharmacist or provider follow up. At the time of the phone call, a laboratory appointment to obtain A1c laboratory could be sched-uled, and comprehensive diabetes education was provided. At the end of the quarter, results were relayed to pharmacists through electronic communication. Additional options for relaying results are described in **Table 1**.

Background

Poor diabetes (DM) control (A1c >9) and lack of diabetic monitoring (no recorded A1c within one year) are areas where a health disparity exists at the Madison VA. Overall score for the Madison VA for patients with poor diabetes control is better than the overall score for the VA nationally. How-ever, when patients are separated by race and ethnicity, the scores for Black and Native American patients at the Madison VA are significantly worse than the overall national score average. Scores for Hispanic patients are also worse than the overall national score. Our goal for the quarter is to not only focus on improving DM care, but to also reduce health disparity.[6]

EXAMPLE 2. COMPREHENSIVE COPD MANAGEMENT

Background

This population management strategy focused on COPD. This strategy represents a single quarterly focus. Background information and materials shown in **Table 2** were provided to PACT pharma-cists. Similar workflow strategies were implemented such as in Example 1 to provide comprehensive COPD management.[7]

FINANCIAL PLAN

The VHA operates under a cost containment strategy and largely does not receive payment for pop-ulation health management services from private insurance payers.[5] The cost containment strategy

CASE 11, TABLE 1. Population Health Quarterly Focus on A1c

Goals	1. Review five patients per week who have an A1c >9 and make interventions where needed • Focus first on patients belonging to groups with a health disparity based on data. Examples to focus on may include Black, Hispanic, Native American, rural, or women patient populations
Suggested Interventions	1. Complete chart reviews • Is patient already scheduled for appropriate follow up? • Could additional interventions be made to improve care such as medication changes or referrals? • Is patient followed by an outside provider? 2. Review EHR to ensure ongoing care and update any of the following reminders with the most recent A1c: • A1c Goal Not Entered or reviewed • Diabetic - Annual A1c NEEDED • Diabetic - A1c not in Range 3. Reach out to patients unscheduled to assess diabetes. Utilize motivational interviewing to engage patients in diabetes care
Resources	• Link to "Primary Care Equity Data Dashboard" • Directions on how to access and export data • Example note templates • Pharmacy prescriptions and fill records • EHR data including laboratory values • Society or institution guideline links
Metrics	1. Number of appointments completed from referrals 2. Number of actionable patients requiring intervention before and after intervention period 3. National Score, Facility Score, and absolute difference from national before and after the intervention period • "HbA1c testing in patients with diabetes" • "Poor control of HbA1c in patients with diabetes" 4. Equity Deep Dive statistics on the above measures from the Primary Care Equity Dashboard • Patients per month, score, and absolute difference from national stratified by race and ethnicity
Results	• Modality: Display graphically, verbally, and /or written • Method: Team meeting presentation, email • Feedback: Reflect on intervention, elicit feedback from team

is determined by an annual fiscal budget determined by the government. The VHA provides all services to Veterans from this budget through a single-payer healthcare system. Financial benefits from this case are tied to optimal management of chronic health conditions and preventing need for higher levels of care such as ER visits and hospital admissions.

While this case example does not account for insurance reimbursement, value-based care is becoming increasingly common in the private healthcare sector. Value-based care is where insurance payment is tied to the delivery of quality care.[3;4] Therefore, concepts may be applied to private healthcare systems where payers require reporting of similar population health data and will pay the healthcare system in varying degrees when HEDIS or similar metrics are achieved. This system places an emphasis on improving lower cost primary care services. A separate revenue generating financial case could therefore be drawn in those instances.

Patients in the VHA do not have a co-pay for telephone encounters made for population health management outreach. However, workload credit is based on encounters (completed appointments). Time for unscheduled population health management is included within the work schedule for pharmacists working in PACT which minimizes additional costs to the organization. The project lead will require approximately eight hours per quarter to complete administrative tasks and this represents the primary cost to the pharmacy department. The strategy focuses on using data that is

CASE 11, TABLE 2. Population Health Quarterly Focus on COPD

Goals	Goal: Make at least two COPD related interventions per week

Suggested Interventions	• Complete chart reviews and identify patients:
	  • On controller inhaler with no recent prescription for rescue inhaler
	  • With COPD diagnosis on ICS without LABA/LAMA
	  • With prescriptions for duplicate therapies
	• Collaborate with primary care provider ahead of scheduled appointments to recommend therapy change
	• Reach out to patients unscheduled to discuss
	• Discuss during scheduled phone or in-person appointments for COPD
	  1. Ensure rescue therapy is available
	  2. Address regimens that may be suboptimal
	      Examples: ICS without LABA/LAMA or duplicate therapy

Resources	• Link to "Data Dashboard" • Directions on how to access and export data • Example note templates • Pharmacy prescriptions and fill records • EHR data including laboratory values • Society or institution guideline links COPD resources—GOLD guidelines, institution ICS de-escalation protocols
Metrics	• Number of actionable patients requiring intervention before and after intervention period.
Results	• Modality: Display graphically, verbally, and/or written • Method: Team meeting presentation, email • Feedback: Reflect on intervention, elicit feedback from team

already readily available and is a shared cost across VHA departments and costs for data management are not accounted for in this case.

IMPLEMENTATION PLAN

Steps to implementation of a population health management program are described in **Figure 4**. Before presentation to pharmacy or other indicated leadership, current workflow processes must be analyzed. Barriers to implementing a program should be considered including availability of population health data. Data sources could include a formal report derived from the EHR, refill records, laboratory values, or patient demographics. When proposing the program, the purpose of the program as well as necessary time and costs should be calculated. Internal stakeholders must approve data sharing for each pharmacist. Timing varies in each organization and should be accounted for. When defining the workgroup, consider the scope of the initial program. Consider beginning with all pharmacists in a single strategically picked specialty clinic where interventions may have the best chance of initial success. Program design is considered as the final step where institution-specific guidelines are created. For example, patient identification strategies, outcome measurements, realistic number of achievable goals, and resources needed should be generated. In total, the process of implementation is estimated to take around four to six months.

Supporting Materials

1. Population Health Management Protocol (site specific)

2. Implementation timeline

3. Results spreadsheets

4. Email drafts

1. Data Gathering
- 1-2 months
- Assess current population health management process and identify barriers
- Determine availability of population health data
- Pursue support from pharmacy leadership through project proposal

2. Workgroup Establishment
- 1-2 months
- Define role of project lead
- Identify members of population-health subgroup
- Schedule initial workgroup meeting

3. Workflow preparation
- 2 months
- Determine frequency of population health focus changes
- Identify and refine initial strategic focus based on health system goals or known gaps in care with equity focus
- Determine patient identification strategy
- Determine guidelines for goal creation and create resources for pharmacists

CASE 11, FIGURE 4. Population health management implementation steps

Lessons Learned

1. Pharmacist-led population management is a proactive intervention with the goal of improving the health of a population of patients.

2. A quarterly population management program which aligns facility or national measures with health measures maximizes performance and patient outcomes.

3. Population health data must be accessible in a timely manner for pharmacists to manage the program with autonomy.

4. Well-defined metrics and goals are necessary to measure feasibility and outcomes.

5. Flexibility is key. As facility and national goals change, new focus areas should reflect these changes.

6. Potential pitfalls include questions and difficulties when frontline pharmacists start to incorporate the focus area into their daily practice. The project lead and team must remain responsive and adaptable throughout the quarter.

REFERENCES

1. U.S. Department of Veterans Affairs. I CARE. **https://va.gov/icare/**. Updated November 16, 2021. Accessed November 28, 2021.

2. Institute of Medicine (IOM). *Crossing the Quality Chasm: A New Health System for the 21st Century*. Washington, D.C: National Academy Press; 2001.

3. Institute for Healthcare Improvement. Initiatives: The IHI triple aim. **http://www.ihi.org/Engage/Initiatives/TripleAim/Pages/default.aspx**. Accessed November 28, 2021.

4. Duong NE, Kim D, Hernandez FA, et al. Value-based pay-for-performance gaps in the care delivery framework for a large-scale health system. *Popul Health Manag*. 2021;24(6):691–698. 10.1089/pop.2021.0024. PubMed

5. Carmichael JM, Meier J, Robinson A, et al. Leveraging electronic medical record data for population health management in the Veterans Health Administration: Successes and lessons learned. *Am J Health Syst Pharm*. 2017;74(18):1447–1459. 10.2146/ajhp161048. PubMed

6. American Diabetes Association. 9. Pharmacologic approaches to glycemic treatment: *standards of medical care in diabetes-2020*. [published correction appears in Diabetes Care. 2020 Aug;43(8):1979]. *Diabetes Care*. 2020;43(suppl 1):S98–S110. 10.2337/dc20-S009. PubMed

7. Singh D, Agusti A, Anzueto A, et al. Global strategy for the diagnosis, management, and prevention of chronic obstructive lung disease: the GOLD science committee report 2019. *Eur Respir J*. 2019;53(5):1900164. Published 2019 May 18. doi:10.1183/13993003.00164-2019. Accessed September 27, 2021.

CASE

12

HEALTH SYSTEM SPECIALTY PHARMACY

Matthew H. Rim and Scott L. Canfield

HEALTH SYSTEM BACKGROUND

M&S Health System (M&S) is a fictitious health system located in the Midwestern United States. M&S includes a 500 bed disproportionate share eligible teaching hospital and a number of hospital based specialty clinics including rheumatology, gastroenterology, oncology, and infectious disease. To date, the pharmacy department infrastructure has focused heavily on inpatient operations and clinical services with limited ambulatory clinic presence. The structure does include one internally owned and operated outpatient pharmacy within the main hospital campus that is focused on filling discharge prescriptions. This pharmacy includes one FTE outpatient pharmacy manager, three FTE retail pharmacists, five FTE retail pharmacy technicians, and a pharmacy purchasing supervisor. The outpatient pharmacy team is also supported by a small centralized finance team who primarily performs prescription reconciliation and collection duties.

EXECUTIVE SUMMARY

Specialty drug spending represents over 50% of the total prescription drug expenditures in the U.S. today. New specialty drug development is concentrated in self-administered injectable, oral therapies, and IV infusion therapies utilized in the outpatient/ambulatory setting for complex and chronic diseases. Based on the current drug pipeline, this trend will be continued.[1] Existing and newly approved specialty drugs present opportunities for M&S to provide more integrated care to our patients. About half of health systems similar to us developed their own specialty pharmacy already. Internally, our prescriptions have been diverted to outside entities threatening our integrated care model. Our services are becoming more fragmented, compromising patient safety, clinical outcomes, coordination of care, and the system's total cost of care and quality. Our patients experience delays in starting new treatments and frequent interruptions due to the lack of coordination and communication when they receive their specialty drugs from external entities. The system's outpatient pharmacy is not structured to handle specialty drugs. Specialty drugs require additional infrastructure and resources due to the complex insurance navigation process, payer network requirements, clinical management, accreditation standards, and data requirements for limited distribution drugs. To support our patients and improve our financial strength, M&S Pharmacy Services proposes the development and implementation of an integrated specialty pharmacy within our system. This business case includes environmental/needs assessment with prospective

DOI 10.37573/9781585287130.022

specialty pharmacy business models and a SWOT analysis, business/service description with a pre-scribing data analysis, operating and implementation plans with required FTEs and resources, finan-cial plan with a three year pro forma, and future directions and resource needs.

ENVIRONMENTAL/NEEDS ASSESSMENT

The importance of specialty drugs within health system pharmacy practice has grown rapidly over the past 10 years. Over 88% of large health systems (>600 beds) operate their own specialty pharmacy as of a 2019 survey, with over 48% of health systems similar to our size (400 to 599 beds) doing the same.[2] The definition of "specialty drug" varies depending on source; however, one definition that we believe aligns well with our intended use is cited by the American Society of Health-System Pharmacists (ASHP) and provided by IQVIA, a health information technology and clinical research company. IQVIA defines specialty drugs as those used to treat rare and/or complex chronic diseases and that meet four or more of the following criteria (1) initiated and maintained by a specialist; (2) generally injectable and/or not self-administered; (3) need for additional level of care in the chain of custody; (4) annual cost of therapy of $6,000 or more; (5) unique distribution; (6) need for extensive or in-depth monitoring and/or patient counseling; and (7) require reimburse-ment assistance.[3]

The exponential growth of specialty drugs presents both financial risks and benefits for the organization, as well as an opportunity to create a more integrated and outcome focused patient journey. As more high cost specialty drugs are approved by the FDA, payers continue to narrow specialty pharmacy networks in attempts to control cost and service quality. For the past decade, pharmacy benefit managers (PBMs) and health plans have restricted access to their networks, com-plicating our ability to provide comprehensive and integrated care for patients with both private and governmental payers. Many of major payers for private health insurance and major PBMs are vertically integrated with their own specialty pharmacies, which makes network access increasingly challenging. Most of our patients with private health insurances are not able to receive specialty medications from the M&S retail pharmacy due to payer restricted networks. Despite that limita-tion, Medicare and Medicaid networks are often less restricted and those payers cover the majority of patients seen at M&S. Although Medicare and Medicaid networks tend to be less restricted, the Medicare Part D pharmacy benefit structure does allow payers to also use preferred specialty phar-macies and restricted networks which are likely going to grow across the pharmacy industry.

Many drug manufacturers who launch specialty drugs use a limited number of pharmacies in their distribution networks creating what are commonly referred to as limited distribution drugs (LDDs). Manufacturers may limit the distribution of their drugs for specific reasons (eg, FDA man-dated REMS programs); however, many restrict their network for specialty products in attempts to limit their supply chain complexity, ensure higher quality of services provided, or to ensure access to data or other contractual terms. Specialties such as oncology, pulmonary, and rare diseases have more LDDs, and the trend of using LDD networks is likely to continue to accelerate given the drug pipeline focus in rare disease. Manufacturers of LDDs create a contract to select specialty pharma-cies for their limited distribution network and require frequent data submission, additional clini-cal and operational infrastructure to handle high touch specialty drugs, and one or more specialty pharmacy accreditation. Health systems without a specialty pharmacy and data reporting capabili-ties are typically unable to access LDDs and support their patients. This represents an ongoing and growing risk to M&S.

Health plans use several risk mitigation strategies to control costs associated with high-cost specialty drugs, which can make obtaining access to specialty drugs very challenging for prescrib-ers and patients. Prior authorizations (PAs) for specialty drugs are considered as the most time-consuming and challenging cost containment strategy deployed by health plans. Due to the growth and advancement of specialty drugs and the correlated financial risk for health plans, the PA process has become more rigorous for specialty drugs. Because of the restrictive nature of the PA process, healthcare providers generally view PAs as a burden and barrier to provide care for their patients. Health systems like M&S with multiple specialties and subspecialties, such as oncology, rheumatology and gastroenterology, may experience higher PA burden due to the concentration of specialists and larger patient populations on specialty drugs. Specialty pharmacies often take on parts of this complex insurance navigation responsibility to simplify this process.

According to the ASHP Specialty Pharmacy Resource Guide, organizations evaluating options to address aforementioned problems and market signals should consider the following business models: (1) build in-house specialty pharmacies; (2) develop a partnership; (3) outsource; or (4) manage risk without a formal specialty pharmacy program.[4] **Table 1** summarizes pros and cons of each business model. The most recent National Survey of Health System Specialty Pharmacy Practice published in 2021 indicated that health systems integrated specialty clinics and providers with an in-house specialty pharmacy exceed industry standards.[3] In addition, M&S Pharmacy Services

CASE 12, TABLE 1. Four Prospective Specialty Pharmacy Business Models for Health Systems

Options	Pros	Cons
1. Build an in-house specialty pharmacy	• Use internal expertise • Maximize existing operations (eg, retail pharmacies) • Strengthen and support clinical operations (specialty clinics, prior authorizations) • Realize financial benefit without requiring external relationships • Customize services for the specific patient population	• Require an initial investment to build infrastructure • Long implementation period to be fully functioning • Require resources from existing services such as IT, legal, and managed care department
2. Partnership	• Meet specific needs without much investment (eg, prior authorizations, call center) • Faster implementation • Gain time to build internal expertise • Support	• Difficult to find a right partner aligned with the organization's standard • Require support from the legal and contracting department to execute the service agreement/contract • May require additional quality assurance processes to mitigate nonconformities
3. Outsource (organizations without a retail pharmacy, lack of significant specialty physician groups, limited access to capital)	• Upfront investment is not required • Faster implementation • Realize financial benefits through the 340B contract pharmacy relationship	• Have same cons from the partnership model • Fully rely on the third party (no other options)
4. Manage risk without changes	None	• Scramble to manage patients each time by both clinic and pharmacy staff without proper process and infrastructure • Not able to maintain and expand payer contracts • Not able to join specialty pharmacy network • Not able to gain access to LDDs • Continue to transfer patient care to external specialty pharmacies

conducted the strength, weakness, opportunity, and threat (SWOT) analysis to evaluate the current state of our practice model and identify the specialty pharmacy business model to maximize the organizational competitive advantages (**Table 2**). Based on the gap analysis, evaluation of published resources and careful consideration of the internal capabilities such as a fully functioning outpatient pharmacy, managed care group for pharmacy contracting, and clinical integration with the system's specialty clinics, it is determined that the development of an in-house specialty pharmacy will provide the long-term benefits and flexibility to adjust services to support our patients in this competitive market.

CASE 12, TABLE 2. Strength, Weakness, Opportunity, and Threat (SWOT) Analysis

Strength	Weakness	Opportunity	Threat
• A fully functioning retail pharmacy in place • Integrated practice model with the full access to EHR • Extensive specialty clinics and physician groups • Embedded clinical pharmacists in specialty clinics	• Limited space (retail pharmacy) • Limited payer contracts • Limited access to LDDs • Lack of comprehensive patient management program • Lack of infrastructure to support patients (eg, call center)	• Coordinate patient care with specialty providers and clinic staff • Standardize communication with patients • Invest in clinical and operational infrastructure to support patients and fulfill specialty drug orders • Use internal expertise to develop in-house specialty pharmacy programs (eg, patient management, 24/7 call center, payer contracts, data reporting)	• Increased payer contract requirements • Vertical integration • White Bagging • Site of care restrictions • Limited distribution drug access • Decreasing reimbursements and DIR fees • 340B reform • Complacency

BUSINESS/SERVICE DESCRIPTION

M&S Pharmacy Services proposes the development and implementation of a comprehensive specialty pharmacy program in our system. Our mission is to support patients with complex or chronic diseases reach the best health by providing care in the safest and easiest way at the lowest cost possible. Our vision is to be a leading health system specialty pharmacy through the operational excellence and innovative clinical programs that improve the health of our patient population, which aligns with the overall M&S organization's mission and vision.

Our approach is to fully integrate the new specialty pharmacy processes into our current care model to provide seamless transitions from clinics to pharmacy to receive the prescribed specialty drugs from our providers. Other health systems similar to M&S have developed and shared resources to start and organize new specialty pharmacy operations through ASHP which were utilized to develop our integrated practice model.[5] To achieve this goal, we will require additional operational infrastructure and personnel to provide comprehensive services including prior authorization support, patient assistance navigation, pharmacist patient management services, and data collection and reporting capabilities. This includes hiring and developing a specialty pharmacy workforce, including a specialty supervisor, clinical pharmacists, and specialty technicians as outlined in our implementation plan below.

As indicated in the gap analysis, having a retail pharmacy is one of strengths of our current operations. We propose using our existing retail pharmacy to fulfill specialty drugs initially to jump start the program with nondispensing specialty services (eg, clinical pharmacists and technicians) operating in clinic-based roles to serve as liaison between prescribers, clinic staff, and the dispensing pharmacy operations. It will be important to monitor retail pharmacy capacity and staffing needs as we add more prescription volume; however, we believe incremental dispensing volumes as outlined in this proposal can be accommodated with the existing FTEs through Year 3 of the business plan. We will require additional supplies to accommodate more prescriptions requiring cold chain shipping (eg, coolers, ice packs), which may require a larger future physical space than our current retail pharmacy.

An analysis of M&S prescribing data were performed to identify initial specialty clinics and patient population to offer services. The data were used to estimate specialty patient and prescription volumes across our health system, as well as the current payer mix to determine our ability to process pharmacy claims through the retail pharmacy. The results of this analysis are found in **Table 3**. Pharmacy Services also had initial discussions with key physician and administrative staff in these specialty areas to identify potential champions in each area who are excited to collaborate with Pharmacy Services to roll out this program. All confirmed their willingness to support internal specialty pharmacy services, and their strong desire to receive both clinical and patient navigation support.

CASE 12, TABLE 3. Prescribing Data Analysis for Rheumatology, Gastroenterology, HIV, and Oncology

Disease Category	Unique Patients on Specialty Products in M&S Clinic	Assumed Specialty Rx Dispenses per Patient per Year	Estimated Annual M&S Generated Specialty Rx Dispenses	Estimated Revenue per Prescription	Estimated Payer Mix (% Commercial Plans)
Rheumatology	200	12	2,400	$6,000	50%
Gastroenterology	200	12	2,400	$6,000	50%
HIV	400	12	4,800	$3,000	50%
Oncology	300	6	1,800	$7,500	50%

OPERATING AND IMPLEMENTATION PLANS

Specialty pharmacy team members will initially report to the existing outpatient pharmacy manager, with plans to transition reporting to a dedicated incremental specialty pharmacy manager in Year 2 of the business plan. Specialty pharmacy team members in patient facing positions will operate as part of an integrated care team model, in which the clinical pharmacist and specialty technicians will work within the interdisciplinary specialty clinics where patient clinic visits occur. All patients prescribed a specialty product will receive education and monitoring by a clinical pharmacist, as well as support for financial navigation, proactive refill reminders, and dispensing coordination by the specialty technician. A list of products in scope of specialty services will be maintained by the pharmacy team. The specialty pharmacy team will serve as the point of contact for pharmacy integration needs.

Systems utilized by the specialty pharmacy team will include:

- Electronic Health Record (clinical documentation, patient outreach tracking calendar)

- Pharmacy Dispensing System (prescription processing)

- Prior Authorization Tracking Spreadsheet (results of prior authorization requests and financial navigation)

As part of standard specialty pharmacy services, patients will be offered the option of filling their prescriptions with M&S if allowed by their insurances. When desired by the patient, such prescriptions will be sent to and dispensed by the existing health system outpatient pharmacy, with dispensing and shipping functions performed by the existing outpatient pharmacy staff within the brick-and-mortar pharmacy. When possible, patient education visits between a patient and the team pharmacy will occur face-to-face in the clinic upon therapy initiation. Reassessments will largely occur via telephone unless the timeline for reassessment aligns with their clinic visit schedule for other purposes. The specialty pharmacy technicians will perform proactive patient outreach to coordinate refill dispensing for patients filling prescriptions via the internal pharmacy and initial processing of those prescriptions in the pharmacy dispensing system. Patients who are unable to fill prescriptions with the health system pharmacy will continue to receive pharmacist education and monitoring services while their refill coordination will be managed by their external specialty pharmacies in an effort to avoid duplication of outreach.

The specialty pharmacy team will create and maintain standardized documentation templates for clinical assessments and patient education (initial and reassessment) by disease state or drug where necessary. Generally, patient assessment and education by a pharmacist will be performed prior to therapy initiation, within a month after initiation, and then periodically (at least annually) based on the monitoring schedule appropriate for the medication and patient as determined by the pharmacist and care team.

A phased-in implementation plan over three years will be utilized. The implementation plan will begin with establishing specialty pharmacy services for two disease categories in Year 1 (rheumatology and gastroenterology), followed by annual expansion of scope in Year 2 (HIV) and Year 3 (oncology). The implementation of each service line will be supported by the addition of two FTE incremental clinical pharmacist positions who will focus on the newly established disease category, and similarly two FTE specialty technician positions, all of which will be clinic based. These positions will allow for equal patient:pharmacist and patient:technician ratios of approximately 200:1 for rheumatology, gastroenterology, and HIV with a slightly different ratio of 150:1 for oncology to account for increased patient complexity. Benchmarking for patient and clinician ratios in specialty pharmacy is highly limited, but we believe these ratios are in line with other health systems already providing integrated specialty services within their specialty clinics.

Oversight of implementation as well as ongoing service quality and performance will be provided through a multidisciplinary Specialty Pharmacy Oversight committee, which will have broad representatives of key stakeholders from throughout the institution and include executive health system leadership, pharmacy leadership, finance, clinic leadership, quality leadership, and physician champions. This committee will meet monthly, and review success and quality of the program through evaluation of at least the following measures and outcomes: financial performance, referral volumes, prior authorization volumes and approval rates, patient:staff ratios, and patient and prescriber satisfaction (at least annually). Membership of this committee will be reviewed regularly, with additions of team members in managed care, supply chain, and contracting being likely additions after basic operations are established. Each year, the committee will create and approve an annual program summary document highlighting successes, challenges, and next steps. Distribution of the program summary throughout the health system or incorporation of elements of the program summary within other health system annual reports will be reviewed with executive leadership.

Exploration of the benefits of pursuing specialty pharmacy accreditation will be further considered in Year 2 of service implementation. To identify potential benefits of pursuing accreditation, this exploration will include a review of patient referrals from Year 1 who were unable to fill prescriptions with our pharmacies due to payer carve outs and subsequent exploration of specialty network requirements for the top plans identified. Accreditation offerings from various institutions will be explored and compared, including those offered by URAC, ACHC, and ASHP. Although not required for service initiation, we anticipate specialty accreditation from one or potentially two of these bodies will be required for our pharmacy to meet basic criteria for access to restricted payer and manufacturer networks.

FINANCIAL PLAN

To demonstrate the return on investment, a three year pro forma analysis was developed based on prescription capture. Key elements of the pro forma included estimates of specialty patient volumes (based on previously collected electronic prescribing data), estimated annual specialty dispenses per year per patient, and revenue per specialty prescription by disease category (**Table 3**). Additional key elements and assumptions used to create the pro forma include internal prescription capture rate, revenue per prescription, cost of goods sold (COGS), and costs to provide services such as dispensing costs, delivery costs, personnel costs, and overhead (**Table 4**).

Additional assumptions include: (1) COGS percentage determined based on anticipated 340B mix and review of pricing for the most commonly prescribed products; (2) a maximum internal capture rate of 50% which is achieved by Year 3 of each new disease service implementation and estimated based on past analysis of payer mix and payer specialty network carve outs; (3) 3% annual increase in the number of system generated prescription dispenses to account for expected annual increases in clinic patient volumes; and (4) salary and benefit costs for positions as follows: $130,000 per clinical pharmacist, $50,000 per specialty pharmacy technician, and $150,000 per specialty pharmacy supervisor with each position receiving a 3% annual cost of living increase.

FUTURE DIRECTIONS AND RESOURCE NEEDS

We believe that there will be significant opportunity to grow and expand specialty services within our health system beyond the three year business plan presented in this proposal. In addition to incremental clinical and operational support required for disease category expansion beyond Year 3, additional leadership support and resources will likely be needed. Areas that may require specific additional FTE support include payer contracting, manufacturer relations, accreditation oversight, purchasing, outcomes research, and informatics (eg, medical record customization and data analytics). Additionally, growth may justify needs for additional office space for specialty pharmacy employees or require expansion of our physical dispensing pharmacy footprint to accommodate prescription fulfillment needs. This may require construction to expand the square footage of the existing retail pharmacy, or opening of a new pharmacy location more focused on the dispensing of specialty products.

Partnership with existing health system resources that are external to the department of pharmacy such as managed care, informatics, and contracting will be leveraged wherever possible to promote alignment. However, given the complexities, challenges, and high barrier to entry for access to restricted payer and manufacturer specialty networks, we anticipate dedicated incremental resources in many of these areas will be necessary. Such needs will be further identified as the program matures, and will be communicated to executive leadership. To summarize these needs and quantify additional program growth beyond Year 3, a new two year pro forma will be created during Year 3.

CASE 12, TABLE 4. 3 Year Financial Pro Forma

Pro Forma	Year 1	Year 2	Year 3
Estimated System Generated Prescription Dispenses	**11,400**	**11,742**	**12,094**
Rheumatology	2,400	2,472	2,546
Gastroenterology	2,400	2,472	2,546
HIV	4,800	4,944	5,092
Oncology	1,800	1,854	1,910
Prescription Capture Rate	**13%**	**29%**	**41%**
Rheumatology	30%	40%	50%
Gastroenterology	30%	40%	50%
HIV	0%	30%	40%
Oncology	0%	0%	20%
Total Internal Prescriptions Dispensed	**1,440**	**3,461**	**4,965**
Rheumatology	720	989	1,273
Gastroenterology	720	989	1,273
HIV	0	1,483	2,037
Oncology	0	0	382
Revenue	**$8,640,000**	**$16,315,200**	**$24,252,174**
Rheumatology	$4,320,000	$5,932,800	$7,638,480
Gastroenterology	$4,320,000	$5,932,800	$7,638,480
HIV	$0	$4,449,600	$6,110,784
Oncology	$0	$0	$2,864,430
Cost of Goods Sold (% of Revenue)	**80%**	**80%**	**80%**
Gross Margin on Drug	**$1,728,000**	**$3,263,040**	**$4,850,435**
Total Cost of Service	**($406,800)**	**($993,276)**	**($1,428,587)**
Total Specialty FTE	4	9	13
Clinical Pharmacist (salary + benefits)	$260,000	$527,800	$803,634
Specialty Technician (hourly + benefits)	$100,000	$203,000	$309,090
Specialty Pharmacy Supervisor (salary + benefits)	$0	$150,000	$154,500
Dispensing ($20/Rx)	$28,800	$69,216	$99,300
Delivery Cost ($25/Rx with 50% of Rxs delivered)	$18,000	$43,260	$62,063
Net Contribution	**$1,321,200**	**$2,269,764**	**$3,421,848**
Net Contribution Percent (% of Revenue)	**15%**	**14%**	**14%**

Although not a focus on the initial business plan, we anticipate that need for insurance and financial navigation support within infusion and healthcare provider administered medications will continue to increase across the health system, and that the processes developed and implemented for these functions within take-home specialty products may be able to be adapted to support those needs in the future. Potential scope expansion to support these products will be explored if opportunities and need are identified.

Leadership Lessons Learned (Things to Consider):

1. The exponential growth of specialty drugs presents both financial risks and benefits for health systems.

2. Health systems are well positioned to provide more integrated and patient centered care (maximize your competitive advantage).

3. Health system pharmacy leaders can leverage their system's prescribing and pharmacy claims data to evaluate specialty pharmacy opportunity, and create a targeted plan for implementation, as well as monitor post-implementation progress to create a sustainable business model.

4. Existing health system retail pharmacy infrastructure can serve as a solid foundation when starting a health system specialty pharmacy (HSSP) as long as key start-up resources such as clinical and financial navigation positions are added and proper structure and oversight is outlined.

5. It's never too late to start building your own HSSP. There are many available resources such as the ASHP Health System Specialty Pharmacy Resource Center as well as professional activities from the Section of Specialty Pharmacy Practitioners.

REFERENCES

1. Tichy EM, Hoffman JM, Suda KJ, et al. National trends in prescription drug expenditures and projections for 2021. *Am J Health Syst Pharm*. 2021;78(14):1294–1308. PubMed

2. Pedersen CA, Schneider PJ, Ganio MC, Scheckelhoff DJ. ASHP national survey of pharmacy practice in hospital settings: Prescribing and transcribing-2019. *Am J Health Syst Pharm*. 2020;77(13):1026–1050. PubMed

3. Stubbings J, Pedersen CA, Low K, Chen D. ASHP national survey of health system specialty pharmacy practice – 2020. *Am J Health Syst Pharm*. 2021;78(19):1765–1791. PubMed

4. American Society of Health-System Pharmacists. ASHP specialty pharmacy resource guide. December 2015. **https://www.ashp.org/-/media/assets/pharmacy-practice/resource-centers/specialty-pharmacy/specialty-pharmacy-resource-guide.ashx**. Accessed December 1, 2021.

5. American Society of Health-System Pharmacists. Health system specialty pharmacy resource center. **https://www.ashp.org/pharmacy-practice/resource-centers/health-system-specialty-pharmacy-resource-center**. Accessed December 1, 2022.

HOME INFUSION PHARMACY

Scott Sterrett and Jared A. Austin

EXECUTIVE SUMMARY

The home infusion industry is rapidly expanding, more than tripling its annual net revenue over the past decade. The industry generated over $19 billion in 2019 and is projected to continue growing by 10% or more annually. Various factors are contributing to home infusion's expansion, including payor-mandated site of care restrictions, patient preference, the increasing number of high-cost specialty infusions, and changes brought about from the COVID-19 pandemic.

Health systems are uniquely positioned to succeed in the home infusion marketplace. While hospital-affiliated home infusion pharmacies only comprise about 15% of home infusion pharmacies nationwide, they capture nearly 25% of the market share. Integrated electronic health records, shared system governance, and a unified focus on patient outcomes are just a few of the competitive advantages that health system-operated home infusion programs enjoy. In addition to the positive impacts on patient experience, quality of care, and provider satisfaction, home infusion programs can significantly contribute to the overall financial health of an institution.

While home infusion is a pharmacy-driven service, it involves close collaboration with ordering providers, nursing agencies, and various other professional and technical staff. Internal resources required to implement and grow a home infusion program include a pharmacy director, clinical pharmacists, pharmacy technicians, nurse liaisons, and intake and billing staff. External relationships with nursing agencies, delivery providers, and various drug and product suppliers are also crucial to the program's success.

With a focused investment of resources and the required capital, a new home infusion program can be implemented within 15 months. A dedicated home infusion pharmacy to support a system with 50,000 annual inpatient discharges can be built and furnished for approximately $2 million. Assuming 10-year capital depreciation, the program will be profitable its first year of operation and generate over $2.75 million in net income during the first three years.

To stay competitive in the rapidly evolving healthcare market, it is crucial for health systems to develop internal home infusion programs. It allows systems to focus on quality and patient outcomes across the continuum of care. Systems choosing not to develop a home infusion program will forego expanded revenue opportunities, while also exposing their organizations to continued erosion of infusion margins from ongoing shifts in site of care.

DOI 10.37573/9781585287130.023

SERVICE DESCRIPTION

Home infusion therapy involves the administration of medications to patients intravenously or subcutaneously while in the home or infusion suite setting. A wide range of medications can be administered through home infusion, including anti-infectives, hydration, parenteral nutrition, immunoglobulins, biologics, blood products, inotropes, and other therapies to treat acute or chronic conditions. While home infusion is a pharmacy-based operation, the provision of care is multidisciplinary and includes skilled nursing services, clinical pharmacy services, and close coordination with ordering providers. In addition to medication therapies, home infusion pharmacies provide infusion supplies, durable medical equipment, and myriad other professional services.

Although home infusion therapy was first described in the literature in 1975,[1] it did not become more widespread until the 1980s.[2] Advances in technology that enabled safe administration within the home setting, coupled with the need to contain rising healthcare costs, led to the rising utilization of home infusion therapy.[3] The growth of home infusion has greatly accelerated within recent years, driven by a multitude of factors, including payor-mandated site of care restrictions, patient preference, the increasing numbers of high-cost specialty infusions, and most recently the COVID-19 pandemic. The value of the home infusion industry is now estimated at $19 billion, more than tripling its annual net revenue since 2008.[4]

Home infusion therapy is currently experiencing renewed interest among health systems. A significant number of health systems that do not already own and operate home infusion pharmacies are developing plans to enter the market. While hospital-owned home infusion pharmacies only account for about 15% of home infusion pharmacies nationwide (as measured by membership in National Home Infusion Association, or NHIA), they capture nearly 25% of the market share. The average hospital-owned home infusion pharmacy generates over $28 million in annual net revenue, representing a significant opportunity to supplement revenue streams from ambulatory and specialty pharmacy programs.[4]

Health systems are uniquely positioned to provide home infusion therapy and enjoy many competitive advantages. Integrated electronic health records, laboratory services, and, potentially, home health services facilitate smooth transitions of care and maintain the continuity of records. Internal programs can work within the health system's governance structure to develop clinical pathways and protocols, standardize care, and ensure quality outcomes. In addition to referrals generated upon hospital discharge, systems with owned or affiliated specialty clinics have an additional built-in referral source. Finally, because health system-owned programs share the same mission and finances, they can facilitate earlier hospital discharges, regardless of a patient's insurance or ability to pay.

ENVIRONMENTAL AND NEEDS ASSESSMENT

There has been a paradigm shift in the healthcare environment as payment models have transitioned from volume to value. This shift has resulted in an emphasis on transitions of care, decreasing length of stay, and preventing unnecessary hospitalizations. In 2019 hospital readmissions were estimated to have cost Medicare over $26 billion.[5] In response, the Hospital Readmissions Reduction Program (HRRP) was enacted by the Centers for Medicare & Medicaid Services (CMS) in October 2012. Through this program, CMS began reducing payments to hospitals for excess readmissions.[6]

Home and specialty infusion services provide a vital bridge between hospital and home for more than 3.2 million patients annually. Currently, NHIA estimates that 8% of hospitalized patients utilize home infusion after discharge.[4] Home infusion offers patients the convenience of administering infusion therapy in their homes instead of making daily visits to an infusion center. Improvements in the accuracy and styles of ambulatory infusion pumps have allowed for increasingly complex infusions to be administered in the home setting (eg, TPN or extended infusion antibiotics).

Home infusion services offer hospitals the opportunity to transition patients to lower-cost care settings while still providing safe, high-quality care. In the absence of home infusion services, patients who are otherwise stable and ready to discharge would be held pending completion of infusion therapy. In other cases, lack of home infusion opportunities would result in the indefinite hospitalization of certain patients (eg, TPN and enteral patients). Multiple studies have shown that patients receiving home infusion therapy achieve similar clinical outcomes with lower overall costs compared to those in the hospital outpatient setting.[7,9–11]

The ability to administer infusion therapy in the home setting can be a driving factor in increasing patient satisfaction. One of the main appeals of home infusion therapy for patients is the ease of scheduling and administering their therapies. While most institutional infusion centers have specific days and times of operation, patients administering infusion therapy in the home have the flexibility to infuse at a time and place that best suits their needs. The National Home Infusion Foundation (NHIF) has collected satisfaction-survey data from over 33,000 patients nationwide and reported that 97.6% of respondents agreed or strongly agreed that they were satisfied with the overall quality of services provided.

Within the last five years, many third-party payors have utilized site of care restrictions to move patients from hospital-based infusion centers to lower-cost settings. These restrictions often target high-dollar specialty infusion products. To reduce care fragmentation and retain vital revenue, it has become crucial for institutions to develop infusion strategies that offer alternate sites of care. Home infusion therapy offers a cost-effective, safe, and patient-centered option to maintain continuity of care within health systems.

Health systems choosing not to offer an in-house home infusion program can alternatively contract with a local or national home infusion provider. For 340B-eligible organizations, this can also generate additional 340B revenue back to the system. When initiating services with an external provider, it is important to establish goals and metrics to ensure the provision of quality care. The institution should establish regular meetings with the contracted provider to review metrics and ensure terms of the agreement are being met.

OPERATING PLAN

Staffing

Home infusion therapy is a pharmacy-driven program involving the provision and coordination of clinical, dispensing, and administrative services. Patients are provided with continuous care and support while on service, including the delivery of medications and supplies, comprehensive patient education, 24-hour on-call assistance, and clinical monitoring. A home infusion pharmacy works with the physician, skilled nurses, the laboratory, the patient, and the patient's caregiver or family to coordinate care throughout the course of treatment.

Nurse liaisons are typically the first point of contact within the referral process. These staff members may be positioned in the hospitals or centrally located at the home infusion pharmacy. Nurse liaisons work with the medical team, discharge planners, patients, and caregivers or family members to determine appropriateness for home infusion. They also ensure key requirements are met prior to discharge, including appropriate vascular access, a safe environment for care, and adequate support to successfully complete therapy.

At the same time the nurse liaison is coordinating the clinical aspects of discharge, the pharmacy's intake coordinator works to determine affordability and coverage through the patient's insurance. After a comprehensive benefits investigation, the intake coordinator discusses financial responsibility with the patient and members of the care team, as necessary. These individuals also work to secure required insurance authorizations and coordinate financial assistance programs, as necessary.

After completion of these processes, the patient case is transferred to the clinical pharmacy team. The pharmacist evaluates the patient's medication list, drug allergies, current course of treatment, and treatment goals to confirm appropriateness of therapy and develop a patient care plan. After clinical review, the team enters orders for the medication and all other supplies and ancillary equipment necessary to administer the therapy, which is then sent to the operations team for preparation.

The compounding team, consisting of a pharmacist and pharmacy technicians, is responsible for the preparation, packaging, and labeling of all products in each patient order. In addition to compounding sterile preparations, they also prepare and label all flushes, ancillary medications, supplies, and medical equipment. While packaging, the compounding team takes special care to ensure that all storage requirements are maintained during transit (eg, cold chain or protect from light). The sealed packages are then transferred to a courier service or in-house driver for delivery to the patient's home.

Nursing services are arranged either by the hospital discharge planner or a nursing liaison prior to the patient being discharged home. A home health nurse is responsible for providing an initial patient visit to train and educate the patient and caregivers on the self-administration of medications, maintenance of the IV line, and the goals and side effects of therapy. A nurse periodically visits the patient at home to assess the IV line and site, provide dressing changes, and draw necessary laboratory values specific to the patient's therapy.[8]

Billers and accounts receivable specialists are responsible for developing and submitting claims to third-party payors for reimbursement. Because requirements vary significantly across payors, the billing staff must be adept at utilizing appropriate ICD-10, HCPCS, CPT, and NDC codes and billing modifiers throughout the payment and reimbursement cycle. These individuals are also responsible for managing claim denials, resubmissions, and write-offs.

Metrics

Throughout implementation and growth of a home infusion service line, it is important to track progress, success, and predetermined milestones. While many business metrics are similar across pharmacy service lines, the uniqueness of the home infusion model requires additional monitoring. The following is a detailed, but not comprehensive, list of metrics to consider tracking:

- Referral volume
- Referral conversion rate
- Net revenue
- Cost of goods sold
- Write-offs and bad debt
- Net operating income
- Patient readmission rates
- Medication and supply dispensing errors
- Delivery errors
- Patient satisfaction scores through a third party, validated source

FINANCIAL PLAN

Capital Requirements

Capital requirements will be dependent upon the type, location, and size of facility selected for the home infusion pharmacy. For the purposes of this example, it is assumed that the home infusion pharmacy will occupy its own dedicated space. The facility will need sufficient space for a cleanroom, drug storage and dispensing, warehouse space for supply storage, a loading dock for shipping and receiving, cubicles and offices for staff members, conference space, a break room, and restrooms. Approximately 5,000 square feet should be sufficient to develop and sustain a program for at least five to ten years. **Table 1** provides an estimate of space requirements, while **Table 2** includes some estimated equipment costs. These may vary by location.

CASE 13, TABLE 1. Estimated Home Infusion Pharmacy Space Requirements

Area	Square Footage
Clean Room (Anteroom, Positive Pressure and Negative Pressure Rooms)	1,000
Dispensing and Distribution	500
Warehouse (Storage, Shipping, Receiving)	750
Office Area (Cubicles)	1,500
Administrative Offices and Conference Room	500
Break Area, Restrooms, Changing Room	750
Total	5,000
Construction Estimate	$1,500,000 - $2,500,000

CASE 13, TABLE 2. Estimated Costs of Commonly Required Equipment

Equipment	Estimated Expense
Compounding Hoods	$15,000 each
Equipment for Cleanroom (Carts, Racks, Bins, etc.)	$10,000
Refrigerators/Freezers	$5,000 each
Storage Racks	$15,000

Referral Volume

While NHIA estimates that 8% of discharged patients receive home infusion therapy, this pro forma will conservatively estimate 5% of discharged patients are referred for home infusion. We also assume that employed or affiliated clinics refer a portion of specialty infusion patients for home infusion. The capture rate for referrals is gradually increased over the three-year period, starting at 25% and ramping up to 50%. The estimated number of referrals for a 1,000-bed health system with 50,000 annual discharges is included in **Table 3**.

Staffing

Home infusion is a complex pharmacy operation, requiring expertise from various professional and technical staff. **Table 4** outlines positions required for the successful implementation and growth

CASE 13, TABLE 3. Estimated Capture Rate Based on Hospital Discharges

	Year 1	Year 2	Year 3
Total Discharges	50,000	51,500	53,045
Patients Eligible for Home Infusion	2,500	2,575	2,652
Capture Rate	25%	40%	50%
Patients on Service	625	1,030	1,326

CASE 13, TABLE 4. Home Infusion Pharmacy Staffing Requirements

	Year 1	Year 2	Year 3
Director	1 FTE	1 FTE	1 FTE
Pharmacist	2 FTE	3 FTE	4 FTE
Pharmacy Technician	4 FTE	5 FTE	6 FTE
Intake Coordinator	2 FTE	3 FTE	4 FTE
Nurse Liaison*	2 FTE	2 FTE	2 FTE
Biller/Accounts Receivable	2 FTE	3 FTE	4 FTE

*The nurse liaison positions are recommended to be positioned within the hospital(s) to capture and facilitate referrals. These individuals can also provide bedside teaching and assist with start of care.

of a program based upon volume assumptions provided above. These recommendations allow for a self-sufficient program; however, leveraging support from other departments within the health system (eg, Revenue Cycle or Biomedical Engineering) could decrease ongoing salary expense.

Billing and Revenue Considerations

Home infusion billing is complex, comprising multiple different domains that vary by payor and insurance segment. The following is intended to be a brief, high-level introduction to the pricing of services and various types of revenue. For more detailed explanations of home infusion billing, consult NHIA's Reimbursement Training Center.[12]

Home infusion therapy is billed to various insurance benefits, including major medical, pharmacy, durable medical equipment (DME), home health, and the new Medicare Home Infusion Therapy (HIT) benefits. In general:

- Drugs are primarily billed to the medical benefit, but some payors (eg, Medicare Part D) may cover certain products under the pharmacy benefit. Drugs are billed using a combination of HCPCS (Healthcare Common Procedure Coding System Level II) and NDC (National Drug Code) codes.

- Commercial payors usually reimburse home infusion professional services, supplies, and equipment under a bundled per diem code. The per diem is paid for each day of therapy administered (by the patient or nurse) in the home. Per diem codes are billed to the medical benefit and are sometimes referred to as "S-codes."

- Government payors primarily use separate codes for supplies and pumps. These are often referred to as "equipment and supply codes."

- Nursing visits are generally covered under the commercial per diem structure using CPT (Current Procedural Terminology) codes or under the Medicare Part A home health benefit using G-codes.

Prior to implementation of services, a standardized billing structure should be developed. Charges must be created for medications, per diem codes, equipment rentals, and nursing visits. It is important to note that most payors reimburse based on an established fee schedule rather than a percent of charges. While per diems, rentals, and nursing services are often a fixed fee, drugs may be reimbursed based on a discount off the average wholesale price (AWP), average sales price (ASP) plus a percentage, or maximum allowable cost (MAC).

340B Implications

A health system-owned home infusion pharmacy can be a profitable service without respect to the 340B program. Traditional infusion therapies (eg, anti-infectives, hydration, or total parenteral nutrition) generally have large gross margins. Specialty therapies, including biologics and immuno-globulins, have smaller gross margins, which need to be closely evaluated for financial viability on a drug and payor basis.

Institutions with 340B eligibility will enjoy significantly larger margins on specialty infusion products; traditional products may have some 340B savings but to a much smaller extent. Although specialty infusions make up only about 10% of overall home infusion volume, they account for more than 60% of revenue. As a result, 340B discounts on these products have the potential to add significantly to the bottom line of the service. An estimate of potential 340B savings is provided in the pro forma below to illustrate the potential impact.

Pro Forma

A market analysis, opportunity assessment, and detailed pro forma should be completed to secure required funding for construction, staffing, and program build-out. The example pro forma in **Figure 1** is based on the following assumptions:

- Health system with 1,000 hospital beds and 50,000 annual inpatient discharges in year one. Inpatient discharges increase 3% in years two and three.

- 5% of discharged patients are referred for home infusion.

- Network of employed or affiliated specialty clinics, including allergy/immunology, gastro-enterology, neurology, and rheumatology.

- Mix of 90% traditional therapies (anti-infectives, parenteral nutrition, hydration, etc.) and 10% specialty therapies (immunoglobulin, biologics, blood factors, etc.).

- Payor mix consistent with NHIA averages for health system-owned home infusion providers (approximately 60% commercial, 10% Medicaid, 25% Medicare, and 5% other).

- Nursing services are provided by either an internal home-health division or an external partner or partners. Revenue from nursing services will cover fees owed to the agencies.

- Infusion pump rental, cleaning, and maintenance is estimated at 1% of net revenue.

- Delivery costs (through a local courier or third-party logistics provider) are assumed to be $25 per delivery.

- Cost of goods sold are estimated based on non-340B pricing. A separate line item is included for potential 340B savings, if applicable.

DESCRIPTION	Year 1	Year 2	Year 3	TOTAL
PATIENT SERVICE REVENUE				
Home Infusion Gross Revenue	$20,500,000	$34,000,000	$44,750,000	$99,250,000
TOTAL PATIENT SERVICE REVENUE	$20,500,000	$34,000,000	$44,750,000	$99,250,000
DISCOUNTS AND ALLOWANCES				
Third Party Contractual Provisions	$14,000,000	$23,500,000	$31,000,000	$68,500,000
Provision for Bad Debts	$325,000	$525,000	$687,500	$1,537,500
TOTAL DISCOUNTS AND ALLOWANCES	$14,325,000	$24,025,000	$31,687,500	$70,037,500
NET OPERATING REVENUE	**$6,175,000**	**$9,975,000**	**$13,062,500**	**$29,212,500**
OPERATING EXPENSES				
Salaries & Wages	$1,200,000	$1,600,000	$2,000,000	$4,800,000
Payroll Taxes	$108,000	$144,000	$180,000	$432,000
Employee Benefits	$132,000	$176,000	$220,000	$528,000
Cost of Goods Sold	$4,000,000	$6,500,000	$8,500,000	$19,000,000
Equipment	$60,000	$100,000	$120,000	$280,000
Supplies	$15,000	$20,000	$25,000	$60,000
Dues, Subscriptions, Licensure	$5,000	$7,500	$10,000	$22,500
Delivery Fees	$75,000	$115,000	$150,000	$340,000
Maintenance & Repairs	$5,000	$7,500	$10,000	$22,500
Software Fees	$75,000	$80,000	$85,000	$240,000
Rent	$45,000	$47,500	$50,000	$142,500
Communications	$4,000	$4,500	$5,000	$13,500
Utilities	$10,000	$12,000	$15,000	$37,000
Travel & Meals	$3,500	$4,000	$4,500	$12,000
Depreciation	$175,000	$175,000	$175,000	$525,000
TOTAL OPERATING EXPENSES	**$5,912,500**	**$8,993,000**	**$11,549,500**	**$26,455,000**
NET OPERATING INCOME	**$262,500**	**$982,000**	**$1,513,000**	**$2,757,500**
ADDITIONAL 340B MARGIN, IF ELIGIBLE	$1,120,000	$1,820,000	$2,380,000	$5,320,000
NET CONTRIBUTION, IF 340B ELIGIBLE	$1,382,500	$2,802,000	$3,893,000	$8,077,500

CASE 13, FIGURE 1. 3-Year Pro forma

LEGAL AND REGULATORY CONCERNS

Home infusion pharmacies are required to adhere to all state and federal regulations for sterile compounding pharmacies. Additionally, pharmacies that provide services to Medicare and Medicaid patients must comply with Centers for Medicare & Medicaid Services (CMS) requirements. Finally, most third-party payors require that home infusion pharmacies be accredited by a national accrediting organization to bill for services rendered.

As pharmacy construction is underway, it is important to prepare for licensure with the appropriate state boards of pharmacy for all states to which the pharmacy will ship medications. Regulations for pharmacies that compound sterile preparations may vary by state and could include additional requirements like inspection reports from a third-party organization (eg, accrediting body or National Association of Boards of Pharmacy). Although timelines vary by state, plan for at least three months to complete the required licensure process.

Once the pharmacy licensure process is underway, it is important to obtain both an NPI (National Provider Identification) number and an NCPDP (National Council for Prescription Drug Programs) number. These are both required for contracting and billing purposes. The NPI number must be obtained prior to applying for the NCPDP number. Both identification numbers can be obtained within one week, and it is not necessary to wait for pharmacy licensure approval to start the process.

After receiving pharmacy licensure, and NPI and NCPDP identifiers, the next step is applying for a DEA registration. Since many home infusion pharmacies provide pain management services, a DEA license covering Schedule II–V medications is necessary. This process can be completed within a week.

Because CMS and most third-party payors require home infusion accreditation, it is important to begin preparing for the process early in the project. Common organizations that accredit home infusion pharmacies include The Joint Commission, Accreditation Commission for Healthcare, and Community Health Accreditation Partner, among others. Plan for the accreditation preparation, submission, and site visit process to take at least six to nine months. It is important to coordinate timing so that the accreditation visit will occur shortly after the pharmacy begins serving patients (most organizations require at least five patient records). Failure to obtain accreditation in a timely fashion may result in lack of reimbursement from third-party payors.

Finally, home infusion pharmacies must apply to be a Medicare supplier through the CMS 855B and 855S process. The 855B covers the Medicare Home Infusion Therapy (HIT) program, while the 855S covers the Durable Medical Equipment, Prosthetics/Orthotics, and Supplies (DMEPOS) program. These applications are generally processed within two to three months.

IMPLEMENTATION PLAN

Development of core and supportive services for a home infusion operation is critical in the early phase of a service launch. Appropriate identification, prioritization, and completion of key business functions is necessary to ensure timely program launch and successful long-term growth. **Table 5** outlines key milestones for launching and growing a home infusion program.

CASE 13, TABLE 5. Timeline of Key Milestones for Program Implementation

Timeline for Service Launch		
Activity	**Recommended Start**	**Duration (months)**
Create business plan, identify champions, gain organizational support	Month 1	2
Develop and post pharmacy director position	Month 1	3
Research licensure and accreditation requirements	Month 1	1
Identify pharmacy and office location	Month 1	2
Develop partner agreements for contracted services (eg, wholesaler, product suppliers, software, courier services, nursing agencies)	Month 2	12
Design and build out clean room, pharmacy, and office space	Month 3	12
Staff recruitment and hiring	Month 3	9
Policy and procedure creation	Month 3	6
Committee development and integration with pharmacy enterprise	Month 3	6
Electronic medical record, documentation, and workflow development and integration	Month 6	9
Begin accreditation preparation	Month 9	6
Obtain required licensures	Month 12	3
Implement, manage, and adjust service line up until and after first patient is seen	Month 15	1
Post-Launch		
Activity	**Recommended Start**	**Duration (months)**
Undergo accreditation visit once first patients are served	Month 15	2
Achieve 25% capture rate of discharged patients requiring home infusion services	Month 15	12
Increase patient volumes by 50%	Month 24	12
Double patient volumes from first year	Month 36	12
Increase staffing as needed in response to increased volumes	Month 24	24
Consider internalizing some skilled nursing services (eg, specialty infusions)	Month 24	12
Consider internalizing delivery functions as a cost-reduction measure	Month 24	12

SUPPORTING MATERIALS

Additional operational documents to be considered for inclusion in the workflow, growth, and management of a home infusion service are:

- A collaborative practice agreement or pharmacy-to-dose protocol for pharmacokinetic dosing of medications (eg, vancomycin, aminoglycosides, or TPN)

- 340B contract pharmacy agreement

- Treatment protocols, including:

    ○ Administration equipment and supplies by therapy type

    ○ Infusion administration guidelines

    ○ Anaphylaxis medication orders and management

- Patient education materials, including:

    ○ A welcome packet

    ○ Visual training aids for patient self-administration

    ○ Supplementary drug education

- Marketing materials for clinics and provider offices

- Membership in the National Home Infusion Association

- Processes and spreadsheets or dashboards for monitoring patient volume and financial performance

LESSONS LEARNED

1. Hire an entrepreneurial pharmacy director with training or experience in program development and implementation. Previous experience with home infusion is highly preferred.

2. Engage internal or external resources with experience in designing and building cleanrooms that are compliant with the most up to date United States Pharmacopeia (USP) standards.

3. Carefully evaluate potential contractors to ensure that services rendered meet the organization's needs and quality standards.

4. Develop strong relationships with hospital care management staff and physician office staff to increase referral capture rate and ensure exceptional customer service.

5. Ensure sound processes for benefits investigation, prior authorization, and patient admission to prevent back-end billing and payment issues.

6. Recruit and retain individuals with experience billing services to commercial medical payors and government-sponsored programs like Medicare Part B. These are much more complex than traditional pharmacy benefit billing.

7. The ability to internalize processes like delivery and skilled nursing will lead to greater control over quality and the patient experience, in addition to increasing overall profitability.

8. Implement processes and an internal committee to regularly monitor and identify opportunities for quality improvement.

REFERENCES

1. Levine PH. Delivery of health care in hemophilia. *Ann N Y Acad Sci.* 1975;240:201–7.

2. McAllister III JC. The role of the pharmacist in home health care. *Drug Intell Clin Pharm.* 1985;19(4):282–4.

3. National Home Infusion Association. About home and specialty infusion. **https://nhia.org/about-infusion-therapy/**. Accessed November 28, 2021.

4. National Home Infusion Association (NHIA). Infusion Industry Trends 2020. NHIA. Alexandria, VA.

5. Wilson L. MA patients' readmission rates higher than traditional Medicare, study finds. HealthcareDive. **https://www.healthcaredive.com/news/ma-patients-readmission-rates-higher-than-traditional-medicare-study-finds/557694**. Updated June 26, 2019. Accessed November 23, 2021.

6. Centers for Medicare & Medicaid. Hospital readmissions Reduction Program (HRRP). **https://www.cms.gov/Medicare/Medicare-Fee-for-Service-Payment/AcuteInpatientPPS/Readmissions-Reduction-Program**. Updated August 6, 2021. Accessed November 23, 2021.

7. Polinski JM, Kowal MK, Gagnon M, et al. Home infusion: Safe, clinically effective, patient preferred, and cost saving. *Healthc (Amst).* 2017 Mar;5(1–2):68–80.

8. Centers for Medicare & Medicaid Services. Home Infusion Therapy Services. **https://www.cms.gov/Medicare/Medicare-Fee-for-Service-Payment/Home-Infusion-Therapy/Overview**. Updated August 23, 2021. Accessed November 23, 2021.

9. Wolter JM, Cagney RA, McCormack JG. A randomized trial of home vs hospital intravenous antibiotic therapy in adults with infectious diseases. *J Infect.* 2004 Apr;48(3):263–8.

10. Corwin P, Toop L, McGeoch G, et al. Randomised controlled trial of intravenous antibiotic treatment for cellulitis at home compared with hospital. *BMJ.* 2005 Jan 15;330(7483):129.

11. Kuin S, Stolte SB, van den Brink GR, et al. Short article: Remicade infusions at home: an alternative setting of infliximab therapy for patients with Crohn's disease. *Eur J Gastroenterol Hepatol.* 2016 Feb;28(2):222–5.

12. National Home Infusion Association. NHIA reimbursement training center: Billing. **https://nhia.org/reimbursement_training_center_billing/**. Accessed November 28, 2021.

Glossary

Academic medical centers—Similar to community not-for-profit facilities, academic medical centers are generally organized as tax-exempt under Internal Revenue Service regulations (501 (c)(3)). Their primary purpose is to provide community benefit through various programs and services. Access to capital is mainly through donations (which are usually tax-deductible to the donor), bonds and other debt instruments, and efficient operations. A major part of their mission is teaching new healthcare professionals and funding research. These additional activities carry a higher cost structure, which is often partly offset by other funding sources such as grants, state legislative funding, and so forth.

Accounting methods—The three basic accounting methods used by healthcare organizations are cash basis, accrual basis, and fund accounting.

Accrual basis accounting—Used for most businesses, this method seeks to "accrue" revenues and expenses to the proper period in which they are earned.

Acuity—A measure of severity of illness.

Administrative data—Payment, cost, and activity data generated anytime a patient has an encounter with a provider or facility when reimbursement is sought for those services.

Administrative fees—Fees paid by the hospital for its membership to belong to a GPO and to access the contracts the GPO offers, or fees paid by the manufacturer or supplier of the product. Administrative fees typically range from 1 to 3 percent of the purchase price of the product, and they must be disclosed in an agreement between the GPO and each participating member.

Advance Beneficiary Notice (ABN)—A written notice (on form CMS-R-131) given to a patient before that patient receives items or services, notifying the patient that Medicare may deny payment for that specific procedure or treatment, and that the patient will be personally responsible for full payment if Medicare denies payment. The ABN explains alternative treatment options, quality-of-life issues, and the patient's obligation to pay for the therapy if the claim is not approved by CMS. The ABN must be signed by the physician providing services and by the patient. The patient must disclose any coverage or financial assistance from secondary insurance providers, medication assistance programs, patient assistance programs, or charities.

Adverse Drug Event—An adverse drug event (ADE) is defined as harm experienced by a patient as a result of exposure to a medication.

Affordable Care Act (ACA)—The ACA is a comprehensive reform law, enacted in 2010, that increases health insurance coverage for the uninsured and implements reforms to the health insurance market. This includes many provisions that are consistent with AMA policy and holds the potential for a better healthcare system.

Ambulatory Payment Classification (APC)—The APC outpatient prospective payment system (OPPS) is a reimbursement method that categorizes outpatient visits into groups according to clinical characteristics, typical resource use, costs associated with the diagnoses, and procedures performed. An APC is a diagnostic classification analogous to an outpatient diagnosis–related group.

Average Wholesale Price (AWP)—AWP is a pharmaceutical term that describes the average price paid by a retailer to buy a drug from the wholesaler.

Balance sheet—Lists assets owned by the organization on the left side of the report, and the liabilities owed and the equity of the organization on the right side of the report. Assets must equal liabilities plus equity (or net assets).

Benchmarking—The continuous process of measuring products, services, and practices against the company's toughest

DOI 10.37573/9781585287130.024

competitors, or against those companies identified as industry leaders, so as to find and implement best practice.

Biosimilar—A biosimilar is a biologic medical product that is almost an identical copy of an original product that is manufactured by a different company. Biosimilars are officially approved versions of original "innovator" products and can be manufactured when the original product's patent expires.

Board of trustees—All hospital operations are governed by a board of trustees that commonly consists of members of the hospital's senior management team and representatives from the medical staff and the community.

Budget—A plan for future expenses and revenue, typically over a 12-month period. A budget does not represent the actual amount of money available to be spent, but is a plan based on history and on an understanding of the future. The pharmacy budget is designed to be a thoughtful, data-driven forecast of future expenses and revenue, and a yardstick for measuring financial performance over the course of the financial year.

Budget variance—The difference between the budgeted amount and the actual amount spent for a period. Variances can be described as positive (expenses lower than forecast; revenues higher than forecast) or negative (expenses higher than forecast; revenues lower than forecast). Variances can also be absolute: the total actual amount is higher irrespective of volume, or volume-adjusted.

Bundled contracts—Contracts for multiple products produced by a single manufacturer. This type of contract is usually anchored by a key product in a competitive market, along with several other products for which the manufacturer has competition from other suppliers.

Business plan—A document with a standard format and structure that clearly explains the what, why, when, who, and how of the project. It is a comprehensive explanation of the opportunity, the people involved, the money required to implement the plan, where the resources will come from, and

what financial results the opportunity is likely to produce.

Capital budget—Typically comprises items that cost more than a fixed threshold amount (eg, an expense greater than $5,000) and that have a useful life greater than a specified number of years (eg, five years). Capital expense budgets are typically set several years in advance. Pharmacy examples include installing new IV admixture hoods, remodeling a pharmacy, or building a new pharmacy satellite.

Case mix index (CMI)—Indicator of acuity to recognize the additional cost and resources required to care for more seriously ill patients.

Cash-basis accounting—Recognizes income and expense only when cash is received or disbursed. It ignores liabilities for purchases made but not yet received, and for assets earned but not yet collected. Cash-basis accounting is typically limited to individuals or small community organizations.

Centers for Medicare & Medicaid Services (CMS)—A federal agency in the U.S. Department of Health and Human Services (DHHS) that administers the Medicare program and works with state governments to administer Medicaid and the State Children's Health Insurance Program (SCHIP). CMS establishes program policies in accordance with congressional mandates through regulations, transmittals, and directives to fiscal intermediaries.

Clinical decision-support system (CDSS)—A centralized data warehouse to analyze combined administrative, clinical, and financial data.

Community-based (or not-for-profit) facilities—Generally organized as tax-exempt under Internal Revenue Service regulations (501(c)(3)). Such facilities provide community benefits through various programs and services, and they are funded mainly through donations, bonds, other debt instruments, and efficient operations.

Competitive environment analysis—Research report that includes an overview of the pharmacy's competitors, their nature, the number, and their advantages and vulnerabilities. This research also considers the overall size of the market in terms of gross dollars and net profits, clients and customers, and growth trends over the past three to ten years. The analysis should include any external or internal trends that would affect the potential for success or failure, as well as how this proposed venture would succeed in such an environment.

Continuing education—Instruction that is beyond the requirements for entry into a profession. Continuing education may include courses, programs, or organized learning experiences.

Continuous quality improvement (CQI)—A management philosophy that asserts that most things can be improved upon. CQI is an approach to quality that builds upon traditional quality assurance methods by emphasizing the organization and systems. CQI emphasizes process improvement and supports the use of objective data to assess and improve processes.

Contract purchase—Purchases made through membership in a GPO.

Contribution margin—The amount by which total departmental revenue exceeds total departmental expenses.

Cost accounting system—(or cost-allocating system, or decision-support system) A process that uses information from the hospital's general ledger system applied to individual patient accounts from the hospital's billing system to perform detailed data analysis. Used to allocate the hospital's total cost to the patient database with no comparisons to budget, or a standard cost.

Cost-containment plan—Documents areas in which targeted interventions may improve quality and reduce cost.

Data element—A reported metric (eg, volume statistic, expense, revenue) within a productivity monitoring system.

Departmental outsourcing—The outsourcing of the management of the entire pharmacy department.

Diagnosis related group (DRG)—A system used by Medicare to classify inpatient hospital services in which hospitals are paid a fixed rate for specific diagnoses. A DRG is expected to have consistent hospital resource use. DRGs were developed for Medicare as part of the prospective payment system. A DRG is assigned based on diagnoses, procedures, age, sex, and the presence of complications or comorbidities.

Direct expenses—Expenses that can be clearly identified as having been incurred in the operation of a department of the hospital.

Direct time study—A series of direct observations of a task to determine the average time required to complete the task and to assign a standard deviation to the average measurement.

Disproportionate Share Hospital (DSH) program pricing—(or 340B drug pricing program) A federal program for eligible safety net providers that gives discounts on the cost of pharmaceuticals; typically, to qualify for 340B pricing, a hospital must provide care to a certain percentage (>11.75%) of low-income individuals.

Earnings Before Interest, Depreciation, Taxes and Amortization (EBIDTA)—Net revenue less operating expenses equals earnings before depreciation, interest, taxes, and amortization (EBIDTA for for-profit reporting) or the excess of revenues over expenses (for not-for-profit reporting).

Expense—A payment made by the health system to others for value received. Pharmacy expenses can be divided into three categories: supplies, human resources, and other expenses.

Fiscal intermediaries (FI)—Fiscal intermediaries are regional and state Medicare contractors that provide reimbursement review and medical coverage review. Medicare fiscal intermediaries are private insurance companies that serve as the federal government's agents in the administration of the Medicare program, including the payment of claims.

Fiscal services—The collective name for a number of different departments often led by the chief financial officer. Fiscal services can sometimes simply refer to the accounting department.

Fixed expenses—Expenses that do not fluctuate as volumes in the hospital change. Examples include the monthly lease payment for office space or equipment and core staffing levels in some revenue-producing departments and such overhead departments as administration, human resources, and fiscal services.

Flexible budget—An interactive budget that adjusts the static budget based on the actual volume and mix for a period of time.

Food and Drug Administration (FDA)—The FDA is responsible for protecting the public health by ensuring the safety, efficacy, and security of human and veterinary drugs, biological products, and medical devices; and by ensuring the safety of our nation's food supply, cosmetics, and products that emit radiation.

For-profit facilities—Generally organized as taxable entities. Besides their organizational mission, their primary focus is on generating a return for the shareholder or owner(s). Access to capital is mainly through the sale of stock, debt instruments, and efficient operations.

FTE—A full-time equivalent employee, computed by dividing the number of man-hours for the period by the number of man-hours a full-time employee would be paid for that period.

Functional outsourcing—The outsourcing of a specific function within the pharmacy, such as nuclear radiopharmaceuticals, intravenous compounding, clinical services, packaging services, and after-hours order entry.

Fund accounting—Typically used by governmental entities and academic medical centers, fund accounting establishes specific funds for a variety of uses, such as the equipment replacement fund and the general fund. The general fund serves as the operating fund for the entity.

Gap analysis structured method—Used to document the difference between where a

particular department or process is versus where it should be.

Gross revenue—The total amount of revenue billed, based on the established charging structure.

Group purchasing organizations (GPOs)—Organizations whose primary service is developing purchasing contracts for product and nonlabor service agreements that their membership can access. By pooling the purchases of their member hospitals, GPOs can negotiate lower prices from suppliers and manufacturers.

HCPCS coding—The process of organizing data into meaningful categories for analysis. The HCPCS code set is one of the standard code sets used for this purpose. The HCPCS is organized into two principal subsystems, referred to as level I and level II of the HCPCS. Level I of the HCPCS comprises the CPT (current procedural terminology), a numeric coding system maintained by the American Medical Association (AMA). The CPT is a uniform coding system comprising descriptive terms and identifying codes used primarily to identify medical services and procedures. Level II of the HCPCS is a standardized coding system used primarily to identify products, supplies, and services not included in the CPT codes.

High-priority medications—A list of 60 to 80 drug products that represent as much as 80 percent of total annual medication expenditures.

Home infusion center pharmacies—Specialized pharmacies that primarily mix, prepare, and dispense infusions, injections, and other products for use in the home and in other ambulatory settings.

Human resource expenses—Consist of the salary and benefit costs for pharmacists, pharmacy technicians, pharmacy managers, and others.

ICD-9-CM classification system—The International Classification of Diseases, ninth revision, clinical modification (ICD-9-CM) is a coding system based on the World Health Organization's ninth revision, International

Classification of Diseases (ICD-9). ICD-9-CM is the official system of assigning codes to diagnoses and procedures associated with hospital care in the United States. The ICD-9-CM is designed for the classification of morbidity and mortality information for statistical purposes, for the indexing of records, and for ease of data storage and retrieval. The ICD-9-CM classification for diagnoses and injuries is grouped into 17 chapters that are typically arranged by body systems. These codes can be up to five digits in length, permitting detailed descriptions.

Implementation plan—A plan with a timetable indicating key milestones.

Income statement—(or operating statement, or statement of revenues and expenses) Reports financial performance of the organization for a designated period of time. It details revenues earned and related expenses incurred in the operation of the organization.

Indirect expenses—Expenses such as employee benefits, or depreciation, which are similar in nature to revenue deductions in that they require an allocation to be made.

Institute for Safe Medication Practices (ISMP)—ISMP is an American 501 organization focusing on the prevention of medication errors and promoting safe medication practices. It is affiliated with the ECRI Institute.

Institutional Review Board (IRB)—An institutional review board (IRB) is a committee formally designated to monitor, review, and approve biomedical and behavioral research involving humans. The IRB focuses on the protection of the rights and welfare of research subjects.

Integrated delivery networks (IDNs)—Networks of facilities and providers, usually anchored by one or two large hospitals (many times teaching hospitals), and several smaller community or rural hospitals, clinics, and other alternate sites of care, that work together to provide care to a specific market or geographic area.

Internal benchmarking—(ie, internal productivity monitoring) A process of measuring current department performance against performance over time, comparing current and future department performance against prior department performance.

Key indicators—List of performance measures used to monitor changes in financial operations over time; reviewed at least annually to be sure that the reports and ratios focus on the current main issues.

Letters of commitment (LOCs)—Letters that the pharmaceutical supplier requires the provider to sign in order to access the program. LOCs may be managed by the GPO to track membership enrollment in the program, or by the pharmaceutical supplier, in which case the GPO may not be able to reliably track which members have enrolled in the program.

Local Coverage Determinations (LCDs)—(or local medical review policies) A local coverage determination (LCD), as established by Section 522 of the Benefits Improvement and Protection Act, is a decision by a fiscal intermediary whether to cover a particular service on an intermediary-wide or carrier-wide basis in accordance with Section 1862(a)(1)(A) of the Social Security Act (ie, a determination as to whether the service is reasonable and necessary).

Long-term care pharmacy—A pharmacy designed specifically to meet the needs of those in long-term care. Most medications administered in such a pharmacy are oral dosage forms, and the remaining comprise injections and infusions.

Lost charges—Patient-chargeable items for which pharmacy appears to have provided a dose through the first dose process or cart fill, when a second replacement dose is requested by nursing because the initial dispensed dose cannot be located. The replacement dose is then billed back to the HCO for chargeback to the department in which the loss occurred.

Mail-service pharmacy—A pharmacy that mails drugs to patients. Such a pharmacy is often a cost-saving alternative to the traditional retail pharmacy.

Managed care—A highly competitive arena in which the primary strategy is to offer a comprehensive bundle of healthcare services for a set fee over a specific amount of time, using principles of health management and financial control. Managed care is a risk-based business and a form of insurance.

Market—Group of customers, with a set of common characteristics, who want to buy the service.

Market competitive clause—A clause that often exists in generic pharmaceutical contracts to allow for price reductions if competitors within the generic class offer a lower price to GPO members.

Marketing plan—A plan to inform potential customers of the new service and ongoing marketing efforts. A marketing plan should include an overall strategy and may include tactics for each target group. Collateral materials and media should be described to provide additional insight on how the new service will be promoted. The plan should include a schedule for introducing the new service and for promoting, as well as a general plan for tracking results of the marketing effort.

Medicaid program—Title XIX of the Social Security Act is a Federal/State entitlement program that pays for medical assistance for certain individuals and families with low incomes and resources. This program, known as Medicaid, became law in 1965 as a cooperative venture jointly funded by federal and state governments to assist states in furnishing medical assistance to eligible needy persons. Medicaid is the largest source of funding for medical and health-related services for America's poorest people.

Medicare program—A Federal entitlement program that provides access to and pays for medical care for people age 65 or older, for people under age 65 with certain disabilities, and for people of all ages with end-stage renal disease.

Medicare Prospective Payment System (MPPS)—The MPPS was introduced by the federal government in October 1983, as a way to change hospital behavior through financial incentives that encourage more cost-efficient management of medical care. Under PPS, hospitals are paid a predetermined rate for each Medicare admission. Each patient is classified into a diagnosis-related group (DRG) on the basis of clinical information. Except for certain patients with exceptionally high costs (called outliers), the hospital is paid a flat rate for the DRG, regardless of the actual services provided. MPPS introduced the fixed-price payer into the hospital profit box.

Medicare's Low-Income Subsidy (LIS) benefit—Federal assistance that can increase a patient's cost savings by paying part of their monthly premium, annual deductibles, and monthly prescription copayments under the Medicare Part D program. This extra assistance can be worth as much as $3700 annually for an individual patient.

Medication budget—The health system's plan for medication expenditures during the budget period. The medication budget is the sum of the high-priority, new medication, nonformulary, and low-priority budget components, minus the savings identified in the cost-containment plan.

Medication Therapy Management Services (MTMS)—Services provided by the pharmacy, which optimize therapeutic care (including managing and monitoring drug therapy in patients receiving treatment for cancer or chronic conditions such as asthma and diabetes, consulting with patients and their families on the proper use of medication, conducting wellness and disease prevention programs to improve public health, and overseeing medication use in a variety of settings, such as home care settings, hospitals, ambulatory care settings, long-term care facilities, clinics, and intensive care units).

Minibid—A bid conducted for a specific drug or contract if the awarded supplier decides it cannot continue to be price competitive.

Monthly operating statement—A monthly accounting of expenses and revenues prepared by the finance department. The monthly operating statement details the pharmacy's performance against revenue, expense, workload, and additional selected indicators.

Net present value (NPV)—NPV is a financial metric that seeks to capture the total value of an investment opportunity.

Net revenue—Gross revenue less deductions for negotiated discounts, mandated contractual adjustments, and the write-off for charity care. It is the real measure of the revenue earned by the hospital.

Nonacute care facility—Medical treatment facility that does not address urgent or severe needs. A nonacute care facility may include physician offices, retail pharmacies, clinics, long-term care facilities, home care agencies, and other alternate sites of care.

Noncontract purchase—Occurs when a pharmaceutical purchase is made though neither the GPO nor an individual member contract.

Nonformulary agents—Those drugs not found on a hospital or health plan's approved drug list; such drugs may not be covered or may result in a higher copayment.

Off-contract purchase—Occurs when the member hospital does not purchase through the GPO agreement but through an individual contract with the supplier or another GPO or distributor agreement with the supplier.

Operating budget—A forecast of the daily expenses required to operate the pharmacy, including labor, drugs, supplies, and other support below the capital expense threshold.

Operational benchmarking—(Also commonly referred to as "external benchmarking" and "external productivity monitoring") A system whereby hospitals submit department-level data (usually on a quarterly cycle) into a vendor-managed financial and operational comparative database to compare departmental operational and financial performance to peer organizations.

Order management—Everything the pharmacy does to understand, translate, perfect, and prepare the physician's order for fulfillment. Order entry, or order review, usually comprises a large part of this process.

Outlier payments—Provisions within the Medicare Act provide for Medicare payments for cases that incur extraordinarily high costs (outliers). These payments are made to Medicare-participating hospitals in addition to the basic prospective payments.

Outsourcing—A contract between a health system and an outside company to provide pharmaceutical services or management.

Overhead—Cost of the indirect services that support the pharmacy but are not directly paid by the pharmacy. These include housekeeping, heat and air-conditioning, electricity, health system administration, health system purchasing, information systems support, human resources, finance, and others.

Patient assistance programs (PAP)—Patient assistance programs are run by pharmaceutical companies to provide free medications to people who cannot afford to buy their medicine. PAPs provide opportunities for individuals with no insurance or prescription coverage to receive low-cost or free pharmaceuticals.

Patronage fees—The portion of the administrative fees returned to a GPO's membership each year. Most GPOs subtract operating expenses from the administrative fees and return the remainder of the fees to their membership each year. The percentage returned to the member hospitals varies among GPOs.

Pay-for-performance(P4P)—Compensation for high-quality care, based on established quality indicators.

Peer group—A grouping of like hospitals or hospital departments.

Per diem rate—Fixed-price per patient day; most favored payment methodology of health insurers.

Per Member Per Month (PMPM)—A fixed payment per month that is received for providing services to a member.

Percentile—A relative ranking of performance versus a compare (peer) group. In operational benchmarking, percentiles range from 0 to

100 percent, and better performance is typically signified by a lower percentile ranking.

Performance agreements—Contract agreements designed to reward hospitals for increased use of a specific product within a therapeutic class. Performance agreements typically have multiple tiers, each of which is associated with a product price. Tiers are differentiated based on a market share percentage scale, the total number of units purchased, the total of dollars spent, or a combination of these attributes. The price a member pays for a contracted product decreases as the market share percentage for the product increases, the total units purchased increase, or the total dollars spent increase. Performance agreement calculation of market share is usually based on a market basket of competitive products, whereby the contracted product usage is divided by overall usage of all other products in the market basket.

Pharmacy Benefit Managers (PBMs)—A PMB is a company that manages prescription drug benefits on behalf of health insurers, Medicare Part D drug plans, large employers, and other payers.

Pharmacy informatics—The effective acquisition, storage, organization, analysis, management, and use of information in the delivery of pharmaceutical care and the delivery of optimal medication-related patient care and health outcomes.

Pharmacy residency program—A pharmacy residency is an organized, directed, postgraduate training program in a defined area of pharmacy practice. It provides the knowledge and experience that pharmacy practitioners need to face challenges in today's complex healthcare environment, while also providing essential skills to meet the practice demands of the future.

Prescription drug benefit—A contract that defines the benefits, including formulary coverage, copays, deductibles, and caps according to the specifications of the employer, who is picking up most of the expenditures. The prescription drug benefit portion is often defined by the plan and priced on a per member per month (PMPM) basis.

Procedure analysis report—Depicts the current price, current month and year-to-date volumes, and gross charges for each procedure code in the pharmacy and includes departmental totals of volumes and revenue.

Productivity ratio—A measure of productivity (output/input). Productivity ratios are often divided into labor productivity ratios (eg, hours worked or paid per unit of output, hours worked per 100 orders processed, doses dispensed per hour worked) and cost-based productivity ratios (eg, expense per unit of output, drug cost per 100 orders processed, total pharmacy cost per patient discharge).

Rebates—A percentage of the total purchase cost of the product returned to the purchaser. Rebates are meant as an incentive to purchase more product. Rebates are also used to hide the actual price of the product either from the pharmacy distributor or from other competitors.

Regulatory environment investigation—Research such as a regulatory environment investigation considers the unique regulatory issues associated with the pharmacy business. Such research must be thorough and is as important to success as any other financial factor in the project evaluation.

Reimbursement analysis—A research report that considers the reimbursement issues unique to the business venture, outlining any advantages, leverage, or limitations to be considered. The reimbursement analysis should include a realistic appraisal of how reimbursement issues will affect the project and its chances for success. Strategies for maximizing any advantages and for dealing with the challenges should be a part of this research, and they should become a fundamental component of the final business plan.

Relative value unit (RVU)—Depending on the cost type, this RVU can be the actual cost per unit, labor minutes per unit, or a weighting factor that helps distribute the cost accordingly.

Replacement cost—The resources and monies expended to replace a separated employee. These resources include the cost of identifying and attracting applicants, conducting screening interviews, testing or other assessment of competency, preemployment administrative expenses, travel and moving expenses, and recruitment or other incentive payments.

Residency Program Director (RPD)—A licensed pharmacist responsible for direction, conduct, and oversight of the residency program.

Responsibility accounting—Responsibility reports show the department manager their responsibility in the financial picture. The report presents only those items that the manager is, or should be, directly responsible for in their department. The most common responsibility accounting report is the monthly department operations report.

Responsibility Center Management (RCM)—RCM is a budgeting model under which revenue-generating units are wholly responsible for managing their own revenues and expenditures.

Retail pharmacy—A community pharmacy in which drugs are sold to patients.

Return on investment (ROI)—A structured calculation of the operating cost and revenue changes that the health system will incur with the new capital expense. ROI calculations are often stated in the number of months or years that a capital purchase takes to pay back its purchase cost.

Revenue—Money received for products or services provided to customers. Pharmacy revenues consist primarily of patient charges, which may arise from doses administered in an inpatient setting or from prescriptions dispensed in an outpatient setting.

Reverse auction—A bid process where multiple suppliers bid for a contract through an electronic auction process. Through the auction process, the price is driven down rather than driven up (hence the term reverse auction).

Salary accrual—An estimate of the amount of salary and wage expense incurred between the end of the last pay period of the month and the end of the month used to properly match expenses to revenue.

Self-reporting—Relies on staff to document the amount of time required to perform an activity. Self-reporting studies are best conducted in situations of low to moderate activity volume with easily definable start and stop times with little variation in activity interpretability.

Specialty pharmacy—A pharmacy that stocks, prepares, and dispenses drugs to patients, primarily to those in the home or in other outpatient settings. The drugs dispensed are limited in number, but they tend to be expensive, and they frequently require administration by self-injection. These drugs are often not routinely stocked in a neighborhood pharmacy.

Staff development—A structured development plan created between the staff member and the department manager to improve performance. Staff development is another plan for the career growth of particular individuals within the department. Formal education may be included, such as the Master of Business Administration (MBA) or other specialized education programs. In some organizations, a formal mentoring program may be available for managers or for peak performers who wish to advance.

Staffing plan—A plan that creates an optimal relationship between the available resources (hours of pharmacist and technician work time) and the coverage hours and activities of the pharmacy and that seeks to achieve the greatest utility and output while meeting the human needs of staff. The basis for a staffing plan includes the scope of services of the pharmacy, practice standards and regulatory requirements, the leverage provided by the skills and competencies of the pharmacy staff, the capabilities of automation and technology, and an understanding and acknowledgement of the support needs at practice interfaces with physicians, nurses, and others who work in the medication use process.

Standard cost accounting, product costing—Process of determining the price of a product by examining the various expenses accumulated in the development and sale of that product.

Statement of cash flows—Final financial statement. It identifies the sources and uses of cash in the organization. The statement must tie to the cash balance reported on the balance sheet.

Statement of owner's equity or fund balance—Provides a detailed account of the equity balance at the beginning and end of the reporting period. The net income or loss (excess of revenues over expenses, in the case of a not-for-profit organization) is often the most significant transaction. Net income increases equity on the balance sheet; net losses decrease equity.

Static budget—Snapshot of expected costs; not adjusted or altered after the budget is submitted.

Stepwise analysis—Method of variance analysis that lines up all the factors being analyzed, starting with all factors at their budgeted level. At each step in the analysis, one of the factors is shown at its actual level rather than at its budgeted level.

Stop loss provision—Contract provisions in which additional payments to the hospital are generated from the insurer when an individual admission reaches a certain charge level (similar to outlier payments). These additional payments can take any form (per diem, case rate, percentage of charges), with percentage of charges being preferred by the hospital financial manager.

Strategic plan—A document describing the resources required, the costs incurred, and the benefits realized in acquiring those resources to achieve long-term goals.

Strategic pricing—A pricing method that analyzes each procedure code by payer source (charge-based or cost-based). Strategic pricing places as much of a price increase as is possible on procedures with high usage by charge-based payers and as little as possible on procedures with a high usage by cost-based payers generating a higher net return for the hospital.

SWOT (strengths, weaknesses, opportunities, and threats) analysis—A structured strategic planning method that results in a report that enables the pharmacy to evaluate how to enhance strengths, mitigate or eliminate a weakness, and capitalize on an opportunity, and that helps the hospital plan how to deal with threats.

The Joint Commission—The Joint Commission is a United States-based nonprofit tax-exempt 501 organization that accredits more than 22,000 U.S. healthcare organizations and programs.

Therapeutic interchange—To modify the market share of drugs in a specific therapeutic class by moving market share toward one product in a class by deeming products therapeutically equivalent to the medication prescribed. Examples of therapeutic categories in which interchange programs may be considered include antiemetics, antimicrobials, and erythropoietic growth factors.

Time standard—The mean time required to perform a task.

US Pharmacopeia (USP)—USP is a not-for-profit, science-driven organization that has an established process for convening independent experts in the development and maintenance of healthcare quality standards. The process is public health focused, leveraging current science and technology, and draws on the expertise of scientists and healthcare practitioners while providing opportunities for public input from stakeholders throughout the standards' progress. The USP Compounding Expert Committee is responsible for the development of General Chapter <797>.

Variable expenses—Expenses that fluctuate as volumes in the hospital change. Pharmacy drug cost is an example of a variable expense—the more patients the hospital has, generally the higher the total drug cost, and the fewer patients a hospital has, the lower the drug cost.

Variance—Differences between the budget and actual expense expressed in absolute dollars and as percentage differences.

Veterans Health Administration (VHA)—The VHA is America's largest integrated healthcare system, providing care at 1,298 healthcare facilities, including 171 medical centers and 1,113 outpatient sites of care of varying complexity (VHA outpatient clinics), serving 9 million enrolled Veterans each year.

Volume budget—The number of admissions, patient days, CMI, outpatient visits, emergency department visits, and other activities for the budget year; prepared by the CFO.

Volume indicator—The frequency with which activities occur, often reported as a mean frequency when nonautomated sources are used to provide the frequency.

Weighting—A method used to recombine a department's varied work outputs equitably to produce a single figure that represents the department's entire output. Weighting can also be defined as a measure of time to perform one unit of each department output.

Work sampling—A method to estimate the percent of time that staff spend on various activities; an indirect method of establishing time requirements. The work sampling method of measurement is best for measuring the relative frequency of all tasks staff perform, and for measuring intermittent activities that are not closely structured in time, that occur infrequently, and for which data would thus require an inordinate amount of time to collect through direct observation.

Workload unit—A unit of measure to monitor financial performance. On the inpatient side patient days, number of admissions, and number of discharges are common measures. On the outpatient side patient visits, such as emergency room or clinic visits, are common indicators. For those organizations that provide traditional retail prescription services, prescription volume is also a common measure.

Technical terms outlining the function of Medicare, Medicaid, and other reimbursement and financial functions of the Department of Health and Human Services and the Centers for Medicare & Medicaid Services (CMS) were researched and validated at the time of publication. Readers are referred to these websites to ensure that their understanding of the terms, and that use and function of these terms are current. Websites: www.cms.hhs.gov, www.cdc.gov, www.hhs.gov, www.medicare.gov.

Index

DOI 10.37573/9781585287130.BM